Postcodes: the new geography

Postcodes:
The new geography

J. F. Raper, D. W. Rhind and
J. W. Shepherd

Dedication

We dedicate this book to Frances,
Christine and Jean.

Longman Scientific and Technical
Longman Group UK Ltd
Longman House, Burnt Mill, Harlow,
Essex CM20 2JE, England
and Associated Companies throughout the world

copublished in the United States with John Wiley & Sons, Inc., 605 Third Avenue, New York, NY 10158

First published 1992

British Library Cataloguing in Publication data
A catalogue record for this book is available from the British Library.

Library of Congress Cataloging-in-Publication Data
ˈA catalogue record for this book is available from the Library of Congress.

Printed and Bound in Great Britain at the Bath Press, Avon

Contents

List of Colour Plates

(plate section can be found on pages 130-1)

Preface

In 1985, I was asked by the Secretary of State for the Environment to chair a government Committee of Enquiry into the Handling of Geographic Information. At that time, few outside a select band knew anything about such information. Fewer still appreciated the revolution that was coming in the use of information and how our society was rapidly moving towards an 'information economy'. The image of geography as a subject was still little more than an encyclopedia of assorted 'facts' about different parts of the world to many lay people. Why then did the government set up such a committee, especially one so antipathetic to committees in general?

The answer is an interesting one and has relevance to this book. A number of previous studies, notably the Ordnance Survey Review Committee's report of 1979 and the House of Lords' Select Committee on Science and Technology report on satellite remote sensing and digital mapping in 1984, had prepared the ground. They identified the trends in the rapid decrease of computing costs and the huge potential for organisational benefits from the corporate use of a precious resource viz. data. They also suspected that there could be much wider use of geographical data if users were familiar with what is possible, had the tools and skills to do it and if the basic 'framework data' were made routinely available for the whole country. By 'framework data' they meant the topographic skeleton provided by Ordnance Survey and standard sets of area boundaries. Unhappily, neither committee had the time, human resources or remit to investigate matters further but the Select Committee recommended that a suitably broad-ranging study be set up to investigate how the potential might be brought to reality. The then Secretary of State for the Environment deserves much credit for his foresight in backing their proposal.

My Committee was broadly based. We took evidence from over 400 organisations or groups; we argued over many things but produced a unanimous report on time. More important, that report did not gather dust like so many other official documents. It was sold worldwide and had to be reprinted to meet the demand. In one sense we were lucky: we reported just at the most appropriate time. Geographical data handling had come of age.

One matter we debated for some time was how to standardise the way in which data are 'spatially referenced' or located in space; chaos and error would certainly ensue if many different spatial references were employed since there is rarely an exact conversion possible from one to another. Many different choices were available. In the end, we concluded that two different systems should be employed because they were ideally suited to different situations. Those two systems of spatial referencing are coordinates on the British National Grid, designed and supported by Ordnance Survey, and Royal Mail's Postcode system. We urged government to exploit the ease of linking one data set to another which comes about if it is based on use of one or other or both of these two systems.

Significant progress has been evident since we reported – the 1991 Census of Population in Scotland, for instance, has been largely built on a Postcode basis and the resulting data may therefore be used much more flexibly than hitherto. Unsurprisingly therefore, I am delighted to write this preface for a book on Postcodes. The pleasure is increased because the three authors have all made significant contributions to the science and practice of handling geographic data from their well-known base in Birkbeck College. For all these reasons, I wish the book well and commend the use of Postcodes.

Chorley

December 1991

Lord Chorley was chairman of the UK government's Committee of Enquiry into the Handling of Geographic Information (1985-7). He is chairman of the National Trust and was previously senior partner in Coopers and Lybrand, the international accountancy and management consultancy practice. Though trained as an economist and accountant, his involvement with geography has been long-lasting and has included being President of the Royal Geographical Society.

Foreword

We are grateful to many people for the help they have given us in writing the book. We are particularly grateful to Professor John Beaumont, Head of the Business School at the University of Bath, for writing the chapter on marketing for us. Peter Bibby of Halcrow Fox and Associates also contributed significantly to chapter 9. The permission of the Department of the Environment to reproduce part of their directory of spatial data sets held by government (appendix 3) is much appreciated. The support of the Association for Geographic Information, in particular Maxine Allison, in providing a copy of the relevant section of the directory is gratefully acknowledged.

Appendix 5 and other material on the National Grid is drawn largely from various OS Information Notes, from Harley (1975) which was sponsored by the Survey and from other OS sources. Some of the examples cited in chapter 8 were kindly provided by CACI Ltd and by Pinpoint Analysis Ltd.

Individuals like Jack Archibald, Bob Barr, Mike Blakemore, Ruth Blatchford, Peter Burnhill, Jill Collins, Nick Green, Andrew Larner, David Martin, Helen Mounsey, Stan Openshaw, Ralph Robbins, George Robinson, Mary Short, Gurmukh Singh, Susan Squires, Frank Thomas and Paul Winterton helpfully discussed postcode-related matters with us. Alex Clark at the Office of Population Censuses and Surveys provided vital information on the Central Postcode Directory and Bob Butcher and Dave Elliot did the same on sampling methodology. Friends in other countries like Fred Christ, Don Cooke, Rudolfo Nuñez del la Cuevas, Alexandra Fonseca, Wolfgang Kainz, Philippe Miellet,

Joe Mousset, Bengt Rystedt and Henk Scholten all provided valuable comparative material. Whilst not acting as entirely disinterested volunteers, Samantha and Jonathan Rhind kindly carried out some field trials of the accuracy of Royal Mail's Postcode Address File. Our special thanks go to Peter Clark, Keeper of the Royal Geographical Society (RGS), for determining the National Grid Reference of the front door of Lowther Lodge, the home of the RGS.

Most individual authors are dependent to some degree on colleagues in their organisation for support of some form; we are certainly no exception. Our colleagues in the Department of Geography at Birkbeck College - notably Merle Abbott, Teresa Connolly, Elsa João, Peter Gale, Siân John, Simon Lewis, Xavier Lopez, Duan Ming, Sandra Randell, Graham Sadler, Jean Shepherd and Ann Wilkes - all helped in various ways, usually to impossible deadlines. Particular mention must however be made of Tina Scally who put a prodigious amount of work into creating acceptable diagrams for the book on her Apple Macintosh computer: many of these originated in poor quality scraps of paper or faded faxes. Apple Computer (UK) Ltd facilitated this by their gift of Macintosh computers to found the Apple Mapping Centre in Birkbeck's Department of Geography. The support of the Economic and Social Research Council in funding the staff and equipment in the South East Regional Research Laboratory (SERRL) at Birkbeck which maintains and analyses many of the data sets used in this book, is also acknowledged. The Birkbeck College Photographic Unit also took certain of the colour photographs most efficiently and effectively.

Julietta Edgar was our main liaison with Royal Mail though Alan Brewer and Anne Wine were also invaluable sources of information and support. Pete Douglas, Nick Francis, Stuart Pretty and John Williams also provided useful insights to Royal Mail's operation and plans, and Ron Clatworthy provided data for figure 3.1. Readers unfamiliar with the organisation might wish to know that Royal Mail is the letters business section of the Post Office though the historical development of Postcodes was initiated by the Post Office itself.

Finally, it is a pleasure to record our thanks to our publishers, Longman Group UK Ltd and their staff for producing the book in a much shorter time period than is usual. Coping with a triumvirate of authors is never easy and this particular group, we suspect, was even more difficult than usual.

Acknowledgements

We are grateful to the following for permission to reproduce copyright material:

The Automobile Association (Kingswood Ltd.) for Fig. 5.16, Table 4.8 & part Plate 8 © The Automobile Association 1991; Bartholomew (Greater London Street Atlas) for Fig. 5.3 based on OS data © Bartholomews; British Telecommunications plc for Table 9.1 & part Table 9.2 (BT); CACI Ltd. for Figs 8.3, 8.4 & Plate 7 © CACI Ltd.; Clansouth Ltd. for Fig. 8.6; Department of the Environment for Tables 1.1 (DoE, 1987) & 10.1 (DoE); EGIS Conference Bureau for Figs 9.3, 9.4 & 9.5 (Dowie *et al.*, 1991); Environmental System Research Institute (ESRI) for Figs 1.5 & 1.8 (ARC/INFO User Manual); the authors, R. Flowerdew & M. Green for Figs 9.6a-f (Flowerdew, Green & Lucas, 1991); the author, Dr. A.C. Gatrell for Fig. 4.2 (Gatrell, 1989); General Register Office for Scotland for part Figs 6.1 & 6.2 (GRO(S)); Geomatrix Ltd. for Part Plate 8 © Geomatrix Ltd; Geoplan (UK)/Market Profiles Ltd. for Fig. 4.4 (Geoplan) Chas. E. Goad Ltd. for part Fig. 4.5; Halcrow Fox & Associates for part Figs 9.7-9.10a & part Table 9.2 (HFA); the Controller of Her Majesty's Stationery Office for Figs 4.3 (OS), part 4.5 (OS), part 5.4 (OS), part 5.6 (OPCS), part 5.6 (OS), part 6.1 (OS), part 6.2 (OS), part 9.10a & b (OS), A5. 1-A5.5 (OS), Tables 4.7 (OPCS, 1991), 6.1 & 6.3 (OPCS) & part Plate 3 (OS) © Crown Copyright; Infolink Ltd. for Figs 9.1 & 9.2 (Infolink); The Institute of British Geographers for Fig. 1.1 (Owen *et al.*, 1986) & Table 1.2 (Openshaw, Wymer & Charlton, 1986); the author, W. Kainz for Table 3.3; Kellogg Company of Great Britain Ltd. for Plate 4; Macmillan Magazines Ltd. and the author, D.G. Kendall for Fig. 1.6 (Kendall, 1971) Copyright © 1971 Macmillan

Magazines Ltd.; McGraw-Hill Publishers for Table 8.3 (Parkinson & Parkinson, 1987); Pinpoint Analysis for Tables 8.4, 8.5 & part Plate 3 © Pinpoint Analysis; Royal Mail for Figs 2.1, 2.2, 3.1-3.3, part 5.4, part 5.6, 10.1, Tables 2.1, 3.1, 4.6, 10.2 & Plate 5; Royal Mail (PAF on CD) for Figs 2.3, 5.5, 5.7-5-9, part 9.7-9.10a & b, Tables 2.2-2.7, 4.1, 5.1, 5.4, 8.1 & Plate 2; The Royal Statistical Society for Fig. 9.11, Tables 4.2, 4.3 & 9.3 (Wilson & Elliott, 1987); Sloan Management Review Association for Fig. 8.2 (Gorry & Scott Morton, 1989) Copyright 1989 Sloan Management Review Association.

Whilst every effort has been made to trace the owners of copyright material, in a few cases this has proved impossible and we take this opportunity to offer our apologies to any copyright holders whose rights we may have unwittingly infringed.

Introduction

Why this book exists

A book on Postcodes[1] intended for the general public yet written by a group of academics requires some explanation. The first reaction of those browsing the bookshelves may be that this is simply the unreadable preaching about the inexplicable! We hope that further reading will dispel such an uncharitable view because there is a very good reason why we devoted time to writing this book. The reason is that Postcodes are important to all of us, and becoming ever more so, yet this fact is little understood.

In later pages, we try to explain why all this is true. We also try to anticipate what is going to happen with Postcodes in the future and suggest new applications where profit or other value can be gained through the use of Royal Mail's invention.

The original idea for this book came from Royal Mail but they have not influenced what we have written. They have, of course, contributed examples, illustrative materials and criticism. We are grateful for all of these but what is contained herein is our interpretation of the present and our anticipation of the future.

The very core of our argument is that something designed and funded for one purpose *can* be useful – even vital – for many others. The Postcode cannot conceivably be ideal for many of these additional purposes. But, in practice and associated with Ordnance Survey grid references, it is the best overall solution we are ever likely to have: the cost of having several

---

[1]We use 'Postcode' whenever we discuss the Royal Mail's product since that is how they treat it but use 'postal code' whenever we talk generically (e.g. about postcodes worldwide) or 'postcode' when we quote others who have used it thus

totally different ways of defining the geography of the country, each best-suited to different purposes, is far too high even for the nation state. Moreover, the postal system is based upon the physically observable (and hence familiar) world of postal addresses. For this reason, a UK government Committee of Enquiry recommended in 1987 that:

> the preferred basis for holding and/or releasing socio-economic data should be addresses and unit postcodes (Department of the Environment 1987, p. 89)

In using the Postcode, we get something for nothing since it already exists and can be used 'freely'. But what can it be used for? To appreciate the breadth of its applications, we must first realise just how often we all rely upon a knowledge of geography.

The secret world of geographers

Everyone is a geographer. We all have to navigate and make decisions which take account of where other things or people are located; *where* is an everyday factor in all our lives. Such decisions are often critically important for our employers and our families. Yet perhaps 99% of us do not realise that, in making these decisions, we are momentarily becoming geographers.

Geography is about the inter-relationships of people and their whole environment. Geographers think of 'environment' not simply as the physical factors of the lie of the land, the weather, the flow of rivers and so on. It also includes the place to place variation of the society and communities in which we live, the organisations in which we work and even the ideas and conventions that shape our lives. It might be objected that this embraces nearly every aspect of our knowledge about the world and other academics do make such objections from time to time. The important point, however, is the way that geographers use the notion of 'environment' and the physical fact of geographic space to integrate a multiplicity of information about the countries, regions and places in which we reside, work and take our leisure. It was for this emphasis on the way things are inter-related that a recent leader in *The Times* newspaper referred to geography as 'the queen of sciences'. We naturally see no reason to dispute this judgement!

Geography, then, is about bringing things together which are relevant to our needs as human beings and doing this in as rigorous and objective a manner as possible. But geography, like most of life, involves some subjectivity. Each of us looks at reality from our own viewpoint. Rather fortunately, however, our concerns overlap with those of many other people even if they are rarely identical. In Britain, for instance, geographical variations in taxes (such as the Poll or Council Taxes) normally affect our near neighbours in similar ways to ourselves even if they affect those people in far-flung places quite differently. As another example, global warming (if it happens) may affect everyone on the planet, but this will occur in different ways. A family living in the Maldive Islands, for instance, may have to emigrate since nowhere there is more than six feet above present sea level. Even if places do differ in their properties, linkages between them are often critical. After some global warming, the inhabitants of the UK may also enjoy warmer weather and even produce good red wine in the south of the country – but only if the Scots and Welsh can be persuaded to supply enough water to the parched south east of England.

All this can be summarised in two 'laws' of geography:

- most things influence most other things in some way;
- nearby things are usually more similar than things which are far apart.

How do we describe *where*?

Both amateur and professional geographers therefore have to deal with the differences between places and the interactions between places, actions and events. To do this, we obviously need ways of describing the environment which are understood *in the same way* by everyone. The most vital geographical tool is therefore a method of describing *where* things exist or happen.

At the global scale or for a whole continent, we have little choice but to use latitude and longitude. Using this, we can calculate how far apart are London and Rio de Janeiro (5770 miles) if their respective latitudes (51° 30′ North and 22° 53′ South) and longitudes (0° and 43° 17′ West) are known. Elementary calculations using the same information can tell us the time it is in Rio (9 am) when it is noon in London. It must be stressed that there is nothing immutably fixed or sacrosanct about all this reference framework. Where the lines are drawn is simply a matter of convention and familiarity. In the 1880s, there was a huge international argument about whether the Prime Meridian of longitude should pass through London (the winner) or Paris. Yet this simple concept of dividing the world up 'around its circumference' and also 'up and down' between Poles provides a tool of universal value.

Within countries, especially small ones, latitude and longitude become clumsy to use, are not familiar to many people and form a totally invisible system - we do not have these lines marked on the ground (except at Greenwich on the Prime Meridian). Part of the problem may be reduced by use of National Grids or referencing systems. These are best thought of as a flat sheet of graph paper on which position is measured in miles or kilometres, and fractions of them, eastwards and northwards from one fixed point, the origin of the Grid. The location of the front door of the Royal Geographical Society in London, for instance, is TQ 27 80 to the nearest kilometre but is TQ 26729 79635 to the nearest metre in British National Grid coordinates, relative to the origin west of the Scilly Isles. If the TQ code is converted to numbers, the front door of the Royal Geographical Society is seen to be 526,729 metres east of that point and 179,635 metres north. It will become obvious later in this book that the British National Grid is invaluable for many purposes. A more detailed description of it is given in appendix 5 but a summary of it in relation to the Postcode is given in chapter 2.

Yet, even if such grids are easier to use than is a latitude and longitude system, they are still not very convenient for many purposes. Other alternative methods of spatial or locational referencing also have their own advantages and disadvantages. Place names, for instance, are convenient but idiosyncratic and duplicates occur. For many purposes, therefore, we need a geographical tool which is familiar and readily used. The obvious one to use is the postal address. Its problem is that it is too detailed for many needs and, because of the wide variation in the forms of the address and frequent spelling mistakes, is not easy to use in a computer system. The last point is even more important as computers progessively invade ever more of our lives.

Thus we need something that provides the ability to divide up the country into small areas or large ones, is simple to understand, can be related to everyday experience and is easily handled by computers as well as human beings. This is the Postcode, born out of the postal system and founded upon postal addresses. Its value will become still clearer as the book progresses and the vital role of computers in linking together different data sets and analysing the results is explained. In summary, then, the Postcode arrived just in time to make 'within-country' geography easy for all of us to describe and understand. Now we hope you understand why we wrote this book!

The structure and contents of the book

The book falls neatly into four inter-related parts. In the first, covering the first four chapters, we describe the nature of the Postcode and its original purpose in the delivery of the mail. The corresponding situation in other parts of the world is also described since practice there differs somewhat. In addition, the various Postcode products and services currently available from Royal Mail and other organisations are outlined. As indicated in the previous paragraph, use of Postcodes is much easier when we use computers so the second section (chapter 5) describes the kind of tools used for coping with and exploiting Postcode-based data. Both hardware and software are covered; so far as the latter is concerned, Geographical Information Systems (GIS) and the simpler mapping tools are described in detail. The third section deals with the non-postal uses of the Postcode, notably in the Population Census, in target marketing, in town planning, in the health service, education and elsewhere. Finally, we look to the future in reviewing what is likely to happen as the use of the Postcode expands.

Repetition has been deliberately introduced in various places as we suspect that the book will not be read from cover to cover but will be sampled for information on particular topics. For this reason, we have tried to make chapters self-contained though we have included cross-references to other parts of the book where more details are given on that particular topic. References are given to other important publications which are described in the bibliography. For ease of reading, we have also removed much technical detail to the appendices, together with contact addresses (and their Postcodes!) where appropriate. Finally, and as a matter of policy, we have tried throughout the book to avoid the sorts of acronyms and specialist terms which professionals use, irrespective whether they are in marketing, Royal Mail or any other sector. Where acronyms are used they are included in a glossary at the end of the book. We have also tried to make the text cheerful and easily read. We hope you, the reader, approve of these efforts.

The nature of Postcodes and their role in postal services

CHAPTER 1   Postcodes and places

This is a book all about Postcodes. Though they are called different things in different countries and vary somewhat in detailed form, most countries now use them to speed the delivery of mail. But they are also taking on another and more substantial role: they are becoming a widely used and general way of describing the position or location of places, areas or objects on the earth. Because of their familiarity (many people use Postcodes to refer to neighbourhoods) and because of their ability to describe location, they have the potential to expand the value of many data sets which include or could include Postcodes. Indeed, it is no exaggeration to say that Postcodes are going to be vital in future to the way in which we allocate resources, target our marketing and describe how any part of the country differs from its neighbours. All of that, however, is a story for later. To understand the real significance of Postcodes, we need to start with some notions about something very basic – geography. We also need to know something about the nature of information itself and how we can add value to it so as to enhance its range of applications. This chapter therefore sets the stage for the detailed ones coming later.

Why is geography important?

Like history, geography is inescapable. Most decisions we make are constrained, guided or controlled by geographical information. Thus we determine which route to work to follow on the basis of our knowledge of traffic conditions at particular times; we plan the opening of new schools or the closure of others on the basis of changes in local populations; we elect politicians to speak for the people in a particular area; and we investigate how the incidence of heart attacks or other disease varies from one place to another. Government uses geographical information on the location of particular groups of people, such as the unemployed and the elderly, to target funding; businesses use it to identify likely customers and to site their depots and branches; and it is essential to the operations of the armed forces.

These geographical concerns operate at all scales from the global to the micro-scale: global warming may (in decades) make Birmingham more like Bordeaux whilst the failure of a street light in a particular place may facilitate crime. But as human beings, the majority of our interests are normally local. For that reason, our ability to memorise the juxtaposition of one place to another, to appreciate the very character of each place and to communicate this information to others is the stuff of everyday life. Unhappily, because both the ability and the need are so familiar, they are taken for granted. Without thinking, many humans subconsciously assume the structure of our daily world to be simple and the same for everyone – at least until we go to an exotic spot like Japan or the Middle East.

Yet the human ability to comprehend, sift and summarise geographical information is highly sophisticated. The most powerful computer systems are only now coming within reach of matching certain human abilities in coping with geography, such as in pattern recognition. Research on children shows us that our ability to think geographically – for instance, to use a map for simple route-following exercises – grows rapidly from three or four years of age. By their early teens, most people are capable when trained of quite sophisticated interpretation of the landscape from maps, interpolating height above sea level from contours and orienteering using the map. Part of this geographical ability has grown recently: since TV pictures of weather systems from space became commonplace, we have become used to recognising those parts of countries not covered by clouds and interpreting conditions there for ourselves. We act, then, as human computers in processing massive amounts of information gained from various places, in recognising parts of it that are relevant to our task and then using this as a mental map to guide our actions.

If this is all true, why do we need computers to handle databases of geographical information? The answer to that lies in the type of tasks which we need to carry out, the availability of information and, in particular, the nature of that information itself.

What is geographical information?

It is easy to talk about geographical information by example, as above. But what is geographical information? A UK government Committee of Enquiry spelled this out simply in 1987: it is information which can be related to specific locations on the Earth. It covers an enormous range, including the distribution of natural resources (soils, minerals, etc.), descriptions of infrastructure (roads, houses, schools, etc.), patterns of land use and health, wealth, employment, housing and voting habits of people. Indeed, it goes further, though that Committee – which produced the now-famous Chorley Report (see Department of the Environment (DoE) 1987) – ignored these other areas. Most people involved in handling geographical data would include information on the seas, the oceans and the atmosphere. For the rest of this book, however, we too ignore these important areas which need their own special treatment.

Some examples of information held in geographically–referenced (or spatial) form by the British government is given below in table 1.1 which is modified from that given by the DoE (1987). This is only a small fraction of what exists and much of it is now available publicly. All the data sources cited cover England and Wales (and hence about 88% of the population of the UK). In Scotland and Northern Ireland, different sources often provide the equivalent data; thus the General Register Office is the Scottish supplier of population census data (see appendix 6). The final column indicates, where relevant, whether this data is described by postal address (A) or Postcode (P) and hence, subject to confidentiality restrictions and charges, what may be made available in this form. The use of square brackets, such as [A], indicates that such data could in theory be produced by computer processing from other data. Finally, a more detailed version of part of this table, compiled under the UK government's Tradeable Information Initiative, is set out in appendix 3; it lists all known government data sets referenced by Postcode or postal address. Contact points for the information and for services related to it are given in appendix 2.

Table 1.1 Major types and sources of spatial data in the UK (*Source: DoE 1987*)

Type of data	*Major source(s)*	
Land and property		
Large scale maps	Ordnance Survey maps	[A]
Ownership	HM Land Registry	A
Value	Inland Revenue/Valuation Office	A
Land Use (including land use change planning permissions and availability)	Department of the Environment, local government	A

Table 1.1 *(cont)*

Type of data	Major source(s)	
Land and property *(cont.)*		
Housing stock, Conditions and Building Rates	Department of the Environment, local government	A
Socio-economic		
Population characteristics	Office of Population Censuses and Surveys	P
Medical statistics	Office of Population Censuses and Surveys, Department of Health, National Health Service	P
Labour Market (including employment, unemployment, job vacancies)	Department of Employment	P
Business statistics	Department of Trade and Industry/Business Statistics Office	P
Social Benefits	Department of Social Security	A
Crime statistics	Home Office, Royal Ulster Constabulary, local government	A?
Tourism and leisure	National and Regional Tourist Boards, Countryside Commissions, National Park Authorities, local government	P?
Land use, rural resources and the environment		
Small scale maps	Ordnance Survey	
Agriculture	Ministry of Agriculture, Fisheries and Food	
Natural resources	Natural Environment Research Council, Macauley Institute, Soil Survey, survey companies, oil companies, British Coal	
Forestry	Forestry Commission	
Environmental quality	Department of Trade and Industry, Department of the Environment, National Remote Sensing Centre, local government	A
Atmospheric conditions	Meteorological Office	
Infrastructure data		
Utilities networks	Electricity and Water companies, British Gas, British Telecom	A
TV networks	TV companies	A
Road networks	Department of Transport, OS, commercial map-makers, local government	[A]
Other transport networks	British Rail, London Regional Transport, Water companies	

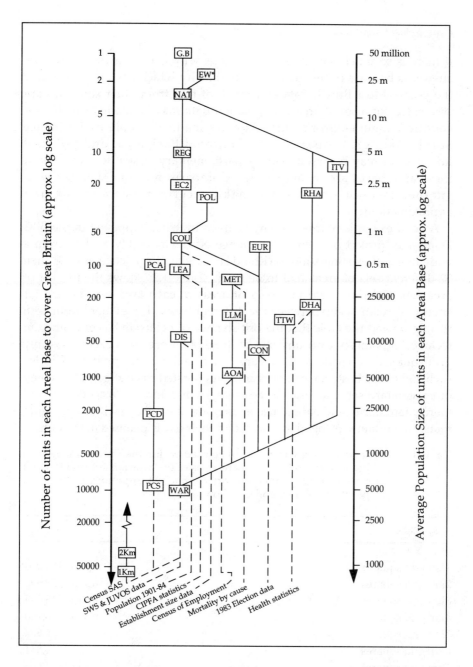

Figure 1.1 The anarchy of geographical area bases in use in the UK. This diagram shows the variety of area bases discovered during the BBC Domesday project to be in use in 1986, together with the relationship between them and the numbers of people they contain on average *(Source: Owen et al 1986)*.

Geographical anarchy

If there is so much data already available, why is there a problem? The answer is because of the geographical anarchy which has grown up over the years. Most British data and much of that from other countries are assembled for a set of areas. Population data may be made available for counties; some environmental data are made available by Ordnance Survey 1km grid squares or by National Park area; and political information may be assembled by parliamentary constituencies. All of these area bases are incompatible. Comparison of one data set with another is only possible by making certain assumptions and approximations.

A good example of this anarchy is given by what happened in the BBC Domesday project of 1986. This pioneered the assembly of data from a wide range of existing sources (Rhind *et al* 1988). In practice, no less than 32 different sets of areas had to be used. Table 1.2 shows the full list of area sets and the (then) numbers of areas in each area set. Figure 1.1 shows the relationship between the different bases. It is evident from both this figure and the table that the British style of Postcode has one inherent technical advantage over any one of these other area sets except possibly grid squares: by virtue of their very small size, any information held for each and every Postcode can be readily aggregated to be a 'good fit' to any other standard set of areas. The advantages therefore of Postcodes are not merely familiarity and ease of use in 'tagging' data; they facilitate bringing many other data sets together - provided their use is planned at the outset.

Table 1.2   The area bases which had to be used within the Domesday System. 'Grid squares' refers to square areas of the British National Grid and printed on Ordnance Survey maps (see appendix 5) (Source: Openshaw, Wymer and Charlton 1986)

Area type	No. of units
1km grid squares	up to 150,000
2km grid squares	up to 23,692
3km grid squares	up to 15,938
4km grid squares	up to 10,950
5km grid squares	up to 7,807
6km grid squares	up to 5,844
7km grid squares	up to 4,566
8km grid squares	up to 3,641
9km grid squares	up to 3,003
10km grid squares	up to 2,507
1981 Census Wards	10,444

Table 1.2 (cont)

Area type	No. of units
Postcode Sectors	8,400
Postcode Districts	2,570
Employment Office Areas	852
Parliamentary Constituencies	650
Districts	488
Travel to Work Areas	334
District Health Authorities	242
Local Labour Markets	280
Functional City Definitions	136
Local Education Authorities	124
Postcode Areas	120
European Constituencies	79
Counties	74
Police Areas	54
Regional Health Authorities	32
EEC level 2 regions	18
ITV regions (best fit)	15
ITV regions non-overlapping version 1	15
ITV regions non-overlapping version 2	15
ITV regions non-overlapping version 3	15
Standard regions	13
Countries (including Isle of Man and Channel Islands for Domesday purposes)	6

The value of data and information

So far, we have used the words 'data' and 'information' almost interchangeably. This is because it is not easy to define the distinctions between 'data', 'information' and 'knowledge' except by example or in the most general of terms. Thus data is usually taken to be 'raw' or little-processed, such as population statistics for a given area; information is taken to imply direct relevance to one or more tasks or policies and generally involves some classification or other processing of the 'raw' data, resulting in (for example) the market size for a product in that area. Knowledge is generally used in a more abstract way but may also be used to denote a set of 'facts', sometimes expressed in statistical form. In principle, then, the data-to-information conversion somehow adds value by creating a new, derivative product without diminishing the value of the original; the converse process is generally impossible. Interestingly, maps are an anomaly because computer-readable geographical data may be converted into other, non-computer-readable data (a paper map, which is widely regarded as information) and this may then be converted back into (different) data by a digitising process. Hence there is a major terminological difficulty: what is data for one person and for one task may be information for others.

The 'commodification' and the commercialisation of geographical information seems to be a relatively recent phenomenon, at least so far as governments are concerned (Openshaw and Goddard 1987). The prices of maps sold by the British national mapping agency (Ordnance Survey) until 1966, for instance, were based only upon the recovery of the costs of printing, of paper and of distribution though copyright charges for copying by users of published maps helped to defray total mapping costs. Prices of large scale maps were raised in 1966 to help meet the costs of speeding the Survey's work programme; seven years later, the organisation was ordered to maximise revenue on all products, subject to certain policy guide-lines (OSRC 1979). For financial year 1991/2, OS was asked to recover at least 70% of its total costs through supply of geographical goods and services. Though other government departments faced much less stringent criteria, the UK government has laid particular stress on trying to identify and publicise the existence of 'tradeable information' derived from *all* the data which it collects (Department of Trade and Industry (DTI) 1990; see appendix 3). The aim has been to exploit such information, through the private sector, in order to generate returns to the tax-payer.

Yet the whole concept of information as a commodity is also less than straightforward. Information does not, for example, wear out through use though its value may diminish with time. The rate of decline in its value will be determined by the rate of change of the features it describes and the advent of competitors. It is also clear that different types of information display different kinds of characteristics: on standard definitions, much digital information could be considered what economists term a public good – it can be copied at near-zero cost and this may well limit the abilities of a vendor to secure acceptable profits.

Despite all this, there are clearly a few situations where the currency of the data *is* critical (such as in many military and in a few civilian tasks). In these circumstances, the market *can* operate to generate (in theory at least) profits. Much more important than this, however, is that the utility and value of spatial or geographic information are often highly related to the expertise, knowledge and imagination of the purchaser and exploiter. In these circumstances, the 'normal' relationships between supply, demand and pricing may well be distorted. In addition, all experience with Geographical Information Systems so far strongly suggests that ultimate value is heavily dependent on the association of one data set with one or more others (see below). Almost by definition, a geographical framework such as given by a set of Postcodes becomes embedded in other data sets and/or these are plotted in relation to it; without this data linkage, almost no other geographical data could be analysed spatially or displayed.

Adding value to geographical information

Like most other information, geographical data or information normally have little intrinsic value. Their value lies in their relevance to the applications to which they are applied. But a special case exists for geographical information, as we hinted above: their potential value may be greatly increased by linking together multiple data sets. The technical aspects of data linkage of this kind are dealt with in chapter 5 while methods used to handle some specific types of Postcoded geographical data are detailed in chapter 7. But here we simply outline the nature of the process. Especially in the UK, this data linkage is often an essential feature since data are collected by different organisations tailored to their own particular purposes, often without regard to other potential uses.

Suppose, for instance, we want to investigate the variations across the UK in the incidence of death from cancer amongst children under 10 years old. To do this, we wish to work with data for each county. Suppose also that (as usual) we have the numbers of people of this age group in each county in one computer file and the numbers of deaths in the group for each county in another file. First, we need to combine or link the two data files. Once this is done, division of one figure by the other for the same county gives the desired answer.

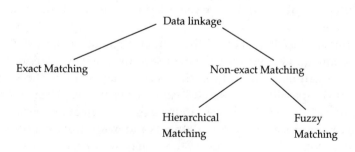

Figure 1.2   Different ways of linking together data using geographical position as the matching key.

If this seems trivial, it is not always so. Consider the different ways in which data sets may need to be linked together (figure 1.2). 'Exact matching' is the operation already described. The operation to bring the two data sets together is easy and is achieved through use of the key which is common to both files (e.g. the county name). Thus the record in each file with the same county name is extracted, the two are joined together and stored in another file. Postcodes would serve as well as county names in this example but we will demonstrate that later.

Sometimes, however, some information is available for more detailed geographical areas than is other information. Typically, frequently collected (e.g. finance or social survey) data are only available for large areas (such as Standard Regions or Countries) but infrequently collected data (e.g. from the Census of Population) are available for very much smaller areas (e.g. groups of Postcodes). If the smaller areas 'nest' (i.e. fit exactly within) the larger ones, then the solution is to use 'hierarchical matching' – add the data for the small areas together until the grouped areas match the bigger ones and then do an exact match. Needless to say, this is readily possible with Postcodes.

On many occasions, however, the small areas do not match the larger ones. This is especially true when dealing with environmental data. The areas for which agricultural information is collected – typically individual farms – rarely match the boundary between types of soil. If we wish to answer questions such as 'What soils are the most productive so far as wheat is concerned?', we need to overlay the agricultural output and the soils data sets and compute what crop productivity exists on each and every type of soil present on every farm. In principle, this is like laying a map on tracing paper over another and noting the combinations of soil and crop productivity (see plate 1). This is not merely laying one picture on top of another and photographing the result; the combinations are held in our computer's database so that we can ask questions about the areas in which each combination occurs.

The fundamental point is that all these operations use geography or space as the common key between the data sets; the relevant parts of the two sets of information are linked together where they relate to the same space. With this capability, we can add value: from the two data sets of soils and crops mentioned above, we can have one combination. From 20 data sets, we can produce 190 pairs of data sets and over a million possible combinations in total. Whilst many of these may well be valueless, the range of applications is inevitably much greater than with each one of the original twenty data sets considered in isolation. All that said, the possibility of carrying out such overlay and hence adding value is greatly affected by the way in which we describe the geography in the data sets.

Fixing a position in space

In practice, we have various possible ways of doing this, some better than others. Which is best depends partly on the area in which we are interested and the tasks we have to carry out. For example, whether we know it or not, we all live on an oblate spheroid called the earth. For many applications carried out within any one small country, the earth's detailed, pear-like shape can be ignored. Some applications, however – such as navigating great distances from one country to another – demand that the pilot takes the three dimensional nature of the world into account if everyone is to arrive where they wish and expect. But many of our needs for information and our perceptions of space are met by thinking of our local world as a two-dimensional place. The directions for walking around a city or for driving rarely need to include details of how to go vertically up or down! Sometimes, indeed, we can go further and think of 'place' in a way that is not tied to strict physical dimensions at all; 'the Pennines' form an area with no generally agreed specific geographical extent and position but that does not stop us from using the term. Finally, we may often describe our ideas of geography not simply in terms of 'objects' embedded in space (like counties in a country) but through the relationships between different 'objects'. Knowing how to go from Westminster to a major railway station in London requires a knowledge of which streets join each other and of a path threaded through some of them (see below).

What then are the tools of our trade that enable us to describe those different aspects of geography which we require for a particular purpose? Clearly, for us to be able to understand and use geographical information demands that the location of the 'object' in question is described in terms which both we and others can understand; it must be unambiguous and economical. To have two or more places with the same location code could make life difficult and long, and complex descriptions inhibit use of information. The location must also be capable of being expressed as accurately as is needed for a given purpose; to steer a course round streets or to deliver newspapers when the information is only accurate to the nearest mile is likely to cause problems. Finally, it helps if it is easily identified 'in the field' and relates in some obvious way to the physical world experienced by the populace at large. In short, the geographical description of place needs ideally to be unambiguous, terse, accurate, familiar and easy to use for a variety of different purposes.

We now consider the different candidates, summarising their advantages and disadvantages. Table 1.3 lists the different ways of defining geographical position and figures 1.3 to 1.8 illustrate how this works in general. Tables 1.4 and 1.5 contain data for figures 1.3 and 1.4 respectively.

Table 1.3 The characteristics of different methods for describing place or geography

Type	Characteristics	Example	Advantages	Disadvantages
Nominal	No relationship between 'objects' can be derived	County name, individual name of house (figure 1.3 and table 1.4)	Simple, familiar	Useless except for distinguishing one place from another. Difficult to handle inside computers because it varies greatly in form
Partially sequenced	Order of house numbers normally in sequence (2,4,6 or 1,3,5,) within a street i.e. some geographical hierarchy implied	Street address (figure 1.4)	Simple, familiar and matches to structure of the real world. Widely used in manual record keeping	Relationship between house numbers approximate, that between streets unknown
Topological	Defines what is next in space to a particular 'object'	'Oxford Street and Regent Street intersect' or 'Kent is adjacent to East Sussex'	Familiar and simple in terms of route following	Does not imply physical distance; normally, maps cannot be made on this basis (but see figure 1.6)
Local geometry	Defines what is next in space to a particular object and quantifies the distance between objects	'the hydrant is 5 metres from the corner of this house' (see figure 1.7)	Easy to understand and use, works well over short distances and where landmarks are common	Not good in rural areas with few landmarks or over large areas. Cannot relate objects described in relation to different landmarks
Global geometry	Defines location in space as compared to a single fixed point (e.g. origin of the British National Grid or the centre of the earth)	'At National Grid reference NT123 456' or 'at latitude 51° North and longitude 1° West'	Works well over large areas; permits calculation of distance between any two objects. Can be used at any level of detail. Simple to handle in computers – standard in form	Not 'natural' on the ground; requires maps to identify location or satellite based position fixing systems

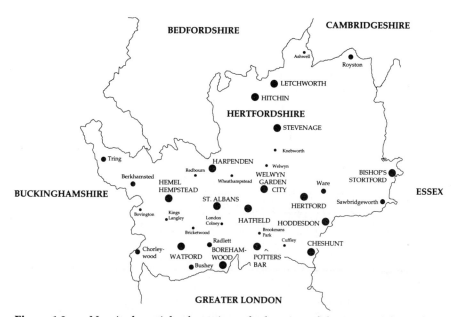

Figure 1.3 Nominal spatial referencing - the location of the 'entities' (towns) is given only by place names. The numbers in table 1.4 refer to the importance of the town on some criterion and this is reflected in the size of type used in the map. Very little can be done with such data except to match information for each town in one computer file with other information for the same town in another file. Even drawing this map required additional spatial referencing (of the global geometry type) !

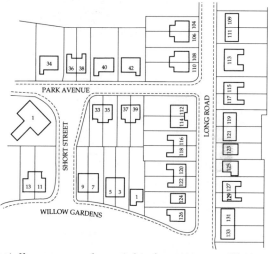

Figure 1.4 Partially sequenced spatial referencing, as illustrated by house numbering within streets. The accompanying list of houses (table 1.5) is sorted by house number within a street and each house has an attribute *(S: Semi-detached house, D: Detached house).*

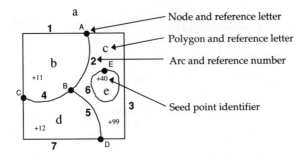

Arc Topology				
Arc #	From node	To node	Left poly	Right poly
1	A	C	b	a
2	B	A	b	c
3	A	D	a	c
4	B	C	d	b
5	B	D	c	d
6	E	E	c	e
7	C	D	d	a

Polygon Topology		
User-ID	Polygon letter	Arc #
11	a	1,3,7
99	b	1,2,4
12	c	3,5,2,6
40	d	5,7,4
	e	6

Node Topology	
Node letter	Arc #
A	1,2,3
B	2,4,5
C	1,4,7
D	3,5,7
E	6

Figure 1.5   The relationships between nodes (the points at which lines intersect), lines (here called arcs) and areas (or polygons) as described using topology. Thus arc 4 is the 'edge' between polygon d and polygon b whilst polygon d is built from arcs 4, 5, and 7 and node B 'receives' arcs 2, 4 and 5. *(Source ARC/INFO User Manual)*

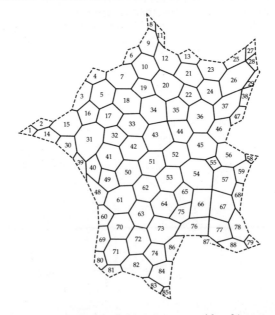

Figure 1.6   This map of the administrative areas (the départements) of France was constructed entirely from a knowledge of the topology of the areas i.e. which polygons were adjacent to which other ones. *(Source: Kendall 1971)*

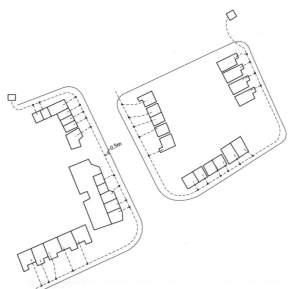

Figure 1.7 Local geometry as used by utilities in digging for buried pipelines or cables (the pecked lines). The workman is instructed to dig at a position defined by its relationship to a particular house and a specified distance in from the pavement edge. In practice, of course, the computer system holds the information as 'global geometry' - each line is stored in National Grid coordinates and the map is produced from them - but these are much less meaningful to the workman.

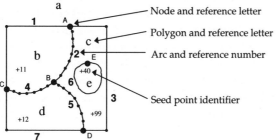

Node and reference letter

Polygon and reference letter

Arc and reference number

Seed point identifier

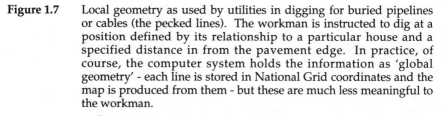

Arc Topology				
Arc #	From node	To node	Left poly	Right poly
1	A	C	b	a
2	B	A	b	c
3	A	D	a	c
4	B	C	d	.b
5	B	D	c	d
6	E	E	c	e
7	C	D	d	a

Polygon Topology		
User-ID	Polygon letter	Arc #
11	a	1,3,7
99	b	1,2,4
12	c	3,5,2
40	d	5,7,4
	e	6

Node Topology	
Node letter	Arc #
A	1,2,3
B	2,4,5
C	1,4,7
D	3,5,7
E	6

Figure 1.8 Spatial or geographical position represented by global geometry; the 'knots' on the lines, each represent the National Grid coordinates of individual digitised points. *(Source: ARC/INFO User Manual).*

23

Table 1.4 County and town names and their attribute type as used to create figure 1.3

Name	Type	Name	Type
Ashwell	4	Hertfordshire	1
Bedfordshire	1	Hitchin	2
Berkhamsted	3	Hoddesdon	2
Bishop's Stortford	2	Kings Langley	4
Borehamwood	2	Knebworth	4
Bovington	4	Letchworth	2
Bricketwood	4	London Colney	4
Brookmans Park	4	Potters Bar	2
Buckinghamshire	1	Radlett	3
Bushey	3	Redbourn	4
Cambridgeshire	1	Royston	3
Cheshunt	2	St. Albans	2
Chorleywood	3	Sawbridgeworth	3
Cuffley	4	Stevenage	2
Essex	1	Tring	3
Greater London	1	Ware	3
Harpenden	2	Watford	2
Hatfield	2	Welwyn	4
Hemel Hempstead	2	Welwyn Garden City	2
Hertford	2	Wheathampstead	4

The types of description in table 1.3 are really just the building 'blocks' or 'primitives' with which we normally work. For instance, we might say 'Durham, Yorkshire and Northumberland will have snow tomorrow'. Inside computers, we can build up complicated areas if we have many small building blocks; there are, for example something like 125,000 areas for which statistics are produced from the British Population Census (see chapter 6). Similarly, we can define areas inside our computer by a list of coordinates (see figure 1.7) which, when joined together by straight lines, locate the boundary of that region.

Table 1.5 Property addresses and house characteristics as shown in figure 14

Location	Number	Type	Location	Number	Type
Long Road	109	S	Long Road	120	S
Long Road	111	S	Long Road	122	S
Long Road	113	D	Long Road	124	D
Long Road	115	S	Long Road	126	D
Long Road	117	S	Park Avenue	34	D
Long Road	119	S	Park Avenue	36	S
Long Road	121	S	Park Avenue	38	S
Long Road	123	D	Park Avenue	40	D
Long Road	125	D	Park Avenue	42	D
Long Road	127	S	Park Avenue	33	S

Table 1.5 *(cont).*

Location	Number	Type	Location	Number	Type
Long Road	129	S	Park Avenue	35	S
Long Road	131	S	Park Avenue	37	S
Long Road	133	S	Park Avenue	39	S
Long Road	104	S	Short Street	1	D
Long Road	106	S	Willow Gardens	1	D
Long Road	108	S	Willow Gardens	3	S
Long Road	110	S	Willow Gardens	5	S
Long Road	112	S	Willow Gardens	7	S
Long Road	114	S	Willow Gardens	9	S
Long Road	116	S	Willow Gardens	11	S
Long Road	118	S	Willow Gardens	13	S

Different ways of describing geography can also be combined. It is, for example, quite common to describe position using a hierarchy of nominal forms of referencing: we, the authors, work in Birkbeck College, within the London Borough of Camden, within London, within the South East of England, within Britain, within Europe and so on. This is, however, clumsy and long-winded. Moreover, what constitutes Europe or the other areas tends to mutate through time; by the year 2000, Europe may be a community of nearly 20 nations rather than the present 12. Such a nominal type of spatial referencing is also difficult to use for any purpose except identifying uniqueness; it is inadequate, for example, as a description of how to get to our front door. It is also liable to be used differently by different people: we also happen, for instance, to work in a particular Family Practitioner area, within a Health District, within a Health Region. Finally, such *ad hoc* nominal means of describing position are liable to be re-arranged by politicians for administrative convenience or other reasons: there is a long history of such schemes being re-arranged in the last 50 years, perhaps most notably the 1974 re-creation of local government areas in England and Wales. If that happens, information for the periods before and after the change cannot be compared if their position in space is described solely in nominal terms.

All relative or nominal forms of position-fixing cause difficulties over large areas. There are, for example, several hundred Acacia Avenues in the UK. This may be avoided by combinations of various schemes: thus the location of a lamp post may be specified and validated by describing it as: 'number M2911, 60 metres north along Stephen Street from the junction with St Cuthbert's Way in Erewhon in the County of Barsetshire'. In practice, however, that is a clumsy way to proceed. Perhaps more important, it limits the use which can be made of the data since it is very difficult to link it to other data in the manner shown earlier.

A reasonable conclusion to be drawn from all this is that different ways of describing geography have different advantages and disadvantages – but some are more useful than others and some are more easy to grasp and observe than others. In an ideal world, therefore, we may wish to use particular methods for describing position for certain purposes and others for quite different purposes. All this means that we need ways of converting one description of location in what is really a spatial or geographic language into an equivalent description in another language. As it happens, Postcodes have many attractions as a tool for conversion of data from one 'language' to another. But, in our view (and also that of the government's Committee of Enquiry into the Handling of Geographic Information – see DoE 1987), two different ways of describing geography in Britain are needed to cope with the whole range of different purposes. Fortunately, their advantages complement each other. The two systems needed are the British National Grid and Postcodes. It should be noted that a separate Grid is used to cover Northern Ireland but the principle is identical. Table 1.6 sets out the relative merits of each. This book is mainly about Postcodes but, because the National Grid is vital for many applications which also use the Postcode, it is summarised in chapter 2 and described in full in appendix 5; numerous references are made to it throughout the text.

Table 1.6   Relative and shared merits of the National Grid and of Postcodes

Geographic System	Advantages	Disadvantages of sole use
National Grid coordinates	• covers whole of Britain • maintained by one organisation • provides consistent geographical resolution (or detail) across whole of country and level of detail may be chosen by the user • defines features or places relative to each other. As a result: – mapping is possible – calculations of routeways and distances between places are possible • is easily handled by computer • can be converted into Postcodes through use of an index	• uses Irish Grid in N. Ireland • no obvious relationship exists on the ground between physical features (e.g. roads or postal addresses) and the National Grid i.e. it is unsuited for delivery of goods. It is 'geographically neutral' and not related to the location of people • some people find it difficult to understand (but see chapter 2 and appendix 5) • few people know the grid reference of (say) their own house
Postcodes	• covers whole of the UK • maintained by one organisation • is closely linked to the postal address and to the 'perceived structure' of geography such as buildings and streets	• does not provide any reliable knowledge of where features (such as Postcoded buildings or organisations) are in relation to each other i.e. mapping, etc. is not possible except in trivial cases

Table 1.6 *(cont.)*

Geographic System	Advantages	Disadvantages of sole use
	• provides a fixed hierarchy of areas covering the country and *ad-hoc* areas can be well approximated by use of Unit Postcodes • are easily handled by computer • can be converted into National Grid coordinates through use of an index	• only works well at detailed level where mail is delivered (geographical resolution is coarse in rural areas) i.e it is a people-related system • finding out what is the postcode of a place has been difficult until recently (see chapter 4)

If we abandoned all other forms of spatial referencing or at least used these two as the basic 'building blocks' of other systems, many of our problems in relating data together and the geographical anarchy already described would be minimised.

Computers and geography

On several occasions already we have mentioned computers. The reasons for this are simple:

- there is a 'lot of geography about' and such machines help us to sift it quickly to find what information is required;

- many tasks for which we use geographical information require calculation (e.g. 'how far is it from Parliament to Downing Street?') which computers can carry out free from error and human effort;

- the computer is increasingly proving to be a convenient method of storing information. Thus some 600 million alphabetic characters – about 12 million average addresses without the use of clever methods of compacting them – can be stored on one CD (Compact Disc; see plate 2). This is more familiar as the Compact Disc is used to store music and each one costs less than £1 to reproduce though the cost of assembling the information and making the master pressing is much higher.

- the cost of computing is still falling dramatically, as figure 1.9 shows. What costs £1 to compute in 1992 would have cost well above £1,000 in real terms when Postcodes were first introduced to the whole of the UK. Some costs have declined even faster: the cost of computer main memory in 1971 to hold and operate upon 600 addresses at any one time was well above £30,000 at 1992 prices. Though one cannot now buy such small amounts of memory, on a *pro rata* basis it would now cost about £1 for a Personal Computer. Not all of this improvement is passed on to end users – more sophisticated software mops up some of the power – but the effects of the change have been dramatic and improved the feasibility of many operations. In turn, this has led to more and more data becoming available in computer form; this in turn again has led to greater use of computers and further falls in price as more are made and sold.

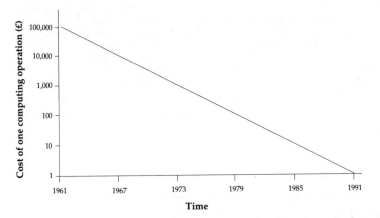

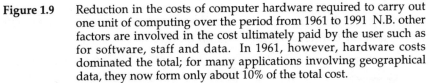

Figure 1.9   Reduction in the costs of computer hardware required to carry out one unit of computing over the period from 1961 to 1991 N.B. other factors are involved in the cost ultimately paid by the user such as for software, staff and data. In 1961, however, hardware costs dominated the total; for many applications involving geographical data, they now form only about 10% of the total cost.

Computing power, however, is no panacea for intelligence and sound working practices. Coping with street addresses inside the computer, for instance, is often a frustrating experience because they vary greatly in form, they are frequently misspelt and they may be ambiguous where two streets have the same name. Without very sophisticated computer software, such problems can cause much trouble. Moreover, administrative records in organisations such as local government which contain street addresses may become out-of-date because it is no one person's job to monitor all changes in the physical fabric of the area. For this reason, a description of geographical position which is simple, regular in form, easily handled by the computer, available as very small building blocks, and which is kept up-to-date by one organisation nationally has great attractions. In the next chapter, we describe how the Postcode meets these requirements. We describe how it is complementary to other methods of description of geography, notably National Grid references. And we set out its advantages and disadvantages which need to be taken into account when planning its use for any of the non-mailing purposes described in later chapters.

CHAPTER 2   What is a Postcode?

How we write our addresses on mail clearly has an effect on how quickly and reliably it is delivered. But clarity is not the only important criterion. The method of defining where the letter is to go is also rather important. A famous experiment carried out in the 1980s by Tobler, the American geographer, involved various friends around the world sending him mail labelled in different ways. He then counted the proportion of those sent which arrived at his Californian home and how long they had taken. The least successful were those labelled only with his name and with his home's latitude and longitude! That sent from Milton Keynes travelled to California via Australia and was appropriately annotated. If nothing else, this demonstrates the resilience of the postal system but use of latitude and longitude is manifestly not the best method of describing destination of mail even if it is suitable for aeroplanes!

To minimise effort (and hence cost) of delivery and to maximise speed of handling, most postal agencies around the world define their own standard method of addressing. The British form is shown below, together with an example:

Name of addressee	David Rhind
Number of house (or name if no number is allocated) and name of street	7 New Place
Locality name (if required)	
POST TOWN (in block capitals)	WELWYN
County name (if required)	Hertfordshire
POSTCODE (clear, well-spaced block lettering is required)	AL6 9QA

To complicate matters slightly, Royal Mail permit a series of exceptions in this addressing convention: for example, where the town name, for instance, is identical to that of the county (such as for Durham or Hertford), then the latter may be omitted. Examples of this can be seen in the latter part of appendix 2, where a list is given of officially-appointed distributors of Royal Mail Postcode products. No compromise is however possible so far as the last item of the address is concerned: the Postcode.

Postcodes are used in many parts of the world but their form differs in different countries. In fact, not all countries yet use them as devices to speed the mail (for example the Republic of Ireland has no postal codes outside Dublin, see Dunlea 1991) though the number is growing. In its simplest form, it is a label that defines a set of mail delivery points. At its most detailed (as in the UK), this set defines a small number (about 15 on average) of mail delivery points; multiples of these are assembled into the load for an individual mail carrier. In countries which have less detailed Postcodes (such as the United States until recently, where it is known as a zip-code), each one defines an area.

A characteristic of all Postcode systems is their hierarchical nature. This is required to steer the mail from its origin to its final destination: it is sent first to the nearest large town and from there it may be sent to a local sorting centre and finally to the individual business or house. All this is facilitated by the encoding of the large town, of a locality, etc. in the code, as is demonstrated below for the UK Postcode. But this hierarchical organisation, covering the whole of a national territory, has advantages for other users as well. It ensures that there is usually a set of areal units appropriate to their particular needs for a given level of detail; even if there is not, new areas may readily be created by amalgamating the basic 'building blocks' (sometimes called 'basic spatial units') provided these are small enough.

The UK Postcode

The UK Postcode is a summary of an address in a form which can be read by computer and thus enables mail to be sorted automatically. It consists of a group of letters and numbers. The format of these letters and numbers conforms to certain standards (see below). Every address in the UK to which Royal Mail delivers has been given a Postcode.

The form of the Postcode

There are about 1.6 million Postcodes covering approximately 24 million addresses in the UK. The distinguishing characteristic of the UK Postcode as compared to the others described in chapter 3 is that it consists of both numeric and alphabetic characters. The reasons for this decision made by Royal Mail were:

- a mixture of numbers and letters is more easily remembered than an all-numeric code;
- a useful mnemonic content can be included in the code which reduces the level of error on the part of the user (e.g. OX is used for Oxford, AB is used for Aberdeen and BD is used for Bradford);
- using numbers and letters gives more code combinations;
- the format chosen allowed continuing use of the historic London and other District codes in almost all cases;
- correspondence is heaviest between conurbations, which means that most mail senders only needed to add three characters to the existing District numbers developed for many cities early in this century to make up the Postcode.

LARGE USER AND NON-GEOGRAPHIC POSTCODES

For obvious reasons, most of this book concentrates on the geography of Postcodes but the non-geographical elements of them must be mentioned for completeness. A Large User Postcode in the UK is issued when:

- a firm or business at a new address regularly receives in a normal day 25 or more items of mail in an urban area, or 50 or more items in a rural area;
- a private mailbox (a PO Box) is provided. This offers the option of an abbreviated mailing address;
- the organisation has opted for Royal Mail to sort mail into groups destined for different internal divisions within the firm.

These Large User Postcodes relate to one delivery point. Generally Royal Mail endeavours to ensure that the Large User Postcode allocated is similar to those in the surrounding area but some flexibility is permitted e.g. if the organisation moves within a Postcode Sector, it may normally retain the use of the same Postcode.

In addition, non-geographic Large User Postcodes are allocated to a small number of organisations receiving an exceptionally large volume of mail. These may differ substantially from the 'normal' geographic Postcode in which the organisation is located. Thus the National Exhibition Centre is allocated the outward code (see below) of B40, even though it is actually located in B37 while the Driver and Vehicle Licensing Centre in Swansea has the exclusive use of SA99. In some cases, PO Box catchment areas are operated: AB9 is the Postcode District for large users in Postcode Districts AB1 and AB2.

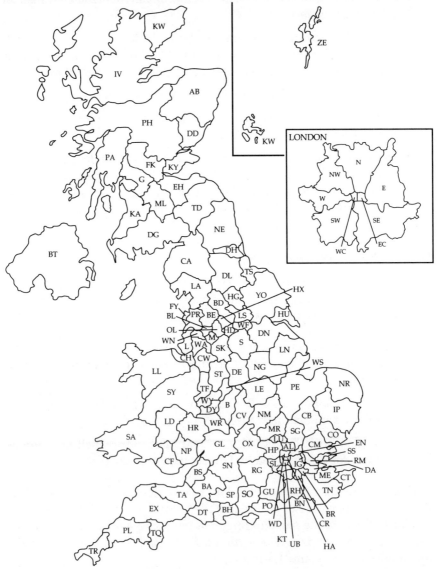

Figure 2.1　　Postcode Areas in the UK *(Source: Royal Mail)*

GEOGRAPHIC POSTCODES

It is sensible to start at the least, rather than the most, detailed end of the Postcode hierarchy. Thus the largest postal unit within the whole country is the Postcode Area (see figure 2.1 for a map and appendix 4 for a full list). Most of these are (or were) centred on major nodes in the national transport network though Fylde (FY) and others are exceptions to this general rule. They are generally denoted by two alphabetic characters, chosen wherever possible to be a mnemonic for the place (e.g. Edinburgh is EH whilst Milton Keynes is MK). Only one alphabetic character is used for the five largest cities i.e. Birmingham (B), Glasgow (G), Liverpool (L), Manchester (M) and Sheffield (S) and the eastern (E), northern (N) and western (W) London Areas.

Each of these Postcode Areas is then sub-divided into Postcode Districts (figure 2.2). These are denoted by a number ranging between 0 and 99; thus AL6 is one Postcode District within the area covered by the St Albans post town north of London. A minor complication occurs in the capital city: a further alphabetic character may be added. As an example, WC1E contains a large part of the University of London (and much else).

Figure 2.2   Postcode Areas and Districts in part of the UK *(Source: Royal Mail)*

The codes for the Postcode Area and the District together comprise the Outward Code. This identifies the town or District to which the mail is being sent for further sorting or forwarding. In Royal Mail's terminology, the remainder of the Postcode – termed the Inward Code and separated from the Outward Code by a space – defines the Sector within the District and the street or individual address to which the mail is being sent.

The structure of the Inward Code is also in two parts. The first is a numeric indicator of the Postcode Sector, using the digits 1 to 9 and then 0. Thus AL6 9 is a Sector within a District within a Postcode Area. Finally, the full Postcode is produced by adding two alphabetic characters. Hence AL6 9QA is the Postcode of the small group of houses in New Place, Welwyn (plate 3 shows an example for another area). In practice, of course, the process can be extended further to define individual houses or individual organisations. The latter are allocated their own Postcode if the volume of mail justifies it: the threshold is normally taken as 25 items per day for new organisations in urban areas or 50 items per day for those in rural areas and 172,000 Postcodes are allocated to such 'Large Users'.

For their own purposes, it is not necessary for Royal Mail to identify each and every house individually; delivery of mail containing a full postal address as well as a Postcode works well using human beings since the system is resilient and (normally) corrects errors at the local level. But for those organisations or tasks which *do* require individual identification of buildings, the Postcode can be extended with additional characters to make it truly unique. Royal Mail has been carrying out experiments with a two character suffix to the Postcode, one of which is alphabetic. This gives 180 different possibilities: for this (and other) reasons, Royal Mail is reducing the maximum number of delivery points in a Postcode to below 100. By the time this book is published, the extreme figures reported below should have been greatly changed though the average number of delivery points per Postcode will not be noticeably affected.

Hints have been given above that, for a variety of reasons, the format of the Postcode is not truly common across the whole of Britain. Table 2.1 shows the variety of formats in use, with A representing an alphabetic character and N a numeric one. All of the variations in format occur solely in the Outcode (or first part) of the Postcode.

Other conventions are that the letter J is not used in either of the first two alphabetic positions of the Postcode (except in Jersey, a separate postal administration) and Q, V and X are not used in the first alpha position. The letters I and Z are not used in the second alpha position (except for the 'one-off' GIR 0AA used for the National Giro bank) to avoid confusion between this and the digits 1 and 2 respectively. The only letters to appear in the third position of the Outcode are A, E, H, M, N, P, R, T, V, X and Y

Table 2.1   Variations in the format of the UK Postcode *(Source: Royal Mail)*

Format	Example	Number of Outcodes in this form
AN NAA	M2 5BQ	70
ANN NAA	M34 3AB	262
AAN NAA	AL6 9QA	1052
AANN NAA	DN16 9AA	1482
ANA NAA	W1P 1PA	9 (Only in W1)
AANA NAA	EC1A 1HQ	49 (Only London Districts EC1-4, SW1, WC1-2)
AAA NAA	GIR 0AA	1 Postcode only is officially sanctioned

The only ones in the fourth letter are A, B, E, H, M, N, P, R, V, W, X and Y. The second, always consistent, part of the Postcode never contains the letters C, I, K, M, O and V since these are easily confused with G, 1 (or 7), R, N, 0 (or Q) and W in hand-written form. Thus some 400 letter pairs are available for use in the last part of the Inward Code, ranging from AA to ZZ.

Postcodes and delivery points

The numbers of Postcodes at different levels in the Postcode hierarchy are shown in table 2.2 as of September 1991. The number of Postcode Sectors approximates to the number of electoral wards but the areas involved do not match; Postcode Districts are five times as numerous as parliamentary constituencies and Postcode Areas are twice as numerous as counties and Scottish regions. The number of Unit Postcodes is approximately ten times that of the next finest nationwide set of areal or spatial units, the Enumeration Districts used for collecting information in the decennial Census of Population.

Of course, the number of Districts in Areas, the number of Sectors in Districts, the numbers of Postcodes in Sectors and the number of mail delivery points in any one of these differ from one part of the country to another. Table 2.3 gives a fuller analysis of the numbers of Postcodes with one delivery point up to those with 20 delivery points Figure 2.3 extends this by showing in graphical form this variation up to 65 delivery points: the histogram is based upon *all* Postcodes in the PAF on CD and

Table 2.2   Numbers of areal units in the standard Postcode hierarchy, as of September 1991 *(Source: PAF on CD 1991/4)*

Level in spatial hierarchy	Number of units
Postcode Areas	120
Postcode Districts	2,679
Postcode Sectors	8,820
Postcodes ('Residential' only)	1,397,754
('Non-residential')	151,765
('Large Users' only)	171, 541
Total Postcodes	1,721,060
Residential delivery points	23,845,162

demonstrates the numbers of Postcodes which have one delivery point, two delivery points, three delivery points and so on at that point in time. This was carried out by an analysis of the Postcode Address File on CD (PAF on CD) dated September 1991 (the latest available when carrying out the detailed research for this book).

In statistical terms, this is normally called a frequency distribution. Clearly the frequency distribution is massively skewed i.e. there are far more Postcodes with very small numbers of delivery points than with

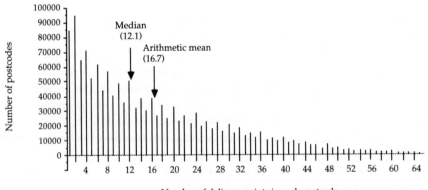

Figure 2.3   Variation in the numbers of delivery points per residential Postcode in the UK *(Source: PAF on CD 1990/4)*

large ones. As a result, the average number of delivery points per Postcode (approximately 17 if large users and non-residential Postcodes are excluded from consideration or 14 if they are included) is not very meaningful. The best single statistic to use is the median value. This is the value such that an equal number of Postcodes are above and below it on the frequency distribution. Its value is 12 and this may be said to be the most typical number of delivery points in a wholly residential Postcode in Britain for the PAF on CD of September 1991.

Table 2.3   Variation in the numbers of delivery points per Postcode in the UK
(Source: PAF on CD 1990/4)

Number of delivery points	Number of Postcodes
1	84137
2	94544
3	64775
4	71220
5	52207
6	61657
7	44245
8	56458
9	40577
10	48051
11	35533
12	50396
13	31891
14	38656
15	30353
16	38718
17	26710
18	33998
19	24637
20	32529

Two other aspects of the histogram are worth describing. The first is that Royal Mail seem to have a penchant for even numbers of delivery points when designing Postcodes: the number of Postcodes with even numbers of delivery points is consistently greater than is the next larger odd number category. Thus there are more Postcodes with two delivery points than those with one, more with four delivery points than with three and so on!

The second aspect is that only 3% of Postcodes have more than 50 delivery points; only 0.2% have more than 100 delivery points though a long 'tail' exists to the frequency distribution i.e. a few odd Postcodes have large numbers of delivery points, there being two Postcodes with 155 delivery points, two with 199 points and the extreme case being Postcode EC4V 3EH with 511 delivery points. The 29 extreme cases are listed in table 2.4 and details of the most extreme one are shown in table 2.5, as derived from the PAF on CD of September 1991 (the most recent available before the completion of the book). Note that these extreme cases were scheduled to be split in early 1992 to remove any Postcode with more than 100 delivery points, and so these observations represent a 'snapshot' in time.

Table 2.4 Postcodes with more than 150 delivery points (DPs) as derived from the PAF of September 1991 *(Source: PAF on CD 1991/4)*

Postcodes	DPs	Postcodes	DPs
EC4V 3EH	511	EC2Y 8DE	328
WC1N 1AN	303	WC1N 1AQ	276
EC2Y 8DD	249	CM2 6JQ	215
EC2Y 8DL	204	BN27 3JW	201
S1 2AP	199	BL1 2AR	199
CV1 3HT	196	EC2Y 8DR	190
BN43 6JQ	189	EC1R 0LN	185
EC4Y 0DT	184	CA2 6TW	182
EC2Y 8DN	178	CA2 7XH	177
SW5 0PA	172	PR3 1PJ	170
NG3 4JA	162	CR0 4HB	162
NW3 4HT	159	RG6 4HN	157
NW1 8UE	155	LE7 8NX	155
SO3 2FP	154	S65 2LJ	153
RG6 3HA	152		

Table 2.5 Details of the Postcode with the most delivery points in the UK in September 1991 *(Source: PAF on CD 1991/4)*

Premise	101-611 /QUEENSWAY
Street	UPPER THAMES ST
Post town	LONDON
Postcode	EC4V 3EH
User category	R (residential)
Sortcode	09304
Grid East	53220
Grid North	18070
Wardcode	28E22
Delivery points	511
NHS Code	F10

Keeping the Postcode up-to-date

It is self-evident that the building of new housing, commercial or industrial premises will lead to some need for changes in the Postcode system. Equally, demolition of property leads to Postcodes being (temporarily at least) redundant. If the objective of each Postcode describing a small group of properties is to be maintained, new codes must be created and old ones deleted from the master database maintained by Royal Mail, the PAF.

Under some circumstances it is necessary to recode existing Postcodes. This is avoided whenever possible but if there are, for instance, no more permutations available within an existing Postcode Sector then a new Sector is created by adding an extra digit; other reasons for recoding include making internal 'circulation' operations more efficient. Some Sectors in Derby and Leicester, for instance, had to be recoded because of exhaustion, whilst the 1990 recoding of Aberdeen where AB3 addresses were changed to AB33 ones was due to the inadequate basis of the original coding. Whenever recoding takes place, all delivery points in the affected area are notified and all Postcode product users are also notified by Royal Mail.

In addition to this periodic and unavoidable necessity, regular up-dating of the PAF is carried out. The magnitude of the change varies with the state of the local and national economy. The updates originate in the local Postcode Areas. Though quality checking procedures are in place, it is obvious that some variation in the rate and accuracy of reporting must occur between the different Postcode Areas. Hitherto, updates have been published quarterly but will be assembled and disseminated every month to those customers requiring them by the end of 1992.

Comparison of the 1991/4 version of PAF on CD with that of 1990/4 provides insight into how the Postcodes on PAF may change over a calendar year. It is stressed that this is not necessarily typical since Royal Mail spent £2 million on enhancing the PAF and the Postcode system by establishing a 'task force' to improve the quality of the PAF in 1991. Prior to this initiative, it was determined that between the middle of 1989 and the end of 1990 the average gross change to PAF was 0.2% per month (or 2.4% per year assuming each change affects a Postcode only once). This is a higher rate of change than the 1.2% quoted in the Chorley Report for the mid 1980s. Royal Mail claims that the 'task force' improved the accuracy of the PAF by 4% in 1991 (equivalent to 1 million delivery points), and approximately 20% of Postcodes saw some change during that period. This is not borne out by the results in table 2.6, but the latter's contents include both natural change and the first stages only of this reorganisation and enhancement.

Table 2.6 Changes in Postcode and delivery point (DP) numbers between September 1991 PAF on CD and that of one year earlier. *(Source: PAF on CD 1990/4 and 1991/4)*

Date	1990/4	1991/4
Number of Postcodes:		
Residential	1,415,096	1,397,754
Non-residential	132,042	151,765
Large User	174,539	171,541
Total Delivery Points	23,673,809	23,845,162
Residential Postcodes only		
New Postcodes	–	84,898
Postcodes not in the 1991/4 PAF	102,240	–
Postcodes with different DPs	–	106,620

Many of these figures show relatively small changes (the total number of delivery points has only increased by 0.7% and 1,312,865 residential Postcodes are identical in both files) but substantial change has taken place at the micro-scale. A more striking example of the changes within the file is that some 84,898 Postcodes appeared in PAF 1991/4 for the first time and 102,240 in the PAF a year earlier had disappeared (table 2.6). As shown above, the numbers of delivery points in 106,620 Postcodes changed in the year: as this book went to press in December 1991 the total number of delivery points was known to have reached 24.5 million. Most of the changes were very small, to cope with individual building infill or to correct errors, as is shown by table 2.7.

Table 2.7   Changes in the number of delivery points in a sample of Postcodes between the 1990/4 and 1991/4 versions of PAF on CD *(Source: PAF on CD 1990/4 and 1991/4)*

Postcode	Delivery points in 1990	Delivery points in 1991
AB1 0AD	8	7
AB1 0DR	4	3
AB1 0DX	19	18
AB1 0HX	5	4
AB1 0JE	16	18
AB1 0JP	10	9
AB1 0LJ	2	3
AB1 0LR	4	3
AB1 0LT	5	4
AB1 0NB	3	4

The National Grid

It is sensible at this stage to describe the British National Grid in outline since the complementary nature of it and of Postcodes has already been stressed. Full details are given in appendix 5. For now, however, the key points to remember are that:

- the Grid was designed by Ordnance Survey in response to the recommendations of the 1938 Davidson Committee which called for a uniform basis on which to create all official maps of Britain (it excludes Northern Ireland, which uses the Irish grid);

- it can be thought of as a sheet of graph paper covering Britain, the origin of which is off the Isles of Scilly. Thus the position of any point in the country can be measured in relation to this origin along an eastern axis and along a northern axis. The address in Welwyn given earlier as an example of correct postal referencing has an Easting coordinate of 523 kilometres and a Northing coordinate of 216 kilometres to the nearest kilometre;

- clearly a curved surface (the surface of the earth on which Britain lies) cannot be 'flattened out' onto a sheet of paper without distortions being created. To minimise these, Ordnance Survey designed the National Grid map projection specifically to exploit the shape of Britain. The line of zero distortion thus runs down the long axis of the country and distortion errors increase outwards from this broadly to the east and west. For almost all purposes, and certainly for those described in this book, these distortions are insignificant;

- the level of geographical detail can be chosen by the user. Extending the number of digits used for both the Easting and the Northing coordinates increases the resolution or detail. The location of the front door of the Royal Geographical Society (RGS) in London is TQ 27 80 to the nearest kilometre but is TQ 26729 79635 to the nearest metre in British National Grid coordinates, relative to the origin of the Grid west of the Scilly Isles. If the TQ code is converted to numbers, the RGS front door is seen to be 526,729 metres east of that point and 179,635 metres north;

- for the convenience of users, Ordnance Survey has created a Grid whose coordinates are both alphabetic and numeric. Thus the country is divided up into 100 kilometre squares which are known by two letters, such as TQ (see appendix 5 for a diagram showing these letters). The rest of the coordinates are numeric and give position within that 100 km square;

- Royal Mail does not use these alphabetic characters but instead converts all National Grid coordinates to numeric representations, as in the RGS example above – except that the huge bulk of the National Grid coordinates held on the PAF at present are only to 100 metre resolution (10m in Scotland). Thus Royal Mail version of the National Grid coordinates for the RGS should be 5267 1796 where the last two digits showing zero are missed off;

- the simplest way of recording the National Grid position of a Unit Postcode is to define one coordinate pair consisting of an Easting and a Northing for some place within the group of delivery points which it comprises (Plate 3). This is adequate for many purposes, assuming the coordinate is specified to a sufficiently high resolution (which is not true in PAF at the time of writing; see chapter 4). Where the whole of an area (such as a Postcode Sector) is to be defined, a sequence of National Grid coordinates is given around the area's boundary (see figure 1.8). Usually, the points are chosen sufficiently close together to be joined by straight lines and these will be so short as to give an acceptable approximation to curves when viewed normally. (see chapter 5).

As we will describe later (see chapter 4), an index which relates Unit Postcodes to the National Grid has long been available and many other products can also be obtained which provide the boundaries of Postcodes in National Grid coordinates.

The source of the National Grid coordinates used by Royal Mail

The origins of the National Grid coordinates held in the PAF go back to the 1970s. They were created for the Department of Transport's Regional Highway Traffic Model (DTp's RHTM). This involved a sample survey and those questioned were asked to identify the origin and destination of their trips by Postcodes. At that time, no index of Postcodes to grid references existed so DTp created one. The method which they used was suited to their immediate purpose but not to subsequent needs and the technology available to them at that stage to 'capture' the data was primitive. The convention was adopted that the grid reference measured was of the first delivery point in the Postcode. At best, therefore, this introduced some bias in the results. The procedure was carried out largely by hand and results were only recorded to 100 metre resolution: this ensures that many Postcodes in urban areas have the same National Grid reference as their neighbours (the rectangular pattern which results is obvious in figure 4.2a). Moreover, errors occurred as a result of the digitising process: many delivery points were allocated not to the nearest 100 metre grid corner but to some other grid 'corner', often rather further away (as indicated in figure 4.1). Checking of all this was difficult because of the nature of the operations carried out. In short, the digitised versions of the coordinates were highly error-prone and some of these errors were invisible to the casual user but the data were almost certainly adequate for their initial purpose. Since they existed, however, the data were pressed into service for other tasks.

The coordinates were incorporated at an early stage into the Central Postcode Directory (see chapter 4) maintained by the Office of Population Census and Surveys (OPCS) but were not included in PAF on CD until the late 1980s; PAF itself does not contain them, although Royal Mail makes them available as the Postzon File (see chapter 4). In the course of their stewardship of the coordinates, OPCS have significantly improved the quality of the file. Various other plans have been laid to improve radically both the resolution and the reliability of the grid referenced data but, at the time of writing, none of these had reached fruition in England and Wales (though the situation is very different in Scotland where the inferred boundaries of Postcodes are now available in computer form; see chapters 4 and 6). The most interesting plan was perhaps that to replace the modified RHTM coordinates with others derived from an averaging of all the coordinates of individual component properties digitised by Pinpoint Analysis Ltd (see chapter 4 and Plate 3); this was intended to produce ten metre or one metre resolution Postcode centroids but appears never to have been widely implemented. At present, then, the grid references in the PAF are up-dated as new Postcodes are created, as existing ones are split and as redundant ones are deleted – but the fundamental basis for them is unchanged, being a progressively improved but still error-prone and low resolution set of DTp's RHTM coordinates. The situation is likely to improve substantially in future since Ordnance Survey plan to build a database of National Grid coordination for each and every property in Britain and to hold this together with postal addresses.

Conclusions

The creation of a national Postcode system has been a massive investment for Royal Mail, running to many millions of pounds. It is being constantly updated and, especially in the period from 1990 onwards, has been significantly improved with an investment of over £2 million. This last point is important since in chapter 4 we examine the quality of the Postcode data and find that earlier versions of the PAF data sets (at least) contained sizeable errors though many of these were largely irrelevant to the needs of Royal Mail itself and only significant for certain non-mailing operations.

Even if significant errors do remain, we should still distinguish between the system and its implementation. There is nothing else to compare with the Postcode system as a way of describing the population geography of the country which is immediately meaningful to the bulk of the population, highly flexible and inexpensive. In addition, almost nothing else exists at present to compare with PAF as a summary of our built environment. For these reasons, we strongly support the strenuous efforts to improve the currency of the Postcode database presently being implemented by Royal Mail. Whether they will be able to reduce all types of errors to truly negligible levels is a matter of debate. Other authors have suggested that the optimal solution would require the involvement of other parties and we discuss some aspects of this in the final chapter when we consider the future.

CHAPTER 3

The use of the Postcode for
postal purposes

The primary purpose of a Postcode is to speed and to reduce the cost of
mail delivery. It does this by facilitating the automated handling of
letters. However, because of the unpredictability of handwriting, the
public's ability to ignore guidelines on how to lay out and describe an
address and the variations in the size and shape of letters and parcels,
total success in automation is impossible to achieve. As in many other
areas connected to computing, the last few per cent of success costs
progressively more. This is summed up by the often-quoted 80:20 rule –
80% of the desired goal is achieved for 20% of the total cost but thereafter
the figures are reversed. In terms of the postal service, the target is
therefore to automate operations to the extent where further additions
become prohibitively expensive. Most people in the industry think this is
somewhere beyond the 90% level but it clearly varies greatly for different
types of mail. Royal Mail's ability to influence the behaviour of the
customer also varies with different types of mail: discounts can be offered
to organisations sending correctly Postcoded mail in bulk but this
incentive is not really feasible so far as individuals mailing one or two
letters is concerned.

The UK situation

In this section of the book, we set out how the Postcode is used
operationally within Royal Mail itself and how the Postcode came to be
introduced. First however, we describe how the volume of post has
changed over the years and how this has fostered the need for automation.

The postal business

Table 3.1 and figure 3.1 show the growth in mail handled by Royal Mail. As with all numerical results cited in this section, these derive from Royal Mail. Over the five years to 1989/90, there was a 34% increase in volume of letter mail.

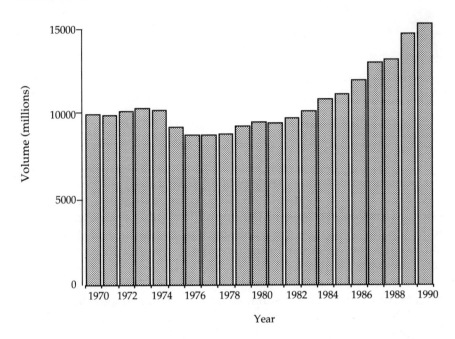

Figure 3.1   Changes in volume of all types of mail handled by Royal Mail and the Post Office over a twenty year period. The mix of mail type has changed significantly within this period. *(Source: Royal Mail)*

Table 3.1   Growth of mail letter volume up to 1989/90 *(Source: Royal Mail)*

Year	Volume (millions of items)
1989/90	13,193
1988/89	12,365
1987/88	11,995
1986/87	11,116
1985/86	10,421

Of this total volume, the various business segments contribute very differently to the volume and the difficulties in handling of the mail. Five market segments have been identified. These are as follows:

- Preaddressed mail
  Business Reply
  Freepost
  (recently renamed Response Services)
- Presorted high volume business mail
  Mailsort
  Presstream
- Non-presorted high volume business mail
  Postage Paid Impression (PPI) excluding Mailsort
  'Paid' stamps
  Post Office
- Low volume business mail
  meter franked
  stamps (part)
- Consumer mail
  stamps (part)

Preaddressed mail is addressed not by the mailer but by its correspondent. As there are relatively few such correspondents, ensuring that the correct Postcode is used is relatively easy and highly effective. The market segment includes business replies, such as payment by consumers to credit card companies and utilities using envelopes provided with each bill sent out. Presorted mail is clearly of great

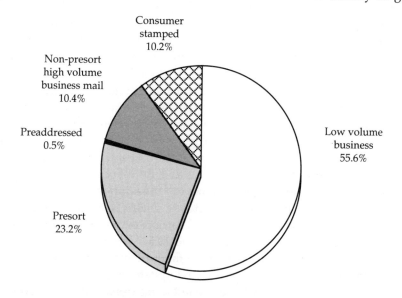

Figure 3.2 The relative sizes of the different market segments of mail handled by Royal Mail in 1990 *(Source: Royal Mail)*. Figures do not sum to 100% because of minor rounding effects.

importance to Royal Mail: some 4,000 customers presort mail on a Postcode basis because they get significant discounts when 90% or more is provided in this form (subject to other conditions of the presort contract).

The first three of these business segments are dominated by only about 6,000 customers. Figure 3.2 shows how over half of Royal Mail's workload arises from low volume business mail. Perhaps most striking is that only three out of ten items of mail now arises from individual items stamped and posted by the customer, and only one out of ten is classified by Royal Mail as 'social mail' (see plate 4 for an example of a typical social mail promotion).

The history of the Postcode

The origins of the existing UK Postcode go back as far as the middle of the nineteenth century. They arose from the rapid growth of London in the earlier years of that century. So rapid was this that the then Post Office could no longer regard the city as a single town from the viewpoint of sorting mail. Thus the division of London into Postal Districts in 1857-8 effectively divided the capital into smaller and semi-independent postal towns. Sir Rowland Hill, the designer of the first stamp and the man who introduced the uniform postal rate for the whole country, carved up London into eight such Districts. These were denoted by letters representing compass points, such as N (Northern), E (Eastern) and WC (Western Central). Thereafter, all mail from the rest of the country was sent directly to the appropriate office. Between 1864 and 1912, cities such as Liverpool, Manchester, Dublin and Sheffield followed this lead.

Towards the end of the nineteenth century in London – then the world's largest city – the situation became clogged again. Initially as a war-time labour-saving device, a suffix on the Postal District denoting the Postcode Sub-District was introduced formally in 1917. The allocation of the numbering was alphabetical. Thus the Eastern District became E1 whilst Bethnal Green Sub-District became E2 and Bow became E3. Glasgow followed London's lead and was the next to introduce such numbering in 1923. Subsequently the original Postcode Districts in London became Areas and the Sub-Districts became full Districts in modern terminology.

The next stage in the saga came in the 1950s when the first post war investigations into the mechanisation of mail sorting were made. It soon became evident that a more sophisticated system of coding was required and that a major exercise would be needed to maximise the use of the new Postcodes by the public. Experiments based on Norwich in 1959 onwards led to the decision to use an alphanumeric (i.e., including both alphabetic and numeric characters) Postcode. Even after much publicity, however, these Postcodes were only used by less than half the senders of mail in the areas concerned. Despite internal doubts about the wisdom of the Postcode within the Post Ofice at that time, a revised version was introduced in Croydon in 1966 and proved more successful. By 1974, the whole of the UK had been allocated Postcodes and Norwich had been recoded. The use of the Postcode has grown over the years; overall, some 71% of all mail in Financial Year 1990/91 contained a correct Postcode of the recipient. From the viewpoint of Royal Mail, the exercise has been an extended but successful one.

The current use of the Postcode within Royal Mail

Thus far, we have blithely announced that Royal Mail finds the Postcode valuable in its operations. To appreciate the advantages and disadvantages of the Postcode system, we need to understand rather more of how it is actually used in the delivery of letters and parcels.

HANDLING LETTERS INSIDE ROYAL RAIL

The stages which letters generally go through once they are brought to a sorting office are as follows:

- *segregation* of the mail into first and second class categories;
- *'facing'* them so all are aligned in the same direction;
- *cancelling* them by printing the date and time of cancellation on the stamps.

The most advanced sorting offices do these actions automatically.

Converting the Postcode to machine-readable form Originally this was achieved by an operator receiving the letters one at a time and typing the Postcode on the letter onto a keyboard; this then prints a series of phosphor dots on the envelope to indicate both the Outward and Inward codes. The more modern way is to use Optical Character Readers (OCR; see Plate 5). Royal Mail have installed 46 of these between 1987 and 1991: each OCR reader can deal with up to 30,000 items of mail per hour. It automatically reads and analyses the typed or printed addresses on letters and prints the translation of the Postcode as the series of phosphor dots. Much simpler machines can then read these dots at later stages in the letter's progress. Royal Mail are, however, carrying out a trial with customer-supplied barcodes and with machines which will be able to decode these as well as the phosphor dots (see chapter 10).

Presorting　　After the letters are coded, they are presorted by another machine. By reading the codes, this divides the mail into three sections – local and regional mail and items not suitable for further automatic sorting.

Automatic Sorting　　The final part of the outward sorting takes place at the Letter Sorting Machine or LSM. This carries out a 'fine sort' for one area of the country, such as London and the South East. By reading the phosphor dots, the LSM sorts the letters into any one of 139 different selections. The sorted letters are then bundled, labelled, bagged and dispatched to the local sorting offices.

Inward Sorting　　On arrival at the local sorting office, the letters are fed through another LSM and sorted into delivery walks. At this stage, selections of mail to individual firms or even to departments within a firm are made. The machine has the capacity to sort down to individual Postcodes. Items bearing no Postcode are, of course, manually sorted. Each walk is designed to be completed between 0700 and 0930 hours and consists of about 400 potential delivery points i.e. about 25 or so Postcodes.

Letters which are fully Postcoded and pass through this system are typically sorted ten to 20 times more rapidly than those done by hand. Mail which cannot be sorted by machine therefore runs the risk of being delayed in delivery. Recent research carried out for Royal Mail by an independent market research company has shown that at the time of writing in late 1991, Postcoded mail achieves, on average, a 3.8% higher quality of service (relative to delivery targets) than non-Postcoded mail. This improvment rises to 5.3% for long distance mail. Moreover, such a system permits Royal Mail to make some changes to the postal delivery system without disturbing the geographical coding familiar to those sending the mail.

The extent of use of the Postcode on mail

It is obvious that some types of users of Royal Mail are more liable to use the Postcode than others. The most obviously successful users are the users of Royal Mail Response Services where envelopes are normally preprinted and will not be delivered without the correct Postcode. The extent of successful use of the Postcode within the five market segments identified earlier are are shown in figure 3.3. In essence, business users in the presort/preaddressed market segment average just under 90% of correct use (some mail in these segments are addressed by the user e.g. Freepost), whilst individually stamped mail manages only around 65%. Strenuous efforts are now being made by Royal Mail to increase these figures, with the aim of raising the overall success to over 90%. One approach is to enhance general awareness of the Postcode by promotions (see plate 4).

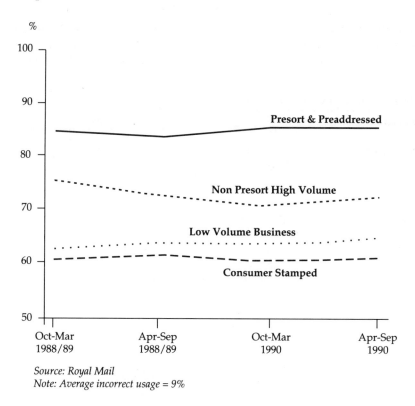

Source: Royal Mail
Note: Average incorrect usage = 9%

Figure 3.3   Accurate Postcode use in 1988–90 by different mail business segments *(Source: Royal Mail)*

The use of Postcodes in other, selected countries

The UK is by no means alone in having a postal code system. Indeed, it was not the first to adopt one for the whole country though its approach is more geographically detailed than others. Can we learn anything from the systems in use elsewhere? This section reviews the equivalent systems in some carefully selected other countries in an attempt to answer this question.

At present, there is no international standard form of postal code (although some countries use similar forms) or even of a postal address–unlike the situation for telephone numbers. Table 3.2, for instance, gives the locally-approved addresses and postal codes of the subsidiaries in different countries of the well-known computer software firm, Microsoft International. It is clear that different conventions are used in different countries. This lack of standardisation is both a disadvantage and an advantage. Omitting one digit by error when telephoning from Paris to Austin, Texas will get you a number in Athens, Greece; if they do not answer (or even if they do) you may be unaware of your error. In general,

Table 3.2 Forms of address and postal codes in different countries

Microsoft Ltd	Microsoft AB	Microsoft SARL
Excel House	Box 27	12, avenue de Québec
49 De Montfort House	S-164 93 KISTA	91957 Les Ulis Cedex
READING	SWEDEN	FRANCE
UK		
RG1 8LP		
Microsoft B.V	Microsoft SpA	Microsoft GmbH
Postbus 364	Centro Direzionale	Edisonstr. 1
2130 AJ Hoofddorp	Milano Oltre	D-8044 Unterschleißheim
NEDERLAND	Via Cassanese, 224	BUNDESREPUBLIK
	20090 SEGRATE (MI)	DEUTSCHLAND
	ITALIA	
Microsoft Pty Ltd	Microsoft Canada Inc.	Microsoft Corporation (México)
PO Box 95	6300 Northwest Drive	Paseo de la Reforma 300-2001
Forestville NSW 2087	Mississauga, Ontario	Col. Juárez
AUSTRALIA	CANADA	06600 México D.F.
	L4V 1J7	MEXICO
Microsoft IBERICA, SRL	Microsoft Co., Ltd	Microsoft International
Lopez de Hoyos, 42	K-Building 5-25, 7 Chome	PO Box 97017
28006 Madrid	Nishi-Shinjuku	Redmond, WA98073-9717
ESPAÑA	Shinjuku-ku, Tokyo 160	U.S.A.
	JAPAN	
Microsoft CH	Microsoft Informática Ltda	
41st Floor, DLI 63 Building	Av. Eng. Luis Carlos Berrini	
60, Yoido-Dong	1253-13 andar	
Yeongdeungpo-Gu	CEP 04571 São Paulo SP	
Seoul 150-763	BRASIL	
KOREA		

postal systems are much more resilient: even if the address (let alone the postal code) is slightly wrong, the mail normally arrives – though it may be delayed.

The variety of addressing and postal code schemes is obvious; to understand why these have grown up, we need to consider the situation in a few selected countries in more detail.

The United States of America (US)

The key to understanding the US postal code system is that it has evolved over three decades or more. To that extent, it may have been the earliest scheme of all. At the time of writing, it is undergoing very rapid change

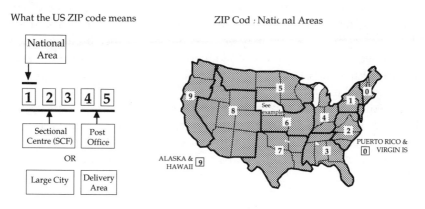

The first digit of a ZIP Code divides the USA into national areas, 10 large groups of states numbered from 0 in the Northeast to 9 in the West.

Example.

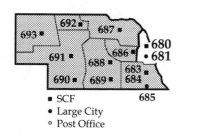

- ■ SCF
- ● Large City
- ○ Post Office

685

Within these large areas, each state is divided into an average of 10 smaller geographic areas which are identified by the 2nd and 3rd digits of the ZIP Code.

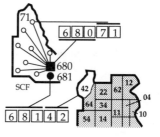

The 4th and 5th digits identify a post office or local delivery area.

Figure 3.4   The structure and geographical meaning of the original 5 digit ZIP code in the USA *(Source: US Postal Service)*

under the impact of automation. The driving force behind this is the cost of labour in the delivery of mail: 83% of all costs in the US Postal Service are labour ones. In general terms, there are about 40,000 ZIP codes, the acronym deriving from 'Zone Improvement Program'. The structure of the original five digit ZIP code is shown in figure 3.4. Thus the code is based upon a three-level hierarchy of nested areas.

Since the late 1970s, the US Postal Service (USPS) have implemented the nine digit ZIP code or, as it is now termed, the ZIP+4 code. This is primarily intended for mail originating in businesses and facilitates offering them discounts for easily-handled mail. The additional four digits enable the USPS automated equipment to sort mail to a specific mail carrier, as the postman and postwoman are called in the USA. The first two digits of the additional four digit element denote a delivery 'sector', which may be several city blocks, a group of streets, several office buildings, or a small geographical area. The last two digits denote a delivery 'segment', which may be one floor of an office building, one side of a street, a firm, a post office block (or group of them) or other specific geographical location. Figure 3.5 illustrates this extension of the geographical hierarchy.

Typed or printed versions of these ZIP+4 codes are read automatically by an OCR and the document is then printed with a bar code on the lower right portion (figure 3.5). This bar code is then used in the US Post Office to sort the letter to the group delivered by individual mail carriers.

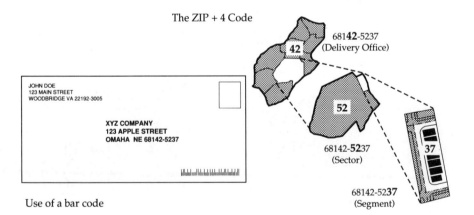

The ZIP + 4 Code

JOHN DOE
123 MAIN STREET
WOODBRIDGE VA 22192-3005

XYZ COMPANY
123 APPLE STREET
OMAHA NE 68142-5237

68142-5237
(Delivery Office)

68142-5237
(Sector)

68142-5237
(Segment)

Use of a bar code

Figure 3.5 The ZIP+4 code and bar coding of letters generated from it in the USA *(Source: US Postal Service)*

Austria

In Austria, the postal codes are four-digit ones based upon post towns. The first digit, however, indicates the administrative province within which the town lies. This is shown below in table 3.3:

Table 3.3   The structure of the Austrian postal code *(Source: W. Kainz).*

1	Vienna
2 and 3	Lower Austria
4	Upper Austria
5	Salzburg
6	Tyrol, Vorarlberg
7	Burgenland
8	Styria
9	Carinthia

The political subdivision of Austria is from the country as a whole to the province (Bundesland), the district (Bezirk) and finally to the town (Gemeinde). Every town has a unique postal code. Thus 8130 is the postal code of Frohnleiten in Styria. Bigger towns (like the provincial capitals) have more than one postal code and are sub-divided appropriately. The capital is treated separately: 1010 is the first district in Vienna whilst 1150 is the fifteenth district in the same city.

France

The French postal code system was inaugurated in May 1965 and initially was based on a two-digit code representing the Département (the local government adminstration). Since then, the system has grown considerably but is under much more local control than is the case in Britain. In 1984, there were 6,002 postal codes in France and there are now believed to be about 7,000.

Since 1972, French postal codes have had five digit numbers. The first two digits still define the département and the others are the *bureau distributeur*, an office which receives and delivers mail. Except for the département number, there is nothing specifically geographical about the postal code allocation; it is simply incremented 'chronologically' as a new office is opened and attempts are made to increment the number by units of ten. Thus Montpellier has five offices whose numbers are 34000, 34060, 34070, 34080 and 34090. Exceptions to this non-geographical incrementalism occur in Paris, Lyon and Marseille where the postal code includes the *arrondissement* number (e.g. 75004 for the fourth Paris arrondissement). In rural areas, one office can serve several communes (the lowest level of local government in France, of which about 36,000 exist). In contrast, major cities have several offices with different postal codes for different parts of towns. Decisions to create a new office are taken at departmental level. The most frequent reason for change in postal codes seems to be to take account of rapid population growth in a commune.

In addition to the standard postal codes, however, there are two other important codes in use in France. The most significant is the CEDEX code. All official organisations that receive more than about 1000 items of mail per day (or which receive less but for which the mail can be handled automatically) are allocated a CEDEX number. This number may be shared with several other organisations and made more specific by use of a *Boîte Postale (BP)* or Post Box. It is frequently 'slotted in' between the postal codes numbers: hence 92126 Montrouge CEDEX is the code for Mediapost (see below). The CEDEX mail is handled by separate offices, called *bureaux cedex* of which about 1000 exist in France; in major towns it is possible to have several such offices, distinguished by number. An example showing the entire possible postal description is:

SOCIÉTÉ TRUC
BP 2503
34180 MONTPELLIER CEDEX 01

Finally, there is a special service, the CIDEX code, for rural areas where houses are scattered around a commune. Mail boxes are placed in one central place and all mail is delivered to them. Each set of boxes is given a CIDEX code but the postal code used is a normal one.

Detailed information about individual postal codes has been available since 1990 from Mediapost (see appendix 2). Products available include postal codes for the entire 36,000 communes, the CEDEX file and the *routage distribution,* a file containing the complete list of streets with postal codes for all towns with more than 50,000 people.

Germany

The postal codes system is (at least at the time of writing in mid 1991) in a state of rapid change as a consequence of the integration of the separate systems in East and West Germany. The revision is expected to be complete by 1995. The original western system was based on eight postal districts centred on the major towns, each being allocated a four-digit number as shown below in table 3.4:

Table 3.4   The structure of the old West Germany postal code

1000	Berlin	5000	Köln
2000	Hamburg	6000	Frankfurt
3000	Hannover	7000	Stuttgart
4000	Dusseldorf	8000	München

Figure 3.6   The top-tier postal areas in West and East Germanyin 1991, based around a small number of main postal towns *(Source: German PTT)*.

The process of allocating and up-dating the succeeding three digit numbers to other towns is not entirely clear from German documentation. As one example, however, Bad Lippspringe has a postal code of 4792, being a town within the Dusseldorf region. Figure 3.6 shows the main regions and post towns within them in both West and East Germany.

The Netherlands

The Dutch Post Office introduced use of a postal code in 1978 to cope with the increasing volume of mail and maintain reasonable delivery times without huge increases in staff. It is composed of four digits and two letters preceding the post town name (e.g. 1054 HK Amsterdam). The numbers stand for a town or part of a town and the two letters designate a group of about 25 houses and commercial properties or postboxes. As elsewhere, the four digits are a hierarchical coding structure: the first two numbers represent a region, the third a district within a region and the fourth is an area (or quarter) within the district. At the behest of the Dutch PTT, 30 municipal governments have subdivided their cities into districts. Some 180 cities have designated quarters. As a result, there are about 560,000 postal codes in The Netherlands, of which 373,000 are of households. Excluding postbox postal codes, there are about 500,000 'geographical' postal codes, 3921 four-digit areas, 795 three-digit areas, 90 two-digit areas and nine one-digit areas. Some 30,000 mutations in the postal codes each year are recorded by the PTT. These arise mostly from changes in municipal boundaries.

As in the UK, the mapping of the postal codes boundaries was first done by the private sector. In 1989, Geodan (see appendix 2) created a national map of the four-digit postal codes areas by use of street plans, postal codes books and information from postmen and local post offices; this was compiled at 1: 25,000 scale in the urban conglomeration in the W. Netherlands (the Randstad) and at 1:50,000 scale elsewhere. These data are now sold commercially, along with socio-economic information in a manner similar to the situation in the UK (see chapter 4). Maps of the six-character postal codes are, however, some way off though Geodan have experimented with point grid referencing and hence mapping of these postal codes. To facilitate use of the postal codes the postal code numbers are written on street signs.

Portugal

The postal code in Portugal consists of four digits, followed by the postal name of the town or village concerned. The first digit describes the area of

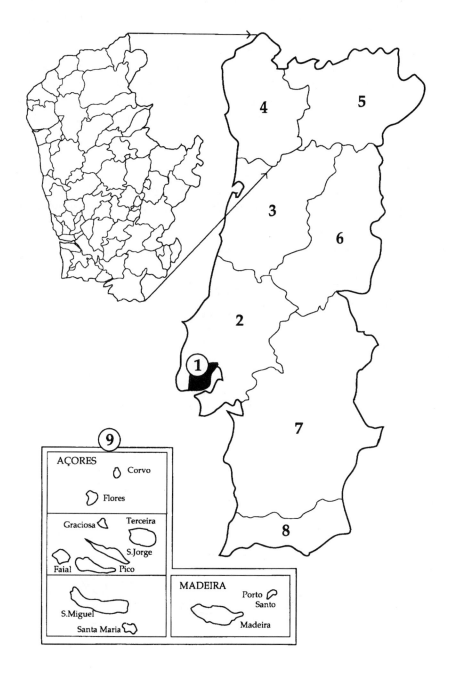

Figure 3.7 The postal code areas in Portugal (Source: Portuguese PTT)

the country in which the post town exists except that Lisbon is designated as one. These areas do not coincide with any others used in the country. The second and third digits indicate a particular postal code centre within that area whilst the fourth digit is zero if the town is a municipality and otherwise is a five. Some 450 postal codes exist in Portugal at present. In addition, special delivery codes (known as 'Codex') exist for organisations receiving large volumes of mail Figure 3.7 shows the Portuguese postal areas for the country as a whole and in more detail for one postal area.

Spain

The Spanish postal code is a five-digit number, made up as shown in table 3.5. Figure 3.8 is a map of the provinces (i.e. the first two digits of the Spanish postal code)

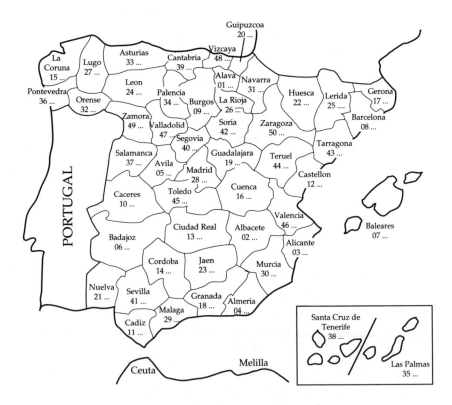

Figure 3.8   The Spanish provinces i.e. the 2 digit postal areas *(Source: Spanish PTT)*

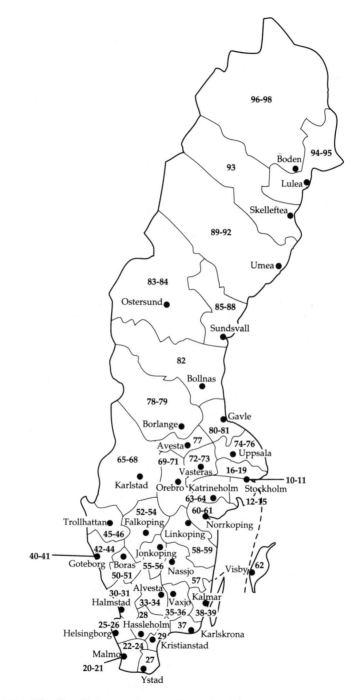

Figure 3.9 The Swedish postal areas (numbers) and regions *(Source: Swedish PTT)*

Table 3.5 The structure of the Spanish postal code *(Source: Spanish PTT)*

Digit(s)	Meaning
1 and 2	Code for the province
3	The forwarding code e.g. 1 indicates transfer or termination in the national capital
4	The route code
5	Distribution or delivery code. The route and distribution codes are used in combination to designate sub-divisions of a large delivery area, postal districts, private and official post office boxes and large users.

Sweden

In Sweden, the basic geographical structure is also provided by the first two digits in a five-digit code. Again, the postal code is written in front of the postal town name: that for the national mapping agency in Sweden is S-801 82 Gävle. The first two digits correspond to a geographical area; one or more geographical areas corresponds to a postal region governed by a regional post office (see figure 3.9). Each such regional post office supervises the allocation of the remaining three digits and approves proposals for changes to their use from the local post office. Whilst changes in the postal code are rare within any one town, the overall situation nationally is changing more quickly. The current situation is summarised in two annual publications, one a list of approved names for post towns, the other a list by post town of the five-digit code which applies to that street (and, typically, one or more others). For the Swedish town of Gävle, the latter takes the form shown in table 3.6.

Table 3.6 A sample of postal codes for streets beginning with A in Gävle, Sweden *(Source: Swedish PTT)*

Adolfslund	803 41 GÄVLE
Albackvägan	805 91 GÄVLE
Albiongatan	802 55 GÄVLE
Apelgatan	
10-22	802 57 GÄVLE
5-, 26-36	802 56 GÄVLE
40-76	802 57 GÄVLE
78-	802 56 GÄVLE

Conclusions on the international scene

Based on the examples cited above (and others such as Canada and Australia), there is considerable international variation in the way in which postal or ZIP-codes are allocated and used. The most common form seems to be the four digit variety but, even within that group, the significance of the digits varies considerably. Those countries which have only a small number of provinces or states (such as Austria or Australia) have typically allocated the first digit to the province. That this is a rather inflexible approach is indicated by the German example (though there, the first digit was allocated to key postal towns rather than to the states or Länder).

It would, in fact, be more surprising if there were not great variations in the international practice of postcoding. At least until very recently, the volume of local traffic constituted the huge bulk of mail sent and received in most places. In these circumstances and especially in the early days of automation of the mail, a national solution was typically imposed. Moving from this to a pan-national solution would involve massive disruption and is, indeed, not necessary since final delivery of mail is always done within the system which understands the local postal code. With just over 200 countries in the world, it is relatively simple to direct mail to the correct country initially by hand. From the moment of its arrival in the 'recipient country', however, sorting by machine is becoming more and more common. This generally involves converting the postal code into some hieroglyphic (like a barcode as in the US or use of phosphorescent dots as in the UK) to ensure that much simpler equipment can re-read the encoded address as the mail progesses through the various stages on its way to its ultimate destination.

Relatively few countries have yet extended the postal code down to the level of very small groups of properties or delivery points. Of those that have, the schemes used in the US, the UK and The Netherlands differ greatly. Canada, whose scheme was based on that used in the UK, has modified it significantly. Few Post Offices seem to have given much thought to the value of geographical ordering of the postal code sequence; each post town is seen as an island in space. Such an approach is feasible when relatively few postal codes are used. In principle, it can even be used with small area postal codes if the entire operation of delivery is automated: for a suitably programmed sorting machine, it does not matter that postal code 99999 and 91111 might be next to each other. For human beings, however, it is highly advantageous to have postal codes which are recognisable and whose relationships to other postal code areas are obvious at least in the most general terms.

The only known postal codes with a structure that intermingles alphabetic and numeric values are those of Canada and the UK though Jersey has recently implemented its own scheme using the UK structure and the Isle of Man will do so by the end of 1992. As used in the UK, such postal codes give some indication of the post town and the structure also seems to render the code more memorable than all-numeric ones. There must be a pleasant irony here for Royal Mail since the Post Office was much criticised by US postal experts in the 1960s for using such an alphabetic code because this was more difficult to interpret by machine. With the improvements in computer technology over the past 30 years (see chapter 1), the UK approach is now manifestly more 'mainstream' than is that in the US: computers are supposed to do the hard work for humans rather than the other way around – and memorising ZIP+4 codes is none too easy!

In short, many postal code systems have grown up from a historical basis of administration, with higher resolution codes added on only as the demands of automation became more evident. Thus postal codes are nationally distinctive at present and likely to remain so even though international standardisation of forms of postal address has long been under consideration. At present, little harmonisation of this kind has been achieved apart from the number of lines of text permitted and the maximum numbers of characters on each line.

CHAPTER 4

Postcode products and
services in the UK

For the person outside Royal Mail, all that has gone before may be largely
academic: he or she is normally interested only in one thing – what use is
the Postcode to me? The answer to that normally lies in the range and
quality of products which exploit the Postcode and the tools for dealing
with these data. The first of these is described here but the tools
themselves, which are fascinating and rapidly developing in their own
right, are described later in chapter 5. We begin with a description of the
products and services which Royal Mail itself produces then examine
other products and services on the market. This chapter is designed as an
overview; technical details of the computer files and the like are available
from the contact points in appendix 2. This section is valuable even for
those who are solely interested in the Postcode as a method of defining
geography and not for speeding the delivery of mail. It demonstrates the
many ways in which the basic anatomy or geography of the country can
be (and is) described.

Royal Mail Postcode products

Postcode directories

The most straightforward descriptions of Postcode geography are given
by these paper directories. Each contains a list of every Postcode for a
defined area. These are arranged by locality and, within that, by street or
thoroughfare. Following a reorganisation of these, some 94 now cover the
whole country.

The Postcode Guide

This paper guide contains information derived from the Postcode Address File (PAF: see below) and includes in-depth lists of post towns linked to Postcode maps and Postcode Directories. Details are given of shared Sectors as well as tables of Postcode Areas, Postcodes as far 'down' as Sector level, to county level and so on. In addition, the Guide features an alphabetical list of commonly used place names in the country, including villages; this shows their post town, county and the relevant Postcode Directory.

The Postcode and Localities Index

The Postcode and Localities Index is a paper guide containing the correct postal addresses for all the place names listed in the PAF (see below) and also serves as an index to the Postcode Directories.

The Post Town Gazetteer

This is an index of post towns in Postcode order showing their county and the outward Postcode (i.e., the first three or four characters, as described in chapter 2). Again it is supplied either as part of the Postcode Guide or separately as a file on IBM – compatible floppy disk or magnetic tape. It does not however contain any address information as such.

The Postcode Address File (PAF)

The PAF is a centrally stored database of every address in the UK to which mail is delivered, together with its appropriate Postcode. This master database is stored at Royal Mail's computer centre and is more or less continuously updated. It contains names but normally only those of businesses; no names of household occupiers are included. The database is the basis for a number of Postcode products available on computer tape (PAF on Tape) or on Compact Disc (PAF on CD; see plate 2).

Where PAF on Tape is chosen, the customer has a choice of different selections and formats in which the data may be provided. For any one product, two types of selection may be made. The first is termed 'Postcode Selection' and provides all addresses within a defined set of Postcode Areas, Districts or Sectors. Address Selection, on the other hand, permits selection of address type: thus residential addresses, small user or large user addresses may be selected. Combinations of Postcode and Address Selection may obviously be made. The current PAF products are now described in turn, starting with PAF on Tape, but note that other products could be extracted from the database holding the data with relative ease.

THE MAIN FILE

This product contains address data in relational database form, with the address elements stored as separate files which can be combined to constitute a complete address. The address elements are held in coded form for compactness and contain keys which point to reference files of address text. Clearly it is unwise to store frequently used names as long text strings on every occasion they are encountered! In reality, the Main File is a misnomer because it comes as a set of files. Whilst it may be considered as one logical file, in physical terms it is supplied as eight separate ones:

- the localities file;
- the thoroughfare file;
- the thoroughfare descriptor file;
- the building names file;
- the sub-building names file;
- the organisations file;
- the address file;
- the Mailsort file.

As long as the address contains each of these address elements then all of these files contains one record for each component held in PAF. The files are all held in ascending order of codes. Updates to the basic table and address keys are provided via products called Changes1 and Changes2.

Since there is no software provided with these data, it is obvious that the bulk data are designed for use on substantial computing facilities with skilled staff and appropriate software. Given such resources, however, the potential uses of the Main File are enormous. As one example, the totality of addresses on it can be used to ensure that each one of those on a customer's database is a feasible one. Products related to this main file are now described.

THE COMPRESSED STANDARD FILE

Unlike the Main File, this contains the address record in a non-encoded format where the address file is not represented by keys but contains all the relevant text. It is therefore relatively easy to 'plug in' to standard word processing and other software such as those for labelling. The records are ordered in ascending sequence of Postcode according to locality, thoroughfare and delivery point. Since the result is much more voluminous than is the Main File, it is rarely sold for the country as a whole but rather for selected areas. The totality of addresses in the whole country, for example, occupies 37 high density computer tapes each 2,400 feet long when stored in this format! Typically, the customers for selections from this file are those with modest computing resources and/or just starting the development of a marketing database, as well as those who are based in just one region of the country e.g. Local Authorities. This product is updated through the Expanded Changes File.

THE RANGES FILE

In this file, each Postcode is listed together with its address range. Thus MK42 9HR is associated with 1-29 Acacia Avenue and MK42 9HH with 2-30 Acacia Avenue in Milton Keynes. It is provided in expanded i.e. 'normal' text form and is updated through Royal Mail's Expanded Changes product. An obvious use for this file is to produce all the addresses within a Postcode selected by, for example, a geodemographic system used to target consumers with particular characteristics (see chapter 8). New Rapid Address Systems incorporating this file can almost instantaneously generate a full address merely from the Postcode and the house number or name.

THE LARGE USER FILE

This contains one record for each and every one of the 172,000 or so Large Users, i.e., those who each receive over 25 items of mail per day (see chapter 2). Typically it is used by companies who wish to contact subscription services, Book and Music clubs, mail order companies or other high-volume users of the postal services. It is also required by all users who wish to obtain the complete set of addresses stored in PAF, since the Large Users are not included in the other tape products.

DELIVERY POINT COUNTS

A variety of different products are available. These may provide information for each thoroughfare within a Postcode, for each locality or for each Sector. The information may be for small or large users, for flats (in reality, all delivery points which have a sub-building name), for residential properties or for properties with multiple residency. The file is periodically rewritten in its entirety, rather than updates being supplied.

POSTZON

This file contains one record for every Postcode in the UK. The information supplied consists of:

- the Postcode;
- the Local Authority Ward Code;
- the British National or Irish grid reference (see appendix 5);
- the National Health Service area code.

Thus there is no address information included though this may be derived by linking with one of the other PAF products. It is the commercial equivalent of the Central Postcode Directory (see later in this chapter).

PAF ON CD

The dramatic changes in computer technology in the late 1980s enabled Royal Mail to provide a subset of the PAF on a 12cm Compact Disc. For each and every one of the Postcodes in the UK is held:

- an encoded form of postal address;
- the number of delivery points in the Postcode;
- the Local Authority Ward Codes;
- the NHS area code;
- the British National or Irish grid reference (see appendix 5);
- the Mailsort Standard Selection code (Sortcode);
- the user category.

In practice, experiments have shown that it is relatively simple as an automated process to expand the PAF on CD descriptions of Postcodes into addresses for individual properties. Table 4.1 illustrates this for one Unit Postcode: details of each of the individual properties (or, more properly, delivery points) have been generated from the compact record for the Unit Postcode as a whole.

Table 4.1 The individual mail delivery points within Postcode SW20 9AA *(Source: PAF on CD 1991/4)*

No.	Street name	Post Town	Postcode	Cat.	Sort Code	Grid East	Grid North	Ward Code	Dpts Code	NHS
2	WATERY LANE	LONDON	SW20 9AA	R	10719	52470	16940	38G14	11	H13
4	WATERY LANE	LONDON	SW20 9AA	R	10719	52470	16940	38G14	11	H13
6	WATERY LANE	LONDON	SW20 9AA	R	10719	52470	16940	38G14	11	H13
8	WATERY LANE	LONDON	SW20 9AA	R	10719	52470	16940	38G14	11	H13
5	WATERY LANE	LONDON	SW20 9AA	R	10719	52470	16940	38G14	11	H13
7	WATERY LANE	LONDON	SW20 9AA	R	10719	52470	16940	38G14	11	H13
9	WATERY LANE	LONDON	SW20 9AA	R	10719	52470	16940	38G14	11	H13
11	WATERY LANE	LONDON	SW20 9AA	R	10719	52470	16940	38G14	11	H13
13	WATERY LANE	LONDON	SW20 9AA	R	10719	52470	16940	38G14	11	H13
15	WATERY LANE	LONDON	SW20 9AA	R	10719	52470	16940	38G14	11	H13
17	WATERY LANE	LONDON	SW20 9AA	R	10719	52470	16940	38G14	11	H13

The obvious use of PAF on CD is to verify and update the mailing list already held by organisations or to form the basis of a new one. But there are a variety of other uses including:

- identification of residential/non-residential codes at various Postcode levels;

- neighbour mailing. Because PAF groups mail delivery points into Postcodes, there is a high probability (see chapter 1) that, if one address has certain characteristics, a number of others at the same Postcode level will also have them. In the absence of detailed information on each and every household, mailing to *all* delivery points within the same Postcode is therefore likely to identify a market previously defined on the basis of a sample of individual households (see table 8.1).

- geodemographic mailing. With the advent of an index defining census Enumeration Districts (EDs) in terms of their component Postcodes, it will be entirely possible to select target EDs on the basis of the census data (see chapters 6 and 8), link this to PAF and extract the addresses of all households in those EDs meeting the specified criteria. That this can now be done easily on a personal, desk-top computer at minimal cost simply reflects the change in computer facilities since the time when these techniques first became popular after the 1981 Census of Population.

The PAF on CD product (plate 2) also contains retrieval software and the main retrieval menu is illustrated in plate 6. Results of searches on specified criteria may be tabulated and copied to a floppy disk or other computer transfer medium. In addition, an extra set of software known as PAF on CD Utilities, written in the Turbo and Microsoft variants of the 'C' programming language, may be purchased. This enables users to use their own programs, yet select data from the PAF on CD.

It should be made clear that not only is PAF on CD an extraordinary resource but that it is relatively inexpensive. At the time of writing, for instance, PAF on tape for a large, multi-user computer system was about £15,000; on a CD, however, the first-year costs were £2,500, these figures dropping significantly in year two onwards. Some 1,200 customers currently use PAF on CD for a variety of purposes. Given the volatile nature of the market and the rate of development of new products, the absolute and relative levels of charging may change. But the present levels seem unlikely to be prohibitive for most business users who need addresses. For those without computer facilities, microfiche copies of PAF can be obtained for about £100 per set (at the time of writing).

How accurate is the Postcode and related information?

Accuracy is a matter of considerable interest to users, particularly (but not exclusively) those who intend to use the data for non-mail purposes: if there are significant errors in the Postcodes, the wrong groups of people might be selected (see chapter 8) or mail may be delayed unduly. It is also sensible to consider not just the Postcode itself but also other information associated with it; the accuracy of the grid references stored for a Postcode is critical for many applications (see below). But what constitutes accuracy in this case? To get a sensible answer, we have to consider separately the different parts of the generally available Postcode data files. Clearly some aspects of the data are much more difficult to get correct than others: as one example, many small businesses are registered at a private address yet there is no obvious sign of them other than the mail received nor is there any unambiguous indication of whether such a firm is still trading. Because of these complexities in building and maintaining a national file of delivery points and associated information, we consider now the accuracy of the different fields in the PAF.

The Postcode Address File is the key Royal Mail product based upon the Postcode. It is emphasised that the results below are all based upon 'snapshots' taken at various moments in time and, moreover, that Royal Mail has recently expended large sums on improving the quality of PAF. Thus some results are almost certainly out-of-date but no newer independently produced or published information was available at the time of writing.

Of the information in PAF, our primary concern is with:

- how complete is the list of addresses?
- how many addresses on the file should no longer be there?
- how accurate and representative are the OS National Grid references?
- whether these results differ significantly between large and small users;
- whether the file is becoming more rather than less accurate with the passage of time.

Four main sources provide us with evidence. The first is Royal Mail itself, the second is an independent review by the England and Wales census agency (OPCS, or the Office of Population Censuses and Surveys), the third is a paper by Gatrell (1989) recounting a comparison of Pinpoint Analysis' and Central Postcode Directory grid reference data (incorporated into PAF on CD in the late 1980s) and the fourth is field work especially carried out for the purposes of this book.

ROYAL MAIL'S OWN STATEMENTS ON ACCURACY

The key accuracy criteria so far as Royal Mail is concerned are whatever affects the speed and accuracy of delivering mail. Thus to have many Postcodes in existence but not on the PAF or to have delivery points not allocated to a Postcode would be a serious inaccuracy. On the other hand, the accuracy of grid referencing is irrelevant to their main task. Following the one million extra changes Royal Mail says it made to the PAF during 1991, Royal Mail analyses indicate they have already surpassed their current in-house accuracy criterion of 99% accuracy. It is accepted though that, at present, the accuracy of names of large users and non-residential delivery points does not match this level and steps are in hand to improve the situation. Royal Mail's own statement of accuracy is as follows:

> The accuracy of the PAF is the subject of continuous scrutiny and adjustment by Royal Mail. The in-house accuracy criterion is being raised to 99% as a minimum in 1992. This is in acknowledgement of the fact that the 100% target will be eroded by the unavoidable time lapse in the process of data capture and by input and output of up to 1%, at least in the short term. An accurate address database is uppermost in the plans for future Royal Mail development of PAF.

In the course of evaluation of the use of PAF as a survey sampling frame (see chapter 9), Wilson and Elliot (1987) compared PAF file contents with households sampled in the 1981 Census of Population post-enumeration accuracy test in England and Wales. The same households were checked to see if they were on the then current electoral register. For that reason, the October 1980 Electoral Register and the December 1980 version of PAF were used. Errors on the Electoral Register and on the Census forms cannot be ruled out though post-enumeration checks showed very low levels of errors in the latter.

Since these dates, of course, the character of PAF has changed substantially but no comparably detailed study has been repeated. For this reason, Wilson and Elliot's findings are reported though they must now be interpreted with caution.

For the PAF coverage check, three sub-samples in the national sample of households were taken:

- a statistically random sample of 444 households;
- all adults who had moved into their address in the 6 months prior to the Census;
- all households at addresses not found in the electoral register;

Of the random sample, 98% were at addresses found in PAF compared with 96.4% in the electoral registers. Part of this will arise from the fact that the registers will not contain households which contain only non-British citizens (since they are not eligible to vote). Moreover, since the lifetime of each electoral register is one year (*cf* the monthly up-dating for PAF from late 1992), OPCS have estimated that their coverage is only about 95.6% at the end of it.

Recent movers are dealt with much better by PAF than by the electoral register. Of adults who had recently moved, the addresses of 95% were in the PAF compared to 75% in the electoral register. The coverage of particular sub-sections of the population, as opposed to the totality of the population, may be of considerable value. Wilson and Elliot claimed that the addresses of 97% of all self-employed and of General Practitioners (GPs) who responded to the Family Expenditure Survey were in PAF.

A known problem of PAF is that Royal Mail is much slower to remove Postcodes and their component addresses than they are to add new addresses. The overall fraction of dead Postcodes (and hence of all postal addresses within them) is not known. Royal Mail deliberately leaves addresses on PAF which are expected to be reoccupied within the relatively short term. This has obvious consequences for mailshots. Royal Mail claim to have improved the situation in various ways, including carrying out a mailshot to all delivery points in the UK and noting which ones were undeliverable. A secondary consideration is also important; small user Postcodes may actually contain firms rather than residents (sometimes they do both – 'the Steamer' Public House example in Welwyn cited below is both a business and a residence but is classified as a residence in PAF). Since this is a common form of ambiguity for certain types of property, Royal Mail plans to correct this problem by structural change in PAF during 1992.

Wilson and Elliot also checked the frequency and reasons for 'ineligibility' of households in the PAF so far as OPCS and electoral purposes are concerned. Of the total in their England and Wales sample, 11% of the addresses in the small user category of PAF did not contain a resident household for these early 1980s data sets. The breakdown of reasons for this ineligibility are shown in table 4.2. This is important for such applications as drawing samples of the population for surveys.

Further investigation of the 11% of ineligible addresses referred to above yielded the data in table 4.2. An examination of the 13% in table 4.2 which could not be traced by OPCS interviewers revealed that, of them, 35% of them do not exist, 20% exist but are ineligible for OPCS' purposes

Table 4.2 Reasons for ineligibility of PAF addresses for OPCS' purposes. Column 3 is derived by re-working their figures and defines a proportion of the total PAF addresses ineligible for the reason given (*Source: Wilson and Elliot 1987*)

Reason for ineligibility	Percentage of sample	Re-allocated %
Vacant	29	3.2
Non-residential	27	3.0
Under conversion	9	1.0
Demolished [and do not exist]	6	0.7
New, not yet occupied	5	0.6
Second home	3	0.3
Not yet built	2	0.2
Holiday accommodation	2	0.2
Derelict	2	0.2
Institutions	1	0.1
Not traced by interviewers	13	n/a
Number of ineligible addresses in sample		**1282**

because they are businesses in the 'small user' category, 25% *do* exist and may be eligible and no conclusions could be reached on the final 20%. When these figures are incorporated with the others and converted into percentages of *all* addresses, the results are shown in column 3 of table 4.2. i.e. these figures are the percentages of all addresses investigated by OPCS which are ineligible for the reason shown.

Perhaps of the greatest concern is that there seem to be major regional variations in these shortcomings. Whilst the England and Wales figure for ineligible adresses is 11% on OPCS criteria, this varies from 7% to 15% according to table 4.3. This may, however, be due to regional trends in the ineligibility factors identified above, for example the higher percentage of second homes in Wales.

Table 4.3   Regional variation in percentage of all addresses 'ineligible' on OPCS criteria *(Source: Wilson and Elliot 1987)*

Region/metropolitan county	% ineligible
N W London	15
N E London	15
Wales	14
E Anglia	11
South West	11
West Yorkshire	11
Greater Manchester	10
Other North West (non-Met)	10
Merseyside	11
South Yorkshire	10
Other Yorks and Humberside (non-Met)	10
S E London	10
Tyne and Wear	9
West Midlands Met Area	9
S W London	9
Other North (non-Met)	8
South East	8
Other West Midlands (non-Met)	7
East Midlands	7

ACCURACY AND REPRESENTATIVENESS OF OS GRID REFERENCES

The representation of the OS or British National Grid References in the PAF is not of vital importance to Royal Mail but is significant to other users of PAF or CD. It is actually given to sufficient digits to provide ten metre resolution on the ground (see appendix 5); but in practice, all the last digits in the X (Easting) and Y (Northing) coordinates are zeros and hence the real resolution is 100m (one example, for 'The Steamer' Public House in Welwyn is 52310 21580; see figure 4.3). The 1.3 million grid references in Postzon and PAF on CD have been taken directly from those in the Central Postcode Directory file (see below). This and other evidence suggests that the conclusions drawn by Gatrell in his 1989 research paper still largely stand though the situation has probably improved somewhat since OPCS did much work to improve the accuracy before the 1991 Census.

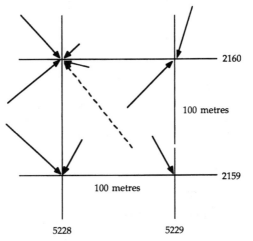

Figure 4.1   Allocation of Postcodes to 100 metre OS National Grid References. Continuous lines indicate correct allocations of Postcode centroids. The dashed line indicates an incorrect allocation.

Figure 4.1 illustrates the principle and practice of allocating individual Postcode centroids to 100m grid references. Gatrell compared the grid references for Postcodes in part of Cumbria held on the Central Postcode Directory (CPD) with those computed by averaging for each Postcode the grid references in the Pinpoint Address Code (PAC) files stored for individual buildings. The former were of 100m resolution, the latter of 1m resolution. Figure 4.2 compares the CPD grid references data with the equivalent but higher resolution data derived from the Pinpoint PAC files; the regularity of spacing in figure 4.2 (a) is clearly a result of the coarse resolution in the grid references in the CPD (and also in PAF on CD).

Figure 4.2   Comparison of the centroids of Postcodes in part of Cumbria as derived from the Central Postcode Directory (a) with their equivalents (b) computed from grid references of individual properties held in the Pinpoint Address Code file *(Source: Gatrell 1989)*

Gatrell found that the mean separation of the Pinpoint data (deemed 'correct' for this study) and that produced by Royal Mail was 96m, with a standard deviation of 66m. Since the maximum possible error if all allocations to the nearest 100m 'corner' were correct should be 70.7m (= the error of a centroid actually located at the centre of the grid square), this is a cause for alarm. The sources of the error are likely to be:

- use of the first address in each Postcode as the grid referenced point, rather than the mean centre (a consequence of the the way in which the PAF file's ancestor was compiled by DTp; this failing is not shared, for instance, by the GRO (Scotland) Postcode data files). See figure 5.4 for an illustration of the alternative ways a centroid could be defined;

- the inadequacy of the mean as a concept (some Postcodes cover clustered sets of delivery points whilst others are partly clustered and partly dispersed);

- some Postcode grid references in CPD (and hence in PAF) are known to be wrong. Gatrell, for instance, found the CPD grid references of two of the 343 Postcodes compared to be more than 500m in error. Ignoring the worst and the best 5% of the matches, the mean value is

90m which suggests these extreme cases are relatively rare. Conversely, 97% of the Postcodes lay within 200m of their correct position and 72% lay within 100m of it.

These are worrying figures for certain applications – many government-allocated resources, for instance, are very sensitive to which side of a boundary a property is based. In principle, the absolute geographical mismatch in urban areas should be smaller but the absolute number (and hence the consequences) of errors may be just as great.

LARGE AND SMALL USERS

Almost all of the above accuracy analysis relates to 'small users' except in so far as the Wilson and Elliot results indicate (unsurprisingly) that many records in this section of the PAF are not residences – they include businesses, empty properties and mixed use by mistake. No published analysis of the quality of the large user file is known to the authors.

As already indicated, much of the information quoted above is now out-of-date. Wilson and Elliot wrote in 1987 but their conclusions relate in part to data in 1980/81. Gatrell carried out his work in 1988/89. Royal Mail set up a 'task force' which made a major effort in 1991 to bring the PAF up-to-date. As yet, the effects of this effort are not statistically demonstrable beyond what has been shown in chapter 2 but it seems extremely likely that the current errors, other than grid referencing ones, are rather smaller than those identified at a much earlier stage by OPCS. Anecdotal evidence for this comes not only from Royal Mail; Wilson and Elliot reported that later checks showed small improvement in the accuracies of certain PAF characteristics.

RESULTS OF FIELD TRIALS ON THE 1990/4 VERSION OF PAF

To give some personal confidence in these results and to bring them more up-to-date, we carried out some field trials of the reliability of the most up-to-date PAF available at the time we were researching this book. These trials were carried out in two highly contrasting areas, chosen to give differing conditions but also for operational convenience. As such, they should be considered indicative rather than representative. Welwyn village in Hertfordshire contains a wide variety of housing (ranging from a Council housing estate to highly priced private housing) with a few non-residential properties. By contrast, the two Postcode Sectors selected in Edinburgh comprised a mixture of shops, offices and tenement housing.

The PAF on CD file used for these surveys was produced in the fourth quarter of 1990 though the accompanying documentation is described as pertaining to January 1991. The surveys were carried out in August 1991. Details for selected Postcode Sectors were printed out by computer (the one used is shown in plate 2) and the descriptions in the file were checked for each and every mail delivery point and for the Postcode Unit as a whole.

The approach followed was to:

- print out a total list of properties within the selected Postcode Sector (i.e. AL6 9) and their descriptions;

- check those in the village itself on the ground and on the most up-to-date OS maps of the area (i.e. from the OS Supply of Unpublished Survey Information which contains the surveyors' own information);

- classify the nature of problems encountered and summarise the statistical extent of problems.

From an extensive on-ground survey, the following results were obtained:

- there were 1866 properties in the 'R' or residential category. This includes houses, pubs, some shops and farms. Many pubs are, of course, both residential and part of the service sector. However, many Welwyn High Street properties, including most of the shops, are classified as 'R' by PAF. A former insurance office (once the village Post Office!) at number 31 is shown as R though it closed in early 1990. The Christian Book Shop closed in 1989 but was still recorded as R in the 1990/4 PAF on CD. Other properties are recorded as R but should be N or L; e.g., numbers 25 and 27 Ayot Green comprise a (working) sawmill, number 25 is the offices and 27 is the mill itself;

- there were 41 'N' or non-residential properties. These comprise offices, service buildings (such as the Fire Station and Telephone Exchange) and council buildings (e.g. the Civic Centre and Welwyn Parish Council buildings);

- there were 21 'L' or Large User category properties i.e. companies receiving more than 25 items of mail per day;

- the total of properties found 'on the ground' and cited above includes some 54 properties not included on PAF. These comprise:

- totally new houses (e.g. two under construction)] 44 in
- other houses   ] total
- ten other non-residential properties, five of them clustered in a group. The others include the Scout Hut, the Lea Valley Water Company Pumping Station, the Welwyn Parish Council building in Kimpton Road and the Little Orchard Nurseries on Rabley Heath Road, opened in summer 1990. It is clear that some of these could not be expected to be in a file of mail delivery points;

- in addition, some errors occur in house numbering in complex areas e.g. Ayot Green is said to include 23 mail delivery points but, on the ground, there are a maximum of 21 – what is implied as three houses for 8 to 12 is in fact one property ('The Cottages'). Royal Mail's task is certainly complicated by the fact that many properties in this area have names, not numbers, and are amalgamations of former individual properties;

- some change is evident yet is not recorded in PAF e.g. conversion of Sisservernes Farm into three permanent residences through conversion of two barns. These must have been in existence for at least one year before the PAF was issued;

- some conversion of category of a property (even without a change in form) has occurred but is undetected; e.g., the former pet shop and residence in 17 Church Street is now only a residence but is still classified as N;

- some 'dead' features still exist on the file e.g. Milford Nurseries have been derelict for some years;

- some properties on PAF could not be found on the ground. e.g. 13-19 Ayot Green.

In summary, therefore, the situation is as shown in table 4.4. On this basis, the overall error rate is approximately 81/1981 or 4% (i.e., incorrectly specified, plus those not included in PAF) but it was much higher (20%) in this area with regard to non-residential properties. The error rate for residential properties was 3%; of those on the file but incorrectly specified, the error rate was less than 1%. It should be noted that some element of judgement is included in this assessment and all types of error are bundled together; some types may also be irrelevant for particular purposes. Many of the errors involve assessments of building function which would be carried out at the time of delivery on the basis of appearance of the property and the nature of the mail delivered. It is outside the scope of the postmen to make enquiries.

Table 4.4 Errors detected in the Welwyn field study (* This does not include the shops classified as 'R')

	Correctly described	Incorrectly specified*	Not included in PAF	Total
Residences	1866	14	44	58
All other properties	115	12	11	23
Total properties	1981	26	55	81

On a superficial assessment this 4% error finding compares reasonably well with recent estimates by Royal Mail (reported in chapter 2) that there has recently been an annual rate of change in PAF of 2.4%. It is clear, however, that the situation is somewhat more complex than this since a number of the errors in this study are quite long-standing ones.

CHECKS ON OS GRID REFERENCES

The accuracy of the grid references was also investigated in the Welwyn study. This was done by noting the distance from the grid reference for

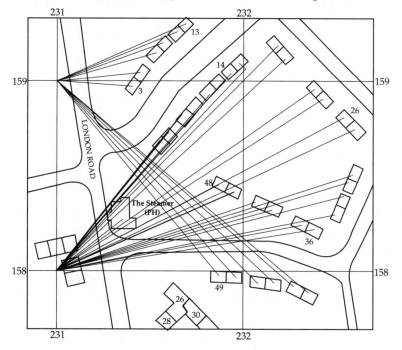

Figure 4.3 Plot of the location of house centroids in relation to the position of the centroid shown in the Postcode Address File for the Postcode which they comprise. This shows part of Welwyn village, Herts and is based upon OS 1: 1250 scale maps *(Source: Ordnance Survey ©. Crown Copyright)*.

each individual Postcode to the centroids of properties within that Postcode. Figure 4.3 illustrates the results. In both cases, some of the allocations are inappropriate. The Postcode grid reference is often far from being the optimal one; odd and even number properties in one street (but different Postcodes) are sometimes referenced to quite different 100m grid references. The conclusion is inescapable: on this evidence, the quality of the grid referencing in the PAF in this part of England at least is worse even than is implied by the 100m resolution of the data.

THE EDINBURGH EXPERIMENT

It is entirely possible that the results of any one field study could be a reflection of the local character of that area. For instance, a wholly residential area where there has been little new development is likely to have low error rates whilst a complex of houses and offices in a rapidly developing part of the country is likely to be much more in error on the PAF. To obtain a little more confidence in the results of the field study, therefore, the same individual carried out a similar experiment in two Postcode Sectors (EH3 7 and EH2 4) in west-central Edinburgh. Here the bulk of the properties were offices, shops and flats (table 4.5).

Table 4.5 Distribution of properties in two Edinburgh Postcode Sectors

PC Sector	Residential	Non-residential	Large User	Total
EH2 4	120	280	80	480
EH3 7[*]	294	387	74	755

[*]Does not include 5 Post Boxes (which were not checkable)

The results from this study broadly confirmed those of the Welwyn one and were as follows:

- one whole street (Lyndoch Park Lane in EH3 7) is not in the 1990/4 PAF (though the smaller Lyndoch Place is) and certain other delivery points found on the ground could not be found in that version of PAF;

- some properties appeared twice in the PAF as both offices and as residences though only having one door to the street;

- flats in one building were sometimes shown as one entity even though there were multiple flats within the block (the standard Royal Mail criterion of a delivery point is a letter box);

- many offices were designated as R (residential) in the PAF;

- the names of firms in offices had often changed from that shown in PAF.

CONCLUSIONS ON THE QUALITY OF DATA IN THE PAF ON CD

Based especially on the findings of the field studies, the following conclusions may be drawn:

- the PAF contains a number of properties which cannot be found on the ground and, vice versa, some properties found on the ground do not appear in the PAF. The frequency of these is greatest in complex areas (often in affluent ones where improvement of properties and fusion of properties has occurred) and the error rate there is sufficient to cause real concern for certain highly demanding applications (see below);

- on all the evidence available, the National Grid references on the English parts of the PAF at least are unreliable for any *local* application. We have been told privately that the variable quality of these is the basis on which litigation is being threatened to one system supplier who has made use of PAF;

- the classification of properties into residential and non-residential ones is inconsistent. In particular, many commercial properties are classified as residential;

- the incidence of errors of all types seems greatest amongst non-residential properties;

- there is evidence of 'dead' properties being left on the PAF and of changes of names of firms not being updated. The incidence of the totality of these errors is difficult to define but may well be as high as 5% of non-residential properties nationally. Errors in residential properties are significantly lower.

The quality of the PAF cannot be considered separately from its use. If, for instance, it is to be used for targeting of mail delivered by Royal Mail itself, the delivery aspect of the process is a minor problem since the system, at least at the level of a statistical abstraction, is clearly resilient. Letters get delivered because local knowledge is used in the delivery process. The quality imperfections impact much more upon the selection of records on some criteria; some records do not exist, some exist which should not and some are described (e.g. by Grid Reference) incorrectly. Even so, some of these errors are also irrelevant for certain purposes – use of the Postcodes for a national map of the incidence of rare events (such as of childhood cancers) or to aggregate data for use at the county level would be perfectly satisfactory. For purposes based upon the individual household or mail delivery point, however, the versions of PAF on CD studied still had significant shortcomings in 1991. This is recognised by Royal Mail and some enhancements have already been carried out by them and by other organisations. Despite these problems, it is significant that all known proposals to build large address databases (such as the one currently being assembled to underpin the Council Tax – being set up at the time of writing) exploit the PAF as the single best available source of data.

ENHANCING THE QUALITY OF PAF

One particular way of enhancing the quality of data is to make comparisons between two independently collected versions of it. Where these agree, considerable confidence can be placed in the result. Where differences appear between the details of the two records (e.g. the property may appear only in one file), this needs investigation. The technical basis for such comparisons is described in chapter 5; here we consider only the theoretical aspects and the data constraints.

There is no shortage of other data candidates for comparison with the PAF. The obvious candidates are:

- electricity, water and gas companies' address data;
- the electoral register;
- HM Land Registry and the Registers of Scotland property data;
- Ordnance Survey digitised maps, from which (in theory at least) property-related information could be generated;
- the British Telecom telephone database.

In addition, developments such as the putative National Streetworks Gazetteer and the possible Land and Property Register (Hawker and Goodwin 1991, LGMB 1991, Pugh *et al* 1991) could provide useful comparators, provided that they were in some respects independently compiled. Many potential data sources (such as the Council Tax Register) are heavily based upon PAF in the first instance. The primary advantages of the annually updated electoral register are that it has statutory force, and following a decision by the Home Secretary some years ago, the register is now publicly available for general use. It is by far the most widely used source of national address (and, by interpretation, property and household) data at present, especially when linked to geodemographic databases for targeting purposes. Moreover, it is made available in computer-readable form at the uniform rate of £18 per 1000 electors (1991 price).

Unhappily, its problems are also manifold: since each local authority sells the data, since many do not accord it a high priority and several different types of computer systems are used to prepare the tapes, the logistics and gestation period involved in dealing with it are both considerable. It does not capture those ineligible to vote, such as non-British nationals, and hence their properties. The advent of the Community Charge has also reduced its coverage, notably in Scotland where as many as 20% of the population may have absented themselves from the electoral register in an attempt to avoid being traced and forced to pay the Charge. Similar lists of strengths and weaknesses can be identified for the other data sets: sales of gas, for instance, do not 'penetrate' anything like all the areas in Britain and Land Registry's records are presently very incomplete.

If there are certain practical shortcomings in the obvious comparator data sets, the crucial problem is more fundamental. The most important difference between the different possible data sources is that they are actually recording different 'entities' or objects (see chapter 5). This complicates the interpretation of what is a genuine difference between the files. The primary objective of Royal Mail is to hold details of each mail delivery point. Hence their records do not describe properties or enterprises which do not receive mail, typically warehouses or buildings which form part of an enterprise which has mail delivered elsewhere (e.g. schools). Buildings which are internally subdivided into flats and occupied by different groups of individuals are also often unknown to Royal Mail (as was demonstrated in our field experiments).

In contrast, the Population Census has a detailed description of what constitutes one household based upon the relationship of the members of the group living together and this is assumed in much socio-economic data. For OS, the rule is 'if subdivisions are not visible, they cannot be mapped'. For the utilities, two different entities are sometimes used: the billing address and the meter address (where the supply is metered). These may be very different; one of the authors pays the telephone bills for a property 500km from his home base. Equally, there may be multiple meters per enterprise (typically church and similar organisations' property is multi-metered). For local government, the entity of importance has recently been the household and individual members within it; the change to the Council Tax currently scheduled for 1993 will take this back towards the former rating basis, the rating hereditament (i.e., the portion of a building, building or group of buildings treated as a unit for tax purposes). For the Land Registry, on the other hand, what is critical is the transaction. Registration takes place only on sale of a plot of land and this may involve multiple properties, zero properties or fractions of one. To complicate matters still further, where the national list is produced from local subsets, duplication is commonplace; students, for instance, often have multiple addresses.

It follows from all of this that some degree of mismatch should be anticipated when two independently compiled data sets are brought together. Given that, the prospect of checking and improving the quality of PAF by comparing it to other, independently assembled data sets is less simple than it seems at first sight. Nonetheless, as the computer tools described in chapter 5 become more readily available and as computer time becomes ever cheaper, some such actions are almost inevitable. In fact, as this book went to press Royal Mail had begun to carry out trials with new software to enable PAF to be compared to other national data sets and Ordnance Survey launched their own plans for an address database derived from their own digital maps and from PAF.

Royal Mail Postcode-related services

It was pointed out in an earlier chapter that there is commercial benefit in using Postcodes so far as the large senders of mail are concerned. The two main services which provide these benefits at present are Mailsort and Presstream.

Mailsort is actually a range of services that provide discounts for customer-sorted volume mailings. The sorting is done using the Mailsort database provided by Royal Mail. To be eligible for the discounts, 90% of a firm's mail must be fully Postcoded. Letters must be sorted into bundles of at least 25 before mailing. The minimum volume is 4,000 letters if posting nationally or 2,000 if posting to one Postcode Area only. Different tariffs are available for those who require next-day delivery or those content for their mail to take up to seven days. Presstream is a similar facility designed for the postage of magazines, periodicals, advertising cards and the like. Again there are different tariffs deriving from the speed of service required.

A key future development in this area will be the use of barcodes on the mail to make the Postcode more rapidly machine-readable. Details of these developments are given in chapter 10.

Other Postcode-related products and services

Many organisations now incorporate Postcodes in their own products so it is possible to obtain the latter from multiple sources though all Postcode information is ultimately produced by Royal Mail. Thomson Directories, for instance, contain Postcode listings for the areas they cover. This section summarises the Postcode-related services available from a wide range of organisations. Their contact addresses are given in appendix 2.

Suppliers of Postcode and address verification systems

Royal Mail has formed alliances with a number of different commercial organisations to market the PAF and other Postcode-related products and services. The specialisms of these organisations are shown in table 4.6 and contact details for all of them are given in appendix 2.

Table 4.6 Suppliers of Postcode and address verification systems. Key: A: Automated procedures. Ml: Manual procedures. M: mainframe or mini-computer software. P: Personal Computer software. *: PAF on CD. x: capability present. *(Source: Royal Mail)*

Company	Postcoding bureaux	PAF on CD distributor	Suppliers of Cross-Matching software	Suppliers of Rapid Access Input Systems
Axciom UK Ltd	A		M	x
Allies Computing			P*	
Anadata Ltd			M	x
Archetype Systems Ltd	A	x	P*	
AT & T Istel Ltd	A			
CACI Ltd	A			
Capscan Ltd	A	x	M,P	x
CCN Systems Ltd	A			
CDMS (Credit and Data Marketing Services)	A			
Centre-File Ltd	A,Ml			
Claymore Services Ltd		x	P*	
Codedit Services Ltd	Ml			
Corporate Publishing Software Ltd		x		
Eltec Ltd		x		
Equifax Europe Ltd	A			
GB Mailing Systems Ltd	A		M,P	x
Hopewiser Ltd	A,Ml		M,P	x
Information for Marketing Ltd	A		M	
Lindor Ltd	A		M,P	x
Mail Marketing (Bristol) Ltd	A			
Optech Ltd		x	P*	
Pinpoint Analysis	A		M	
Printronic International	A			
Quick Address Systems			P	x
ROCC Computers Ltd		x		x
Root 3 Systems Ltd		x	M,P	x
Sintrom Electronics		x		
Technical Information Ltd	A,Ml		P	x
The Computing Group	A		M	x
The WSA Consultancy Ltd		x		
Words and Numbers	A, Ml			

The Central Postcode Directory (CPD)

This is a database which relates all Postcodes in the UK to a number of standard areas. It was created by the Office of Population Censuses and Surveys (OPCS) and the General Register Office (Scotland) (GRO(S)), in conjunction with Royal Mail. The OPCS maintain the module for England and Wales and the module for Northern Ireland, whilst GRO(S) maintains the Scottish Postcode Directory which differs in certain respects. The CPD is based on an earlier one created by the DTp using the then PAF for their Regional Highway Traffic Model (RHTM) project. The DTp file was then enhanced by OPCS with assistance from DTp, General Register Office for Scotland, the Welsh Office, OS, the Department of Economic Development of Northern Ireland, Royal Mail and some local authorities. It covers all of the UK.

The purpose of the CPD is primarily as an aid to the area coding of data and statistical processing in government and the National Health Service, the data being supplied to them via OPCS. The data are also marketed commercially via Royal Mail and are then known as the Postzon file (and have been described thus earlier in this chapter). CPD functions by relating Postcodes to other areal units used by government and Royal Mail customers. It is revised at least twice per year, consists of one computer record per Postcode and each record contains the following information:

- Postcode;
- Year and month of introduction and termination if applicable;
- National Grid Reference (stored as a five-digit Eastings and five-digit Northings, as compared to the OS alphanumeric scheme described in appendix 5);
- Area code describing the county and local authority district in England, Wales and Northern Ireland; region, islands area and district codes in Scotland;
- Electoral ward code or islands area electoral division codes;
- User type (small or large);
- Grid reference accuracy indicator;
- Country code;
- Ward code or county/islands area code accuracy indicator.

The history of the CPD has been an interesting one. In the mid 1980s, OPCS reviewed its status. Some of the results described earlier arose directly from that study. In essence, it was found that about 93% of the ward codes were correct but only 72% of the grid references were correct to 100m. Various options were studied to improve it, notably in a consultancy report produced in 1987.

At the time of writing, however, the CPD is updated by OPCS twice per year on the basis of the latest PAF. CPD contains all Postcodes in the current PAF and all those which were in previous ones but, for whatever reason, have been terminated. Grid references and area codes of new Postcodes are allocated by a computer imputation process using information from other Postcodes either in the same sub-Sector (in 80 to 85% of the cases) or in the same Sector (in 15 to 20% of the cases). In the relatively few cases where this is not possible, the codes and grid references are allocated manually. Changes to country, district or ward codes resulting from changes to the boundaries of local government areas are added to the CPD at the year end in which they take effect. In addition, however, a 'frozen' version of the CPD is produced for the areal units in use at fixed moments in time to facilitate comparison of new and old data (see OPCS 1990 and 1991).

The General Register Office for Scotland (GRO(S)) provides OPCS each January and June with a copy of the Scottish Postcode Directory which contains a more comprehensive set of area codes than that held on CPD. Information is extracted from these for inclusion in the next national CPD. The Scottish directory is maintained in a quite different fashion to that for England, Wales and Northern Ireland: GRO(S) update and maintain maps of Unit Postcodes in Scotland and assign all grid references and area codes manually (see chapter 6).

A continuous process of improvement of CPD is under way but, at present, it is estimated that under 0.1% omissions occur. The two main sources of inaccuracy are:

- straddling. This is unavoidable unless all administrative area sets and Postcodes are made coterminous i.e. fit together exactly. Bias may occur in that the grid reference on CPD is of the first address in any Postcode and this might lie in one area though the bulk of the Postcode could lie in another area. The situation is less severe in Scotland because of the higher resolution of their grid references;

- some grid references allocated at the outset of the Regional Highway Traffic Model project were incorrect. Many of these have since been located and corrected but this could have resulted in the Postcode being allocated to an incorrect ward.

It is interesting to compare the figures for the 'contemporary scene' derived from PAF on CD with those for the continually incrementing CPD. Table 4.7 is reproduced from OPCS (1991). It is not directly comparable with the figures given in chapter 2 because of the slightly different base and because the two sets of figures relate to different moments in time (the CPD is based on an earlier set of Postcodes to those used in the PAF statistics). It does, however, provide a valuable breakdown for the countries in the UK (these counts can also be provided for Local Government Districts, wards, post towns, Postcode Districts and Postcode Sectors by arrangement with OPCS).

Table 4.7 Numbers of Postcodes in Version I 1991/2 CPD, produced in September 1991 *(Source: OPCS 1991)*

Country	Large users	Small users	Total
England	230,078	1,189,759	1,419,837
Wales	10,796	80,922	91,718
Scotland	18,689	144,175	162,864
Great Britain	259,563	1,414,856	1,674,419
Northern Ireland	4,326	35,969	40,295
United Kingdom	263,889	1,450,825	1,714,714

Perhaps of critical importance to readers of this book, Royal Mail takes delivery of the CPD and updates the area codes and the grid references in PAF on CD from it for the whole of the UK.

The GRO(S) Postcode boundary files for Scotland

As indicated in chapter 6, the 1991 Population Census was carried out in a different fashion in Scotland from that in England and Wales. The Scottish Census relied much more on the Postcode system to define the areas used for collecting and reporting the results of the census. One part of this process was that the collections of delivery points making up a Postcode were plotted on maps (see figures 6.1 and 6.2) and boundaries drawn around each Postcode. From these, digitised versions of the boundaries were constructed by the GRO(S). Chapter 5 sets out how these boundaries may be combined using suitable Geographical Information System (GIS) software and any combination of the 163,000 or so Postcodes in Scotland produced for subsequent use in mapping or analysis.

Enumeration District (ED) boundaries in England and Wales

In England and Wales, the 110,000 or so EDs used in the 1991 Census of Population are not assembled from combinations of Postcodes. In one sense, therefore, they may not seem to be a central concern in this book. However, they are very relevant to us because:

- census data for these areas are very widely used, the standard statistics from the Population Census being perhaps the most widely used data set in the UK (see Rhind 1983 and chapters 6, 8 and 9);

- the OPCS is producing an index of Postcodes for England and Wales partly or wholly contained within EDs. In essence, this is an extension of the CPD, and this will facilitate the linkage of census and other, Postcoded data (which is a common occurrence: see chapters 5, 6 and 8).

For these reasons, it is important to record the availability of digitised versions of the ED boundaries. Two separate initiatives have been set up, one led by Graphical Data Capture Ltd (called ED91) and the other by MVA (called ED-Line) whose addresses are given in appendix 2. Both are digitising from the largest scale OS maps necessary to define the boundaries at an accuracy of a few metres. In practice, both organisations are therefore using 1:10,000 scale OS maps and supplementing them from the 1:1250 and 1:2500 scale plans in complex urban areas where necessary. From in excess of 11,000 map sheets they will produce files of all EDs before mid 1992, largely on a county-by-county basis to match to the manner in which census data is provided. Considerable progress has already been made in digitising at the time of writing (late 1991) and numerous county data sets are already available.

Another data set which may be of relevance to users of Postcode data in England and Wales is the officially defined and digitised boundaries of electoral wards. Enumeration Districts fit or 'nest' within wards and hence the OPCS index of Postcodes within EDs also provides a link between Postcodes and wards (the ward code is also given on PAF for each Postcode). The ward is a very important areal unit because of its widespread use in elections (it is used both as the basis of local elections and as the 'building block' from which parliamentary constituencies are created) and for a variety of other purposes; certain unemployment statistics, for instance, are made available for them and the Travel To Work Areas for which important statistics are produced by aggregations of wards. The ward boundaries are periodically re-adjusted by the Boundary Commissioners but, for census purposes, OPCS takes the wards as 'frozen' in 1991. Ordnance Survey has digitised all of these ward boundaries and the contact point for them is also given in appendix 2.

The Pinpoint Postal Address Code

Pinpoint is an organisation which markets data describing the populations of small areas, together with services to facilitate the use of these data. Whilst many other organisations such as CACI have also provided such services, Pinpoint is unique in one important respect: it has created a database containing information for individual properties. This has been assembled from Royal Mail's PAF and by associating with each property a one metre resolution National Grid reference which Pinpoint has digitised from OS's large scale maps. The largest scale OS map available is generally used and, for all the populated areas of the country, this is either the 1:1250 or the 1:2500 scale product. In total, some 230,000 such maps are needed to cover the country at the largest available scale. The result has been the Pinpoint Address Code (PAC), consisting of the address, grid reference, Postcode and some other information for every property in an area. Multi-occupancy of property is recorded in the database. At the time of writing, over half the country is claimed to have been completed, work having begun in the most commercially valuable areas (principally in the South of England). The whole operation revealed inconsistencies between the contents of the PAF and of OS maps; this is unsurprising since OS maps record the physical presence of buildings and PAF summarises the mail delivery points. In the event, however, Pinpoint had to devote substantial resources to solve the inconsistencies but the end result is claimed to be a substantial improvement on anything previously available.

In addition, Pinpoint has begun to assemble their version of a national road network, termed the Pinpoint Road Network or PRN. Again, this is digitised from OS large scale maps and stored in 'link and node' structure (see chapter 5). This records the National Grid references of each road junction and other coordinates between junctions as necessary to capture the curvature of the road centre-line. Street names (or road numbers where appropriate) are held on each digitised link. Other versions of the national road network can also be obtained such as the Present Year Network File developed by the Department of Transport (marketed by SIA-Langton) and OSCAR from the Ordnance Survey, the latter provide by far the most detailed and up-to-date information.

Files of PACs and PRN can be purchased from Pinpoint. Typical applications of these data are:

- bringing together local authority (government) departmental address files to form a corporate database, using the PAC grid reference as the common link;

- mapping health data where the individual's address is coded only by Postcode. The PAC can then be used to obtain the grid reference needed for mapping;

- linking utilities' digitised cable and pipe networks to customer addresses;

- allocating properties to *ad hoc* areas devised by a public or private organisation for the supply of services. This can either be done via the grid reference on each property and digitised boundaries of these areas (via a process known as 'Point-in-Polygon' allocation) or by approximating the *ad hoc* areas with groups of Postcodes then checking each property's Postcode to find which area it lies within. These approaches are described in chapters 5 and 9;

- modelling transport of people or goods. Knowing the origin of journeys as specified by a set of addresses (and hence Postcodes), these can be linked to the road network described by PRN. From this, GIS tools can predict best routes or define the load upon the system as a whole;

Several of these forms of analysis using PAC and PRN have been used in the 1991 London Area Transport Survey being carried out by the DTp and the London Research Centre (on behalf of London Boroughs).

Bartholomew's digital maps of Postcode Sectors

Bartholomew was perhaps the earliest publishing organisation to recognise the potential of Postcodes. At the end of the 1970s, they produced a set of maps at 1:100,000 scale defining Postcode Districts and Sectors. The earliest versions of these were based upon Bartholomew's own map projection which was incompatible with the National Grid. The Postcode Area boundaries have now, however, been converted to the National Grid projection within Britain (in N. Ireland, they are stored in latitude and longitude) by use of a GIS (see chapter 5).

This information has now been compiled so as to be part of Bartholomew's 1:250,000 scale digital map database (1:500,000 scale in Ireland) which is updated continuously as new information is supplied from the National Postcode Centre. The technical detail reveals that encoding such data in computer form is not always straightforward: for instance, at present 'false polygon' boundaries are included within the database. These extend beyond the normal coastline. The benefits of this are two-fold:

- it reduces the data volume since the British coastline is itself highly detailed, being much more intricate than the rest of the Postcode Area boundaries;

- it obviates the need to code separately the many islands with the same Postcode as the adjacent mainland. Such a coding may in any case need to be carried out in different ways for different GIS (see chapter 5).

Because of this pragmatic step, the data may need to be overlaid and 'clipped' by the detailed coastline if, for example, coloured maps of land-only Postcodes are to be produced. Again, this is a step which can be carried out normally in 'state of the art' GIS and is described in chapter 5.

Geoplan's Sector boundaries

The Geoplan product is also a digitised map of Postcode Sector boundaries but is derived from a different source from that of Bartholomew. It was originally constructed in 1985 for the Regional Newspaper Advertising Bureau, with digitising carried out by GDC (see appendix 2). The map source consisted of 204 OS paper maps at 1:50,000 scale on which the Post Office (as it then was) had drawn the boundaries of each and every one of the nearly 9,000 Postcode Sectors. The purpose was to relate the needs of advertisers to their most likely target markets. This was achieved by the following procedure:

- the characteristics of the target market for the product to be advertised were defined and entered in the computer system (e.g. areas with a high proportion of quite affluent families with children under five years). Other constraints could be added e.g. that the area selected had to be within 50km of a distribution plant;

- the computer then searched the database for those census EDs (see chapter 6) which most precisely matched the requirements, based upon use of the Population Census data for EDs;

- these EDs were then compared with the circulation areas of regional newspapers of various kinds. These areas were described in terms of Postcode Sectors and a link was held between these sectors and the EDs. From all this, a list of the most suitable papers was printed out for each product, together with a note of press date, advertising rates and format for advertisements.

Though the boundary data were converted to computer form for this one purpose, it soon became evident that many other applications were

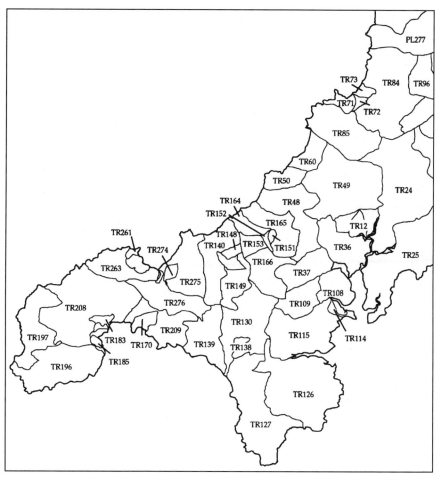

Figure 4.4   A sample of Postcode Sector boundaries as sold by Geoplan *(Source: Geoplan)*

possible for them. In 1991, Geoplan edited the boundaries to bring them up-to-date and marketed them in association with Royal Mail. Figure 4.4 shows the level of detail which these data provide. In this case, the coastline is much more detailed than the internal boundaries (unlike those from Bartholomew's) but this detail has been retained.

Other Postcode maps of Britain

Though not available in computer form, the well-known firm of Geographers' A to Z Map Company publishes Postcode maps of London. These are produced at two scales, a 1:63,360 scale map shows Postcode Districts whilst a series of maps derived from the OS 1:10,000 scale maps shows Postcode Sectors.

AA postal area boundaries for Europe

The Automobile Association (AA) has assembled a number of digitised boundary data sets and place name gazetteers which it is selling via Kingswood Ltd (see appendix 2). For our purposes, the most relevant product is the European map of postal code areas, part of which is shown as figure 5.16. This was compiled on a map of the continent based on Lambert's Conformal Conic projection with standard parallels at 42 and 56 degrees North. As will be obvious from the description of postal code use in selected countries which was given in chapter 3, the postal areas in both the AA map and those available from the national postal organisations directly are somewhat incompatible from country to country in certain respects. Nonetheless, this is by far the most useful Europe-wide product known to us. It emphasises that no postal areas are believed to exist for Ireland! Table 4.8 shows the number of areas present for the countries represented on the map.

Table 4.8 Approximate number of postal areas for each country held in the AA data file in July 1991 *(Source: Automobile Association/Kingswood Ltd)*

Austria	76	Belgium	13	Britain	120
Denmark	21	France	92	Finland	20
Germany (West)	81	Germany (East)	99	Greece	57
Italy	120	Netherlands	31	Norway	30
Portugal	8	Spain	50	Sweden	12
Switzerland	9				

Goad's land use data

For over a century, Chas E Goad has collected and supplied information on the detailed land use in cities and towns. The original purpose was to provide information for fire insurance purposes but currently the information is used for a multiplicity of reasons by customers. Details of 1100 shopping centres in the UK are now held and frequently updated. Extension of business into the Benelux countries, France and Spain has begun. Hitherto, this information has been assembled and sold largely in map form, using large scale OS maps as the base. Now, however, Goad has begun to convert all their information to computer form and, through use of a GIS, is able to produce tabulations and maps to order, showing not only the ownership of properties but their category of use, floorspace (for commercial enterprises) and other information. Since Postcodes of properties are stored with the data, these can be used as a basis for selection. Figure 4.5 shows a sample of output from the database.

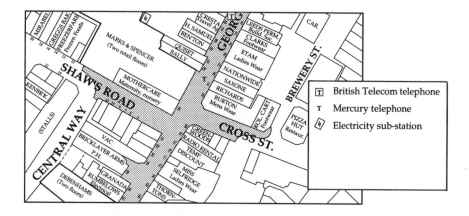

Figure 4.5   A Goad map of part of the shopping centre of Altrincham. Each property is stored as one computer record to which is attached a Postcode *(Source and Copyright: Chas E Goad and Ordnance Survey © Crown Copyright).*

Address list and other information

Partial lists of the addresses of all occupied properties have been compiled (e.g. through lifestyle questionnaires) by a multiplicity of companies; it has been estimated that about 4,500 lists are now available for rental or purchase in the UK. Many of these contain the names of occupants. Some of these lists cover very large fractions of the population and may, in some cases, be linked to or derived from the electoral register to aid national 'profiling' of households (see chapter 8 for some of the uses of these data sets). The largest marketing databases compiled in the UK for list rental purposes are produced by NDL International, ICD and CMT. ICD has recently claimed to have built its database up over several years from 60 million questionnaires. Given that the total population of Britain – every man, woman and child – is about 56 million, it is obvious that there has been substantial duplication in responses and in-built bias (only certain people respond to questionnaires). Nonetheless, this is a massive and valuable database; the attributes attached to each record are chosen to describe 'lifestyle' and are the basis of selection of records for sale to a user. It is this basis of selection and these attributes which form the main concern of the Data Protection Registrar. Almost all such address lists now include the Postcode and hence retrieval is possible on this key; subject to the Data Protection regulations, this may also be used as a means of linking together the address list and other data sets.

Typical of the property address files now becoming available is British Telecom's (BT) new Phone Disc system, launched in April 1991. It consists of software and a CD containing 17 million records for non-ex-directory telephone numbers and is updated every three months (at peak rates, BT claims to change 200,000 records per week which gives some indication of the task of maintaining a database containing names). The cost of this is presently £2,200 per annum. A point of some importance is that this is stated explicitly to be a directory enquiries tool, not a general database; the information has been secured so that it can not be down-loaded. Unlike the Directory Enquiries facility, however, it permits national searches. Retrieval is claimed to be within 30 seconds on a standard PC. As indicated earlier, the 17 million records take up 550 Mb and name, postal address, Postcode and telephone number are stored for each subscriber.

Hence searches can be made on any combination of these characteristics. In principle, only BT's concerns about misuse of the data prevent it being linked together with other data and then used to produce answers to questions such as 'list all the telephone numbers of people living in very high status Postcodes'. Normal output is however available in various forms. Finally, note that the addresses stored on the Phone Disc are those given by customers, and therefore may not be postally-correct addresses.

Finally, the availability of national address databases including details of Postcodes seems likely to expand considerably in the next few years. As we go to press, Ordnance Surrey has announced its intention of creating a high quality, frequently up-dated product of this type and discussions are in progress between them and various other organisations in this field, such as Pinpint Analysis.

Section 2
Handling Postcoded data

CHAPTER 5

Tools for exploiting the Postcode

Postcode information, by its very nature, is voluminous. In paper form, details of the 1.6 million Unit Postcodes fill nearly 100 Royal Mail Postcode directories, requiring a significant investment of time and effort for any business or institution wishing to access large parts of this information efficiently. However, the advent of powerful computers and high-capacity storage devices such as the CD at affordable prices have made it inceasingly practical and cost-effective to store Postcode information in digital form. Computer storage of Postcode information has now made it possible to search through the complete set of Postcodes in only a few seconds and, crucially, it has become much easier to link other kinds of information to the Postcode.

In the context of these technological developments, and with the growing availability of spatially referenced data sets following the publication of the Chorley Report in 1987, there has been a significant growth in the number of Postcode products (which are described in chapter 4). Many of these new Postcode products result from the adoption of the Postcode referencing system by collectors of spatial data sets such as the GRO(S), or by those users who need to access large amounts of address-based data such as geodemographic consultants (see chapters 8 and 9). These developments have followed from a general recognition that the Postcodes are an important 'New Geography', accessible to all, and they have generated a considerable demand for new tools to exploit Postcode-based spatial (or geographical) referencing.

This chapter will be concerned with these tools: what they are, how they work and their potential in spatial analysis. A number of software vendors have developed customised packages which incorporate Postcode referencing with business-related information. But there have been parallel developments of general purpose computer-based GIS which are suitable for management of Postcodes and many other kinds of spatial data sets. These are inherently more flexible than the Postcode-specific software but this characteristic may not be necessary for some users. Before delving into these technicalities, however, this chapter begins on a more philosophical basis by considering how Postcodes summarise geography. This very fundamental matter strongly influences the choice of computer methods for handling Postcodes.

How Postcodes summarise geography – the computer perspective

Both in the Introduction to this book and in chapter 1 we have described how the Postcode system is one way of cutting up the land area of Britain into areas sufficiently small to be used for many purposes. We now revisit this issue, but this time considering it from the perspective of computer manipulation of Postcodes. Again, though, we need to start with the geographical principles underlying the system. The use of computers has many advantages over manual procedures but also makes more stringent demands upon us: in particular, it forces the user to make specific choices about how the world is defined. Computers require precise and unambiguous data sets expressed in text or number form: this is easy to collect for payments in and out of a bank account but rather more difficult when the geography of the real world is concerned.

To begin with, the Postcode can be seen to summarise 'geography' by providing a way of reducing the spatial description of a 'real world' area to a simple alphanumeric code. Geographers refer to the Postcode as a 'representation' of geography, which we can define as 'a means of summarising essential qualities in a likeness'. In this context, the Postcode is the 'likeness', and the 'essential qualities' are all the places in a given locality. Since the Postcode was developed for mail-related activities, for the most part the 'places' are buildings or groups of them and the 'localities' are named areas of habitation. Postcodes are, therefore, representations of human settlement and business activity in particular and not of 'geography' in general. Figure 5.1 shows how Postcodes are simply one form of representation which co-exists with several others, each summarising some aspect of the real world.

As detailed in chapter 2, the Postcode is a hierarchical representation where the places are grouped into localities, and the localities are grouped at two higher levels. In Postcode terminology, the places are described as 'Unit' Postcodes, which are grouped into localities termed Sectors, then Districts and finally Areas at the highest level. Although this is how we see the Postcode from the point of view of geographical principles, in fact Royal Mail created the Postcode system by repeatedly 'splitting' the areas

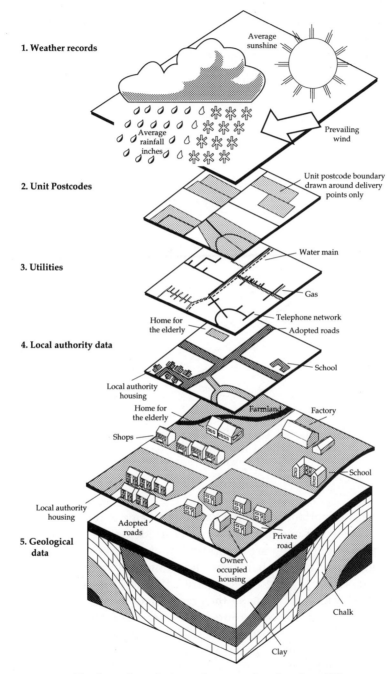

Figure 5.1 The layer-based view of geography showing different possible representations of reality, with Unit Postcodes depicted by shaded areas 'wrapping' around the delivery points

around post towns using local knowledge, rather than by 'lumping' together groups of houses and businesses (see figure 5.2). This makes no difference to the characteristics of the representation scheme, but it is a lot easier to remember the alphabetical sequence of Areas, Districts, Sectors and Units!

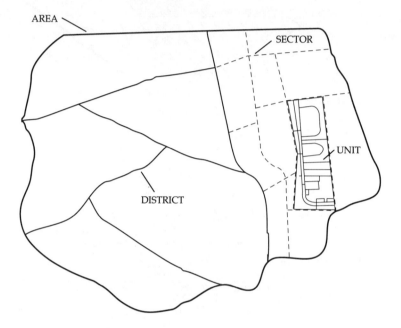

Figure 5.2   Schematic illustration showing the hierarchy of Postcodes geographically. Unlike figure 5.1 the Unit Postcode boundaries have been extended to 'exhaust' space by extending the boundaries to inter-lock with each other

The most important part of the Postcode scheme of representation is the way that Postcodes summarise 'space'. Postcodes can be described as one-dimensional since they are composed of characters which can be put unambiguously into alphabetical and numerical order (see table 5.1). However, the real world has 'extent', that is, it is two-dimensional (ignoring elevation and time for the present) and there is no single natural 'order' into which we can group places (see the features illustrated in figures 1.3 and 5.1). Postcodes are useful to analysts primarily because they incorporate *some* spatial ordering through their hierarchical organisation but also because the description is not burdened with full details of location. Hence, if we acquire a list of all the Postcodes of Birmingham, we can determine that there are 98 Districts dividing up the city but they cannot be located geographically. In other words, we could not guide a helicopter to B21 Postcode District simply by using the Postcode – they do not provide the pilot with a set of spatial coordinates or, as expressed in chapter 1, with 'global geometry'.

Table 5.1 Sequence of a sample of Postcodes for Birmingham in alphanumeric order (note that B2, rather than B20, follows B19 *Source: PAF on CD).*

B19 3XH
B19 3XJ
B19 3XQ
B2 4AA
B2 4AY
B2 4AZ

The Postcode is an economical way to represent geography since it is a way to refer to a particular place without giving details of spatial coordinates. Many organisations find that this is an adequate form of representation: if they wish to send a letter to any single address or group of addresses, they rely on Royal Mail to find a locality such as B21 (the first Unit Postcode of which is actually located at National Grid reference 40290 29010, using the form held in the PAF). For this task, the list of Postcodes is the only aspect of the spatial representation which is needed. Another, non-postal example would be an insurance company which uses Postcode Districts as a means of assigning premiums to customers. The insurance company simply maintains the list of Postcode Districts (see example in table 5.2) and counts the number of claims for each one over a year. At the end of the year, it revises its premiums for those Districts with the most claims and advises its customers of the new premiums by post.

Table 5. 2 Typical house contents insurance premiums for Birmingham Postcode Districts. (*) signifies 'referral area' where insurers reserve the right not to quote a premium as the risk is high

District	Premium tariff
All other Districts	1
B43, B63	2
B1-18, B23-25, B33, B42, B44, B66-76	3
B29-32, B34-38	4
B19-21	*

However, there are many occasions when the spatial coordinate position of each Postcode needs to be known. In the first place, it is presumably helpful to Royal Mail if they can access maps of the boundaries of the Postcodes so that they can assign new codes to new developments. These boundaries need to be placed according to geographical criteria such as the location of roads, railways and rivers (although see figure 5.3 for an

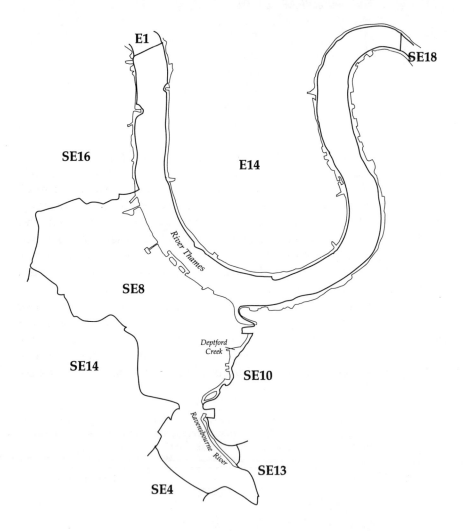

Figure 5.3   The SE8 Postcode District encompasses the surface area of the Thames around the Isle of Dogs, as well as Deptford in SE London, as indicated by the Geographia map from which this is taken. *(Source: © Bartholomew)*

extreme example) and accessibility factors such as bridge locations. Since multiple Unit Postcodes form part of a postman's walk, there is also a need to ensure that they can be grouped to give all workers an approximately equal load. The geographical position of Postcodes is also needed for analysis: for example, it may be necessary to compare the position of a proposed new road with the Postcode Sectors it crosses so that all residents could be contacted by letter.

We can therefore identify two different kinds of representations for Postcodes which both yield precise and unambiguous data sets expressed in text or number form (i.e., data that can be handled by computer). These are those that:

- use a list of the alphanumeric Postcodes which have only implicit spatial ordering (hereafter termed a list-based representation);
- use spatial coordinates for each Postcode providing a full spatial description (hereafter termed a coordinate-based representation).

The clear distinction between these two kinds of Postcode representation marks an important design choice on how to store Postcodes in computers. Simple spreadsheet software, statistical packages or word processors can be used to store and sort lists of Postcodes but specialised software is needed to carry out computer-based Postcode mapping and spatial analysis. Fortunately, with the rapid development in computers over the last few years, there is now a range of software suitable for the manipulation of both list-based and coordinate-based Postcode information. Given the availability of the comprehensive PAF on CD, incorporating basic coordinates for each Postcode (see chapter 4), there is now also a readily accessible source of Postcodes and addresses in computer form which the software can exploit.

Creating spatial representations of Postcodes

The fundamental distinction between the list-based and coordinate-based Postcode representations is a key factor in planning the implementation of Postcode analysis in the computer. Since these representations are expressed quite differently in terms of the data types they use (one is alphanumeric, the other is simply numeric), they require quite different computer implementations. This section describes what can be technically achieved in Postcode analysis with each of the two representations. It focuses on the detailed characteristics of each representation, given the contraints imposed by the need to make it work in existing computers! The two Postcode representations will also be compared with other forms of spatial representation in common use such as those used in the Population Census or in street gazetteers.

It is essential to consider these issues *before* examining the tools themselves. We stress this again because those tools are best chosen and applied on the basis of a fully specified description of the problem at hand. We have seen many projects fail because they were inadequately thought through at the outset. Despite all this, a further note of caution is needed however – we have also seen systems replaced soon after they were introduced because, whilst they did all that was requested of them, users came to realise how much more was possible if only their software were capable of it. The needs of the user often change after he or she has gained experience, so anticipating these changes is perhaps the most difficult element of the planning of new software. Some of the most successful users have adopted a prototyping or 'try it and see' approach to steer a safe course between the evils of excess caution and wild enthusiasm.

List-based representations

If Postcodes, representing areas, are stored simply as lists of alphanumeric codes, we term this a list-based representation. The PAF on CD is a good example of this representation and can enable Postcodes to be linked to several other types of data (see chapter 7). The key element of this representation for use in computers is that it can only be easily linked to other data sets if the corresponding data sets also contain the Postcode. It also 'generalises' the area which the Postcode represents since it does not specify its full spatial extent. If we have to make guesses about the areal extent of a Postcode, we are sure to get it wrong to some degree!

This form of Postcode representation is quite sufficient for many forms of analysis, as in the insurance company example given in table 5.2 above. At present, insurance underwriters for housing cover seem to find that the Postcode District is an appropriate level of resolution for premium calculation (see table 5.2) or at least that the number of residential Postcode Districts (2679) for which premiums need calculation is an acceptable compromise with the resolution obtained. Implicit in such use of Postcodes in isolation from spatial coordinates is that the codes themselves summarise some fact of interest, and the end-user (usually Royal Mail) knows where in the world the places actually are. It must also be assumed that the areas defined by the Postcode are homogenous internally, although this is rarely the case in reality. Hence, to extend the example given above, insurance underwriters normally assume that all houses within a particular Postcode District have the same risk level. This is so because lists of Postcodes are simply labels for pieces of geography, and they do not incorporate any spatial description.

Coordinate-based representations

When Postcodes are stored together with spatial coordinates, we can refer to them as a coordinate-based representation. Usually such a representation can be plotted out on a map, even if there is minimal coordinate information. We can usefully distinguish coordinate-based representations which use a single representative point from those which use multiple points in an attempt to represent the outline of the Postcode on the ground.

REPRESENTATION OF POSTCODES BY A SINGLE COORDINATE POINT

The simplest way to coordinate reference a Postcode is to approximate its position with a single representative point. Several sources of point coordinate referencing for Postcodes exist, based on both public sector and commercial work. Hence the PAF on CD includes a National Grid reference (consisting of Easting or X and Northing or Y coordinates to 100m resolution) for each Unit Postcode. This means that, given appropriate software, it is possible to plot out a symbol at a given location for all 1.3 million plus residential Unit Postcodes creating (in effect) a dot density map for the location of residences. Assuming that the same number of people live at all residential delivery points, this would approximate population density at the maximum resolution achievable from published data (as Population Census returns are aggregated to much larger areas; see chapter 6).

The source of the representative coordinate point used to locate the Unit Postcode in the PAF on CD is a file known as the Central Postcode Directory (CPD) whose genealogy has been described in chapter 4. In this file, the representative point is stated to refer to the *first* delivery point in the range of addresses and was originally established in England and Wales and in Northern Ireland by a clerical exercise carried out from OS paper maps. This point is referenced to the SW corner of the 100m grid square in which the delivery point is found (see figure 4.1). The errors which we and others have found in these grid references and the limitations of the 100m resolution employed are described in full in chapter 4.

Several other alternative approaches to the definition of the representative point can be suggested (see figure 5.4) including placing the point over:

- the middle address of a range (e.g., No. 9 from 1-17) or of a list of delivery points;
- the weighted centroid of the area exactly enclosing the delivery points or a bounding rectangle;
- the weighted centroid of an area enclosing the delivery points and interlocking with adjacent Units to 'exhaust' space.

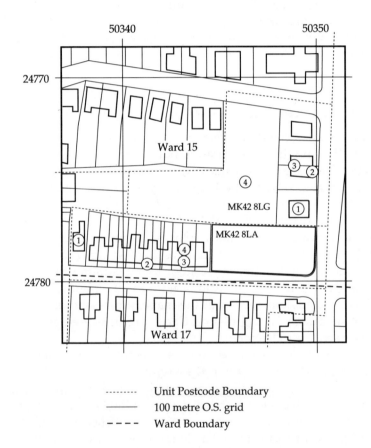

········	Unit Postcode Boundary
———	100 metre O.S. grid
– – – –	Ward Boundary

Figure 5.4 Alternative methods for the definition of representative points for a Unit Postcode. Key: 1 = first address; 2 = middle address; 3 = weighted centroid; 4 = weighted centroid of whole area needed to interlock with adjacent Unit Postcodes and 'exhaust' space (*Source: Royal Mail; Ordnance Survey © Crown Copyright*).

These approaches would all be very time-consuming to apply clerically but can be implemented on the computer given a digital version of the large scale topographic base map (such as the OS 1:1250 plans) on which buildings and other topographic features are recorded. Clearly, any user with access to this data and appropriate software (see section on GIS below) could determine a representative point for all Unit Postcodes in a specified area (such as a Local Authority) in a reasonable time. In fact, the GRO(S) provides representative points to 10m resolution since Scottish Unit Postcodes boundaries exist in digital form, enabling the creation of a more accurate and higher resolution point definition to be carried out automatically.

The representation of a Postcode by a single point is convenient since it is compact and readily available in PAF on CD. It does however greatly limit the accuracy of the potential linkage to other data sets (see below and chapters 6, 7 and 8). Indeed, for some applications, bounded areas rather than a set of delivery points approximated by a single representative coordinate position are *essential*.

One method of generating areas from point grid references for Unit Postcodes is to create Thiessen polygons around the representative point, that is to say, to determine the area which is closer to one point than to any other (see figure 5.5 and also figures 7.3 and 7.4). This is accomplished by joining together all the centroids by triangles, so that all the triangles are as close to being equilateral as possible (i.e., their three internal angles are each close to 60°). There is only one set of triangles which can satisfy this constraint. The perpendicular bisectors of the sides of these triangles either meet in threes or terminate at the boundary, thereby defining a set of Thiessen polygons. These polygons define areas of 'influence' around each point and in the absence of any other information, this is the most reasonable approximation of the area represented by the Unit Postcode centroid. Try joining the centroids by

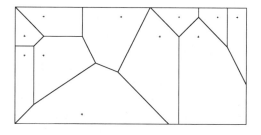

Figure 5.5   Thiessen polygons created around 11 Unit Postcode centroids for the village of Brancaster Staithe, N. Norfolk. The National Grid coordinates of the centroids are given in figure 5.8 *(Source: PAF on CD)*

straight lines in the simple example in figure 5.5 to recreate the triangles, although note that the polygons can become distorted by 'edge effects' when there are only a few points. The value of Thiessen polygons in data linkage is considered further in chapter 7.

REPRESENTATION OF POSTCODES BY MULTIPLE COORDINATE POINTS

We use multiple coordinate points to represent Postcodes in order to create an approximation of the 'real world' shape and location of the area encompassed by the Postcode. In practice, since Postcode boundaries at all levels in the hierarchy are often drawn along topographic features such as roads, river and railways, very many coordinate points would be needed to create a comprehensive representation. There is thus a trade-off between conciseness of description and the need for accurate boundary description. However, a number of products are available on the market which provide such Postcode boundaries at various levels of detail (see chapter 4).

To appreciate how such representations can be manipulated, it is necessary to examine the nature of the spatial relationship between the Postcodes at each level in the hierarchy. Beginning with the 120 Postcode Areas, these are subdivided into Districts and the Districts are subdivided into Sectors. These three upper levels 'nest' into each other precisely, and every part of the land area of the UK falls into a Postcode Area, District and Sector. This makes it possible to create representations of the Areas, Districts and Sectors by creating closed areas from their boundaries (see figure 5.2). Postcode maps on paper are produced by various commercial cartographers showing these boundaries.

However, to create a computer representation of any Postcode boundary, it is necessary to choose between two different types of approach to the creation of interlocking areas. First, we can use closed areas for each separately defined Postcode: these areas are easily created by recording all the points necessary to define the entire perimeter of the polygon. This, however means that the common boundary between Postcodes is duplicated. This is wasteful of space and cartographically unsatisfactory since it is often obvious in the results that some of the boundaries do not coincide where they should. Closed area representation also makes it difficult to nest (say) Sectors inside Districts as this leads to further duplication of boundaries. The solution is the second approach: to create interlocking Postcode zones by using intersecting line geometry. This means that the individual lines separating Postcodes from other Postcodes are stored only once, each line having codes to describe the areas on either side i.e. they are not duplicated. From this, fully nested sets of Postcodes can easily be produced. This requires software capable of storing the inter-relationships between the lines and areas and between the areas and other areas. These are known as topological relationships (see figure 1.8). Both approaches are implemented in commercial GIS software.

Such approaches to interlocking areas are well suited to Postcode Areas, Districts and Sectors. However, at the lowest level in the hierarchy, the Unit Postcode only specifically relates to delivery points (i.e. mostly buildings). This means that Unit Postcodes do not, in one sense, cover the whole UK land area (see the illustration of Unit Postcodes in figure 5.1). Whilst in practice in an urban area Unit Postcodes may form adjacent 'blocks' across wide areas (see the map in figure 5.6), parks and other open space are not usually Postcoded as there are generally no delivery points

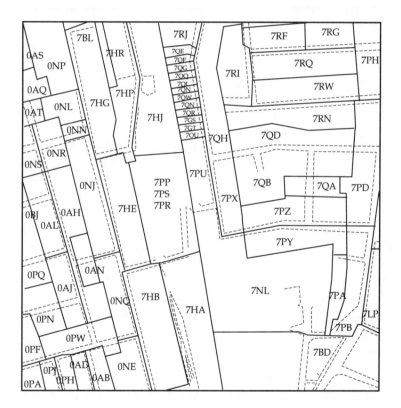

Figure 5.6   An example of Unit Postcode boundaries mapped for part of Hammersmith, London *(Source: Royal Mail and OPCS. Ordnance Survey © Crown Copyright).*

within them. This means that, in theory, Unit Postcodes do not necessarily completely subdivide Postcode Sectors and, unless amended, may leave 'holes' within the area covered by the Sector. This means that if boundaries are to be created for the Unit Postcodes, they must be manually defined so that space is 'exhausted', and all parts of the Sector are assigned to a Unit.

At present, there is only one widely available Postcode boundary product available in digital form at the Unit level. This is the Unit Postcode boundary file for Scotland produced by the GRO(S). This data set consists of boundary files and a representative central point for each Unit Postcode, along with a set of indexes by which it is possible to amalgamate Unit Postcodes into census Output areas (see chapters 4 and 6). GRO(S) made the decision to extend the definition of Unit Postcodes to cover the whole land area of Scotland. This means that, in Scotland, the Postcodes nest into each other at all four levels and there are no 'holes' in this representation i.e. open space between defined Unit Postcodes is prohibited. This has been achieved by extending the boundaries of Unit Postcodes from the minimum required to enclose the delivery point to include surrounding areas. Hence, the Unit Postcode for Edinburgh Castle (EH1 2NG) now includes the surrounding slopes and grounds and not just the buildings defining the delivery point. Clearly some judgement has been applied in devising such a transformation from points to areas.

One other source of digital Unit Postcodes data is Pinpoint Analysis Ltd (see chapter 4) which is carrying out an exercise to define a National Grid reference for every delivery point in Britain. Since the Pinpoint Address Code (PAC) includes the Unit Postcode, it is possible to outline the Unit boundary on the large scale OS base, along with a representative central point (see Plate 3 for an example in the London Borough of Camden). Pinpoint has produced some Unit Postcode boundaries experimentally in London, although these will only be further developed if there is commercial demand. The type of problems encountered in the creation of Unit Postcode boundaries are:

- the co-existence of residential and large business users in the same building;
- vertical 'stacking' of Unit Postcodes in high-rise buildings;
- the extension of Unit boundaries to include open spaces.

In summary, although coordinate-based representations are more time-consuming to create, more voluminous to store and (in the case of the Unit Postcode) more difficult to define, they offer a much more sophisticated linkage to the underlying 'geography' than do list-based representations. The potential of this linkage can be exploited with GIS software enabling very fine resolution spatial analysis, particularly at the Unit level. This is particularly so when the Unit Postcodes have been extended so as to completely segment the land surface, as in Scotland. The next section now considers the potential for linkage of such data with other spatial representations, and this is followed by a look at how commercial software implements these spatial representations.

Relationships to other spatial representations

In the early 1970s, the concept of the Basic Spatial Unit became widely accepted as the 'building block' from which all other areal units might be assembled (see the Chorley Report, DoE 1987). Although Postcodes are widely used, they are only one form of Basic Spatial Unit for which data are collected by organisations across the country. Hence it is necessary to consider how area-, line- and point-based spatial units can be related to each other. Table 5.3 sets out some of the more commonly used types of data sets in three geometric categories:

Table 5.3   Examples of spatial units for which attribute data are collected (usually by government)

Area-based	Line-based	Point-based
Census Enumeration Districts	Transport networks	Price surveys
Administrative areas (ward, district, county)	Street works	Pollution surveys
Travel-to-work areas	River system	Soil samples
Health authorities	Coastal protection	Meteorology
Police divisions		
Electoral districts		

Since these spatial units were created specifically to organise or collect data for different activities by different organisations, they do not usually match perfectly with Postcodes at any level in the hierarchy, except by chance or where there are major topographic barriers (e.g. estuaries) or administrative subdivisions (e.g. between England and Wales).

A major concern for those who use Postcode related information is how to determine a spatial relationship between Postcodes and these other spatial units. Such data linkage can be achieved by comparing lists of data if the spatial units coincide (for example, in Scotland between Postcodes, population counts and local authority data). A typology of matching procedures was discussed in chapter 1; we now describe the theoretical basis for carrying it out. In most cases, however, the spatial units do not coincide and therefore a linkage must be made on an approximation basis, based on use of spatial coordinates.

AREA-BASED SPATIAL UNITS

The ideal form of an area-based spatial unit is 'small relative to the attribute being measured' and is 'internally homogenous'. Such areas should be as equal in size as possible, should be stable over the long term and should aggregate into as many different sets of higher level units as possible. However, such characteristics are rarely found together in one zoning system (see figure 1.1). This anarchy in the data available (see chapter 1) may be the reason why geographers have searched (largely unsuccessfully) for several decades for intrinsic spatial structure in settlement and human organisation.

Hence, on the whole, commonly-used area-based units are irregular and unequal partitions of space – not least their creation has usually been governed by politics or history (*cf* Royal Mail and the development of Postcodes). They are usually not internally homogenous since they represent aggregations of primary units, i.e., people, houses, commuters, patients, incidents of crime or electors (and delivery points). These primary occurrences are usually aggregated into counts for the area in which they exist. However, they could also be recorded as categories or as presence/absence. Note that the occurrences recorded are often only samples and are thus estimates of the true level of occurrences: a good example is a national opinion poll. Many Basic Spatial Units employed by data collectors still do not aggregate naturally, the exceptions being administrative areas and Postcodes in urban areas.

A final problem is that, due to spatial interaction amongst areas, the values for one area may be correlated with the values in adjacent areas. This makes it difficult to look at individual areas in isolation. All these imperfections in the existing spatial units indicate that linkage between area-based spatial units and Postcodes should be pursued carefully, and within wide margins of accuracy. For example, it would be inappropriate to form a predictive model of crime growth across a region by linking crime incidents in police divisions with socio-economic indicators for Postcode Districts without considering the technical effects of sampling and autocorrelation issues (see later in this chapter). Ultimately, we may find that the way in which we have the country cut up for us controls the answers we get unless we set out from the outset to identify just how significant is the form of the spatial framework.

When linkage cannot be made by list comparison, e.g. where spatial units do not coincide, it is necessary to consider area interpolation. This involves the assignment of data from one set of areas to another set of overlapping areas. Several techniques to accomplish this operation are available, depending on the type of data; different approaches are used depending on whether the data are categorical (e.g. ACORN codes for different areas) or a count (e.g. the number of shoppers in a street). If one set of areas is much larger than the other areas, a simple solution based on non-exact matching is to allocate the centroids (representative central points) of the smaller areas directly to the larger areas, using point-in-polygon techniques (see the GIS section below). This is most appropriate for count data since the counts from the smaller areas can easily be assigned to each of the larger areas.

However, if the boundaries of both areas are intersected with each other, then new areas are created with values from each set of areas. If either set of values are categorical then the new areas are labelled by combining the values from each set of areas. In combining soil and crop data, for instance, the new areas will each have a label saying what soil and which crop type is present therein. If the values from both areas are counts, then the values are normally assigned to the new areas in proportion to the area of the component areas. In overlaying the numbers of people in wards with the number of customers in sales areas based on Postcodes, we have to compute the most likely number of people and customers in each of the new areas formed from the two original sets of areas. Several other sophisticated techniques have been proposed when it is possible to characterise the variation amongst the areas by spatially dependent factors such as (say) elevation.

LINE-BASED SPATIAL UNITS

A variety of sets of data are available for networks which might be related to Postcodes. Hence, road or rail traffic travelling along specific links in the network may originate in the adjacent or enclosing Unit Postcodes; street works by the utilities to access or repair plant under the road surface may be assigned to the adjacent or enclosing Unit Postcodes to help schedule works – or even to charge a business nearby for the work done; flows along rivers (especially flood flows) may be assigned to Postcode Sectors for modelling purposes or to Unit Postcodes to provide warnings for emergency services; and coastal protection status along the coastal strip may be used by insurance underwriters to assess the risk to property within coastal Postcode Sectors or (more sensibly) Postcode Units.

In general, unless the Postcodes are already assigned to the linear features concerned (in which case exact matching by list comparison may be used), a spatial operation will be required to check adjacency or enclosure of the linear feature to Postcode zones. Most spatial linkage between linear features and Postcodes will involve an intersection or overlay procedure; this has the effect of allocating appropriate lengths of linear feature to the area of each Postcode (e.g. 'in this Postcode Sector, there are x kilometres of coast at risk from flooding and 370 homes lie within 100m of the coast').

However, it is also possible to assign linear features to Postcodes using non-exact matching if the linear features have representative coordinate points attached to them. Indeed, this is one possible spatial referencing scheme which may be adopted for the National Streetworks Gazetteer in its full implementation in 1993. The procedure needed would then be a point-in-polygon assignment of the representative point to Postcode Sectors or above (also Unit Postcodes in Scotland), or the comparison of the representative point for the linear feature with the nearest representative points for the Unit Postcodes (see chapter 7). It need hardly be stressed that this is an approximate method at best but may be acceptable for some applications.

POINT-BASED SPATIAL UNITS

Several types of point-based Units are used in various kinds of surveys. These include price surveys, for example at all retail outlets of a particular kind and where the premises are located at known coordinate points (see plate 7). They can also consist of repeated environmental sampling of a particular parameter such as atmospheric or noise pollution at known coordinate points, which can be aggregated to (say) Postcode Sectors, averaged over time and reported to the government and the public.

Such point-based units can easily be assigned to Postcodes using point-in-polygon coordinate methods at all Postcode levels (except the Unit level in England and Wales). This implies the placing of all point samples into the appropriate polygon and counting, averaging or taking the modal category from the points and assigning that value to the Postcode record. A simple example of a question to be answered by such means would be 'how many new houses have been built in this Postcode Sector this year'?

Spatial data analysis

Spatial analysis is that type of research which looks for regularity (or departures from it) across space or for coincidence of features which might suggest that one pattern causes another. A good example is the hunt for geographical clusters of deaths from cancer. The availability of coordinate-based representations of the Postcode, along with a wide range of other data sets, has opened up a whole new area of opportunity in spatial data analysis. This is largely due to the speed and efficiency of spatial operations which can be carried out in the new GIS products. Since there is no space here to consider the whole range of approaches or to introduce the fundamentals in a comprehensive way, only the key problems are discussed.

Any review of the potential of spatial data analysis must begin with a caveat: almost all spatial data are based on samples of unknown adequacy from 'domains' whose complete 'population' characteristics cannot be known. This means that it is not usually known how many samples of (say) traffic flows along a road are enough to reflect the complete range of traffic conditions; nor can we know the journey characteristics of *all* cars which pass along the road. Hence, prediction of flows assigned to Postcode Sectors must normally be made with wide confidence bands and must be examined for evidence of systematic variation across space (known as non-stationarity, i.e., the existence of a spatially varying average).

One of the key spatial analysis problems is the Modifiable Areal Unit Problem (also known as MAUP). It arises when data for one level of spatial resolution (either a set of areas or a point data set) are aggregated to another (namely a larger set of areas or from a point data set to a zoning system). This transformation may change the scale and resolution of the original data, amplifying or suppressing existing patterns and may even create wholly new spatial patterns which are a direct consequence of the interaction between the data being aggregated and the properties of the zoning system used for the aggregation. In this situation, the data are changed, new relationships are created and old spatial patterns are altered. The effects of deliberate adjustment of boundaries have, of course, long been known, chiefly in gerrymandering of electoral boundaries, but what we have here is unintentional effects in the use of one set of areas rather than another.

The availability of GIS now makes this previously academic problem of far greater significance. Hitherto, we had little or no choice: our results might well be a nonsense because of the zoning system used by the data supplier, but we had no means of checking. Assuming the data are referenced to small enough areal units (e.g. Postcode Units) or grid referenced, GIS gives the user the opportunity (within limits) to design their own zoning systems, for example by aggregating Postcodes into arbitrary regions, or to validate the stability of their conclusions by testing them at various levels of spatial resolution. Previously, areas used for statistical reporting tended to reflect administrative boundaries which are neither neutral, consistently defined or comparable – nor indeed are their effects on the results of analyses known.

There are two basic approaches to minimising the effects of the MAUP. The first is to use regionalisation methods to design aggregations of building block areas which have known properties. The classic examples relate to the design of functional regions, daily urban systems, and labour markets. These areas have known characteristics and there is some justification for the properties they are given through the design process. The second approach involves a more general type of optimisation: the form of the aggregation to be used is 'estimated' as part of the statistical analysis process. For those who enjoy complexity, the problem can be further complicated by the addition of constraints on either the nature of the areas themselves (for instance on size, shape, or heterogeneity of the areas required) and/or on the quality of the data that are generated (for example, in the forms of statistical distributions or on the spatial autocorrelation assumptions).

Another form of spatial data analysis which superficially seems easy but actually poses special problems is the evaluation of point patterns when little is known about the underlying spatial processes. An important example is the search for spatial clusters of cases of disease, which are usually assigned point locations using Unit Postcodes. Much of the raw information for such studies – typically the home address and Postcode of the unfortunate individual concerned – arises from bureaucratic processes. The objective in this case is to find areas within a study region where the hypothesis that the distribution of points is random breaks down. In other words, we seek to find those places where there is 'unusual' clustering. This is achieved by covering the study region with a lattice or grid and then drawing overlapping circles, for a wide range of radii, around each lattice point. Data are retrieved for these circular search areas and an assessment is made as to whether or not there is evidence of an 'excess' number of cases within the search circle. The circles are designed to overlap by a large degree so as to allow for locational and representational errors in the data being retrieved for the circles. By repeatedly moving the circles by small amounts, these effects can at least be identified and incorporated in the analysis process. Openshaw (1987) has implemented these ideas in his Geographical Analysis Machine (GAM) which has been used to search for cancer clusters.

In summary, analysis of spatial data requires careful planning and execution, since standard data handling procedures often do not transfer well to geographical problems; few cope with nearness or topology as concepts even though those are vital for much analysis of geographical data. In the next section, the tools available for manipulating Postcode representations will be examined together with the means of carrying out both simple, aspatial analyses and these kinds of spatial analysis.

Software and hardware tools for exploiting Postcode data

As we have seen earlier in this chapter, Postcodes can be analysed in one of two forms of representation, i.e. list-based or coordinate-based. At present, list-based representations are probably in wider use due to the simpler computing requirements required and the relative lack of user awareness of more sophisticated possibilities. This section considers first how Postcode lists can be handled in various text data handling packages; and, secondly, it introduces GIS as a more comprehensive means of storing and manipulating coordinate-based Postcode data.

File handling, Spreadsheets, Database Management Systems and Statistical packages

The simplest form of computer representation is a list of Postcodes held in a file created by a word processor or text editor such as that given in table 5.4. This is a simple but structured form of data storage where the rows are referred to as *records* and the columns as *attributes*; in this case the records are a set of Postcodes for North Norfolk while the attributes are street names and Unit Postcode descriptors.

Table 5.4   List of Postcodes and partial addresses for Brancaster Staithe, N.Norfolk *(Source: PAF on CD)*

MAIN RD	PE31 8BJ
COMMON LA	PE31 8BL
ORCHARD CL	PE31 8BN
MAIN RD	PE31 8BP
THE CLOSE	PE31 8BS
MAIN RD	PE31 8BU
BRENTWOOD	PE31 8BZ

A simple set of these records, perhaps numbering hundreds, can be managed in a word processor such as Wordperfect or Microsoft Word although the sorting and manipulation facilities might be more easily carried out in a spreadsheet. A spreadsheet such as Microsoft Excel or Lotus 1,2,3 is a digital version of a large sheet of ruled paper divided into cells by row and column divisions. Spreadsheets are adequate ways to store and manipulate Postcode data running into thousands (see figure 5.7).

However, all these simpler forms of data storage lack the speed, efficiency and security of a DataBase Management System (DBMS), which is specifically designed to store large quantities of alphanumeric data in a

	Postcode	Address	Delivery points
1	PE31 8BJ	MAIN RD	20
2	PE31 8BL	COMMON LA	5
3	PE31 8BN	ORCHARD CL	10
4	PE31 8BP	MAIN RD	25
5	PE31 8BS	THE CLOSE	20
6	PE31 8BU	MAIN RD	21
7	PE31 8BZ	BRENTWOOD	4

Figure 5.7   View of a simple spreadsheet containing Postcodes, addresses and delivery points in Brancaster Staithe, N.Norfolk *(Source: PAF on CD)*

database (note that the database contains the data and the DBMS manipulates it). DBMS provide mechanisms to check that no data are duplicated, that related items of data are consistent with one another and that the data in the database are secure if there is a system fault. DBMS also conceal the details of internal storage of data, ensuring that the user views the data through programs such as report builders or query facilities. Contrast this situation with a word processor or spreadsheet where the user sees the layout of the raw data, has to create and execute search or output operations themselves and must be responsible for all security of the information.

In essence, the PAF is a database of Postcodes and associated information. When supplied on CD, it comes complete with DBMS, reporting and querying facilities. The system may be used as it is or data may be extracted from it and copied into other databases, spreadsheets or word processing packages, where further analysis on a subset of the data could be carried out. PAF on Tape is supplied on magnetic tape stored as eight separate large tables; if such tables have a single alphanumeric value in every row and column, these tables are known as 'relations' in formal terminology. Appropriately, this kind of DBMS is known as a Relational DataBase Management System (RDBMS) because it is based on relational tables which can be linked together in certain circumstances using keys common between pairs of relations (tables).

Relational tables in a database also differ from word processing or spreadsheet files because of the rules which the data must obey (see figure 5.8). Specifically, all records in a relational table must be different from all other records. This can be ensured as long as at least one attribute has unique values for each record; this attribute is known as the primary key. The first implication of this rule is that the records can be ordered in any sequence necessary without destroying any information in the database. This ensures that the relational tables can be indexed using the key attribute and no numbers need to be stored to label the records.

POSTCODE	= PE31 8BJ	POSTCODE	= PE31 8BU
STREET	= MAIN RD	STREET	= MAIN RD
X-COORD	= 579,500.000	X-COORD	= 579,800.000
Y-COORD	= 344,300.000	Y-COORD	= 344,300.000
POSTCODE	= PE31 8BL	POSTCODE	= PE31 8BW
STREET	= COMMON LA	STREET	=
X-COORD	= 579,300.000	X-COORD	= 579,100.000
Y-COORD	= 343,800.000	Y-COORD	= 344,300.000
POSTCODE	= PE31 8BN	POSTCODE	= PE31 8BX
STREET	= ORCHARD CL	STREET	= MAIN RD
X-COORD	= 579,700.000	X-COORD	= 580,000.000
Y-COORD	= 344,200.000	Y-COORD	= 344,300.000
POSTCODE	= PE31 8BP	POSTCODE	= PE31 8BY
STREET	= MAIN RD	STREET	= MAIN RD
X-COORD	= 579,000.000	X-COORD	= 580,100.000
Y-COORD	= 344,200.000	Y-COORD	= 344,300.000
POSTCODE	= PE31 8BS	POSTCODE	= PE31 8BZ
STREET	= THE CLOSE	STREET	= BRENTWOOD
X-COORD	= 579,100.000	X-COORD	= 579,900.000
Y-COORD	= 344,100.000	Y-COORD	= 344,200.000
POSTCODE	= PE31 8BT		
STREET	=		
X-COORD	= 579,000.000		
Y-COORD	= 344,100.000		

Figure 5.8   Records from PAF on CD of Postcodes, addresses, and grid references of Brancaster Staithe, N. Norfolk in relational database form *(Source: PAF on CD)*

The second implication of the key attribute provision is that two relational tables can always be merged together if they share the same key attribute (see figure 5.9). This is an important facility, and one which directly controls the design of the relational tables in the database. Since it is easy to link tables, it is also possible to create relational tables which contain only the less used attributes and link them to the most important tables as and when necessary. This procedure is known as a relational join, and is a fundamental technique in many data linkage strategies since any relational table with a Postcode key can be linked to any other such table with the same key. Note that these facilities are limited to a RDBMS.

123

Once list-based Postcode data is stored in relational tables, a typical RDBMS offers a range of summary and statistical functions. All commercial systems offer simple descriptive statistical facilities such as mean, median and standard deviation of the values of an attribute, mathematical functions such as logarithms, square roots, random number generators, and text functions to enable sorting and substitution. Operations of this kind carried out on a relational table can be used to generate new attributes and tables; alternatively, they can be generated as part of a query and jettisoned once the results are reported.

Query facilities are one of the most powerful aspects of a RDBMS.

POSTCODE	X-COORD	Y-COORD	POSTCODE	DPTS
PE31 8BJ	579500	344300	PE31 8BJ	20
PE31 8BL	579300	343800	PE31 8BL	5
PE31 8BN	579700	344200	PE31 8BN	10
PE31 8BP	579000	344200	PE31 8BP	25
PE31 8BS	579100	344100	PE31 8BS	20
PE31 8BT	579000	344100	PE31 8BT	13
PE31 8BU	579800	344300	PE31 8BU	21
PE31 8BW	579100	344300	PE31 8BW	8
PE31 8BX	580000	344300	PE31 8BX	30
PE31 8BY	580100	344300	PE31 8BY	32
PE31 8BZ	579900	344200	PE31 8BZ	4

Figure 5.9   Simple relational join on Brancaster Staithe Postcode data *(Source: PAF on CD)*

Query languages need to be flexible in the queries they permit yet easy to use and terse. The most widely used one is the Structured Query Language (SQL), which was originally developed at IBM and is now recognised as an international standard for data manipulation in RDBMS (the formal definition of SQL forms the International Standards Organisation [ISO] Standard 9075). As a consequence, it can now be used with many different vendors' products. SQL is flexible since it can be used interactively at a terminal to query the database but can also be embedded in a computer program enabling it to read data from the database automatically. Although the most common SQL function is the SELECT statement which creates reports from the database, it can also be used to calculate summaries of query results. Hence, a simple SQL statement such as:

SELECT (AVG)X-COORD, (AVG)Y-COORD
    FROM POSTCODES
    WHERE LOCALITY = 'BRANCASTER STAITHE'

can be used to compute the average Unit Postcode centroid for the grid reference data in figure 5.8. This query reports a single average value for the Eastings (X) and for the Northings (Y) assigned to each Unit Postcode beginning PE31 8B- (which is the complete set of Postcodes used in that locality). Note that the two attributes could be SELECTed from different tables in an RDBMS.

There are also a wide range of statistical packages which can handle list-based Postcode data. These packages will store and manipulate Postcode data files whose size is constrained (in principle) only by the hardware and system software used; they can be used to compute a range of descriptive univariate (single variable) statistics. The more sophisticated packages such as Systat, SPSS, SAS and BMDP are capable of carrying out multivariate analysis (i.e. several variables simultaneously) on thousands of records. There are basically two approaches to multivariate analysis: in the first approach, rows (or records) in the geographical data matrix are compared, effectively comparing the properties of different places or areas. For example, health indicators held for each Postcode Sector could be analysed to determine whether particular Sectors had several similarly poor values on each indicator; this information could be used to assess whether a screening programme should be launched by mailing all residents.

The second approach is to compare the columns (or attributes) in the same matrix. In doing this, statistical packages are used to assess relationships between attributes using correlation techniques. An example (assuming the data required had been linked together using the 'name' of the Postcode Area as a key) would be to measure whether there was any association between, say, wealth or poverty indicators and health ones for a series of Postcode Areas.

In summary, the RDBMS can be considered the most flexible and powerful form of data storage for list-based Postcode representations even though the most sophisticated statistical packages offer some unique multivariate functions. The RDBMS is widely used in the commercial processing of Postcode-related information, where applications focus on address-related applications rather than spatial analysis through map-type operations. Such applications include rapid addressing from Postcodes given over the telephone; insurance premium determination for houses and cars; determination of dealers or agents for a product or service which are in the same locality; and, most recently, allocation of patients to National Health Service (NHS) areas using Postcodes under the NHS 'internal market' reforms of 1991.

Geographical Information Systems

The key tool for the handling of coordinate-based Postcode information is the Geographic Information System (GIS). GIS are best defined as 'computer systems for integrating and analysing spatial information in a decision-making context', and have also been described as the 'biggest step forward since the introduction of the map' by Lord Chorley in his Report on the 'Handling of Geographic Information' in 1987 (see the Preface to this book). GIS are computer systems which facilitate many of the operations on Postcodes discussed in the previous sections and subsequent chapters: they are optimised for spatial analyses of various kinds. However, since there are now literally hundreds of commercially available GIS products, it is worthwhile starting with the generic aspects of GIS and mapping, and proceeding in the later sections to look at how Postcodes can be exploited using different systems. All of this builds on the properties and constraints built into different spatial representations of postcodes.

It is important to begin by tracing how GIS have developed from computer programs for map handling. Although the map is the customary means of communication for observations and analyses of spatial phenomena, the paper map is – almost by definition – a static record of a particular phenomenon at a given time and place and is therefore inherently limited, especially at times of rapid change in what it portrays. Typically, map users employ the paper map as a 'backdrop' for plotting other kinds of information: Postcode maps have long been used for this purpose. However, as users of spatial data have come to make maps by computer, a shift in the perception of the map has become apparent. When stored in a computer, maps have taken on a new and dynamic form: their content, symbolisation and the area covered can now be changed easily and rapidly. For the first time, users of spatial data can have truly flexible, interactive access to their data and any part of which can be updated in 'real time', i.e. immediately.

It can be argued, therefore, that maps are now better thought of as databases, or collections of information linked by their spatial relationships. In this conception, a paper map can be seen simply as one unique expression of a spatial database which, for example, might show population density mapped by Postcode where the categories of density chosen to segment the values reflect some theory or policy (one cut-off in a map of income variations might be the official 'poverty line'). Beyond the record-keeping and monitoring functions, the GIS also offers much new potential for spatial analysis, based upon use of the same basic data but organised in a different fashion, and is in general a much more efficient way to store spatial information.

HOW GIS IMPLEMENT POSTCODE REPRESENTATIONS IN THE COMPUTER

The functions of a comprehensive GIS can be traced to a range of spatial data handling systems which have evolved since the 1960s in several related fields such as Computer Aided Design (CAD) for engineering drawing, DBMS for storing structured information, automated cartography for plotting maps by computers, and image processing for handling data from satellite remote sensing and scanning sources. These systems developed largely in isolation from each other, partly due to software integration problems and partly because the power of the processing units in computers was inadequate to permit their co-existence until the mid and late 1980s.

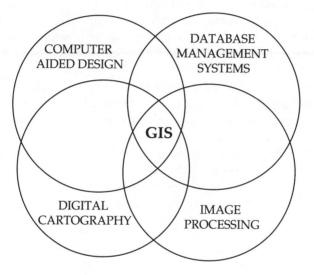

Figure 5.10   Venn diagram showing the types of functionality contributing to GIS

A comprehensive GIS today can be defined as the combination of some of the functionality of each of these systems to form a multi-function, multi-purpose spatial data handling system. The Venn diagram in figure 5.10 helps us to visualise this development and to chart the origin and strengths of particular software packages sold as GIS. Depending on the functionality offered, most packages can be plotted as a dot on this diagram: many will plot in the overlap of CAD and DBMS. Only a few systems can actually be placed in the core GIS category when classified in this way.

It is easy to cite the general functional characteristics of a GIS; hundreds of academic and trade papers have been written on these in recent years (see Maguire and Raper 1991 for a recent compendium). But the most important factor is the types of data representation that the system implements inside the computer. Earlier in this chapter, Postcode representations were divided into list-based and coordinate-based types. We have indicated above that, while DBMS are best suited for the handling of lists of Postcodes, GIS are required for the handling of coordinate-based representations. This is largely because the handling of geographical data and the complexities of spatial interrelationships is a much more demanding problem than is normally met within the DBMS environment. Fortunately, we now see a number of systems that can capitalise on the strengths of both DBMS and GIS.

To create a computer version of a coordinate-based spatial representation, geometric primitives such as points, lines and areas are usually used as the building blocks for the creation of spatial objects such as buildings or regions such as Postcode zones. Such computer representations are created by first measuring locations using spatial referencing systems (an x,y graph is a simple example). The coordinates in the referencing system defining points, lines and areas are measured in terms of x and y units: this is known as *metric information* and is stored in the form of numbers and characters since the computer can not directly handle spatial data such as (say) lines. To complete the representation, the spatial components of the model such as adjacency, connectivity and containment must be ordered and indexed to encode spatial

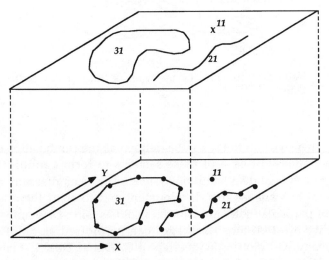

Figure 5.11   Vector representation of some simple point, line and area based features

interrelationships referred to as *topological information*. Collectively, these interrelationships are known as a 'data structure' when implemented in the computer in a specific way. Two alternative approaches are used to implement data structures in the computer; these are known as 'vector' and 'raster' systems and are profiled below.

Vector data structures employ the principles of coordinate fixing as in navigation (see figure 5.11). A point can be described by its distance along each of two axes of measurement, e.g. north and east, while a line can be described as the shortest straight line distance between two such points – a 'vector'. Areas can be represented by any number of lines joined together in a ring and arranged to reflect the specific shape of the area – a 'polygon' (such as a Postcode Sector). In all cases, the only information needed is the coordinates in number form. These can easily be stored in the computer and recalled in the right order when needed.

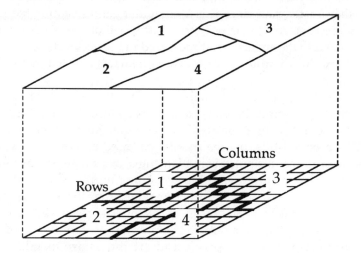

Figure 5.12   Raster representation of some simple point-, line- and area-based features

Raster data structures use a different approach altogether, using regular building blocks to build up the shape of a feature on a grid (see figure 5.12). Using a grid of very small squares (a 'raster'), a point, line or area can be approximated by sets of squares or picture elements ('pixels'), the resolution of the representation being directly controlled by the size of the grid squares. In a raster data structure, the computer keeps a record of which pixels are switched 'on' and therefore form part of one of the spatial phenomena being represented. Generally the pixels are made equivalent to a fixed number of units in the coordinate system so that, for example, if pixels are 10m square, then a road running 140m due east on the ground will require 14 pixels in a horizontal direction to represent it in the computer. Diagonal lines have to be constructed from the best available 'staircase' of pixels.

Use of one or other of these data structures allows the effective storage of spatial phenomena in the computer. However, each of them is best suited for particular tasks. For example, raster data structures make it fast and efficient to combine area-based data from one set of spatial units to another. Vector data structures make it efficient to determine adjacency of areas and connectivity of network linkages. It is therefore increasingly common for GIS to support both types of data structure so that each type of data can be used for the most effective purpose (although it is still necessary to judge whether to capture new data into raster or vector form based on its likely use). Note also that vector data is often seen as more 'precise' than raster data since it is a computer representation based on coordinate geometry. This is only true if the size of the raster pixels is large compared to the smallest unit measured in the vector data, i.e. if you use one metre precision in the vector measurements and ten metre-sized pixels.

To complete the geographical database requires the addition of a unique identifier to all the points, lines and areas represented therein. With this, they can all be linked to associated attribute data such as the Postcode name. This process of linking the coordinate-based descriptions in raster or vector form to the attributes is implemented in a range of ways in the different commercial products. Most commonly, the coordinates are stored in a specially designed file structure whilst the attributes are stored in a RDBMS and linked to the raster or vector data via a key field in a master table. Typically, the database is more rudimentary for raster data since relationships between pixels and attributes are usually more straightforward.

The most recently released commercial GIS store both coordinate data and attributes in a single RDBMS environment with some extensions to the latter to handle spatial data. Hence, the name Geographical Information System is becoming progressively more and more apt as information storage becomes the crucial issue in GIS design and implementation. Increasingly, GIS is seen as a 'database problem'. Decisions on the purchase of a GIS increasingly focus on the structure and performance of the DBMS environment.

A final aspect of GIS and spatial database design to consider is the question of efficient storage of and access to thematic collections of geographical data. Many GIS allow the user to group all the geometric and attribute data together for a particular subject of study in a single

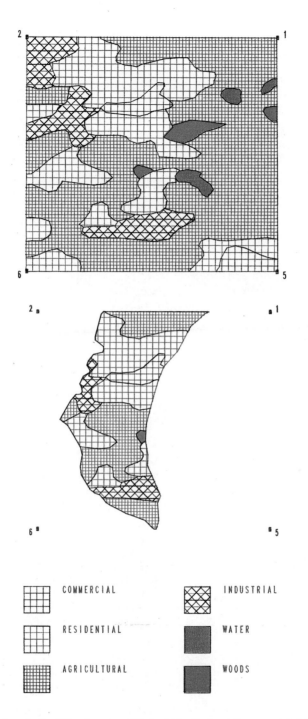

COMMERCIAL		INDUSTRIAL	
RESIDENTIAL		WATER	
AGRICULTURAL		WOODS	

Plate 1 Land use in the Abingdon area of Oxfordshire (*top*) and the same data 'clipped out' using an overlay process and the boundaries of Postcode Sector OX13 6

Plate 2 A personal computer system used for reading and searching the Postcode Address File on Compact Disc (PAF on CD) (*top*); the Postcode Address File on Compact Disc (*bottom*)

PINPOINT POSTCODE CENTROIDS (PPC)

NATIONAL GRID PLANS　　　　　ORDNANCE SURVEY　　　　　PLAN TQ 2199 SW

PiNPOINT

Plate 3 Boundaries and centroids of individual Unit Postcodes superimposed on individual properties. © *Pinpoint Analysis and Ordnance Survey Crown Copyright Reserved*

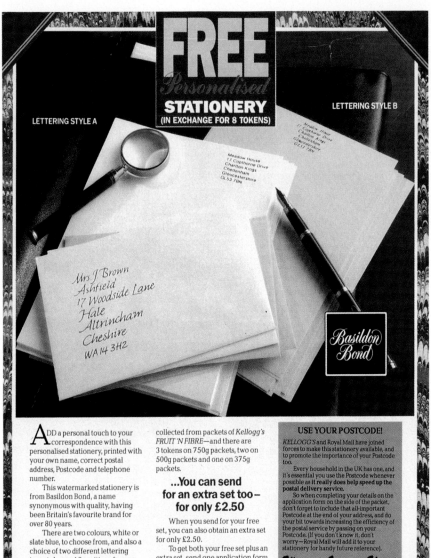

Plate 4 An example of a Royal Mail promotion to foster wider use of the Postcode on social mail, in this case from a breakfast cereal packet (*courtesy of the Kellogg Company of Great Britain Ltd.*).

Plate 5 Automated sorting of letter mail using Optical Character Recognition (OCR) equipment in Royal Mail

⊣Extended Search⊢

PAF ON CD - Extended Search

FULL ENTRY SEARCH
1:Organisation
2:Premise/Street
3:Loc/Town/County
4:Postcode   eh3 7a_   15

KEYWORD SEARCH   5:Org/Prem/St
                    6:Loc/Twn/Cnty
                    7:Street Number
                    8:PO Box
BLOCK SEARCH   9:User Category
                   10:Sortcode
                   11:Grid East
                   12:Grid North
                   13:Wardcode
                   14:NHS Code

Connection: Total: 15

⊣Full Display: 1 of 15⊢

PAF ON CD - Full Display

Street Range   1-7 2-6
Street   COATES PL
Posttown   EDINBURGH
Postcode   EH3 7AA

Delivery Pts   7
User Category   R
Sortcode   05302
Grid East   32424
Grid North   67339
Wardcode   86C24
NHS Code   05

Plate 6 Using a menu provided by the standard PAF software to select Postcode EH3 7AA (*top*); the results of the search – details of Postcode EH3 7AA (*bottom*)

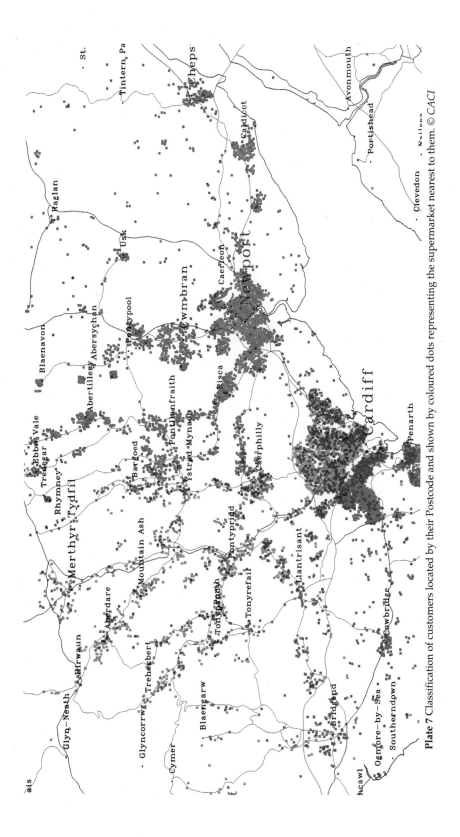

Plate 7 Classification of customers located by their Postcode and shown by coloured dots representing the supermarket nearest to them. © *CACI*

Sector by Sector Penetration of Super Profiles Types A, B, F and I Combined – Within 5 Miles (8 km) of NE33 1

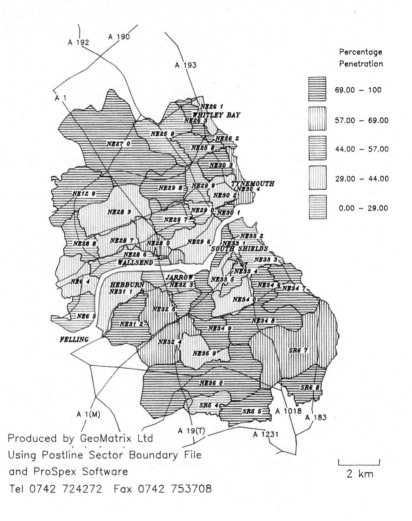

Percentage Penetration

69.00 – 100
57.00 – 69.00
44.00 – 57.00
29.00 – 44.00
0.00 – 29.00

Produced by GeoMatrix Ltd
Using Postline Sector Boundary File
and ProSpex Software
Tel 0742 724272   Fax 0742 753708

2 km

Plate 8 Market 'penetration' of Postcode Sectors dominated by selected types of households and lying within 8km of a particular Postcode Sector. Postcode Sector File © *Geomatrix Ltd.* Coastline © *Automobile Association.*

theme such as 'Postcodes' or 'transport'. This can be implemented as a set of thematic 'layers' in the database (conceptually similar to the arrangement figure 5.1) which can be accessed separately or integrated with each other and with new data sets. The completed database is an integrated spatial *and* non-spatial information system: however, its potential can only be unlocked by applying spatial tools which operate on this structured spatial data (see Raper and Green 1989 for details of a computer-based Tutor called the GISTutor which elaborates all these concepts with examples). We now turn to considering these tools in more detail.

THE FUNCTIONALITY OF GIS

The functions available in a typical GIS can easily be described by the sequence of operations carried out in the creation and analysis of a geographical database. Database creation embraces the decisions made about forms of representation, whether to use raster or vector data, and how to structure the database in terms of thematic sub-divisions. Spatial analysis is concerned at its simplest with viewing retrieved sections of the database and at its most complex with the extraction of spatial relationships from what is stored in the same database. Each of these operations will be briefly described in the following section.

Database creation starts with the acquisition of spatially referenced data, either bought 'off-the-shelf' or created by the user using digital data capture techniques. There are already a number of Postcode products available (see chapter 4). Most of these are in vector form since many polygon operations are easier to implement in vector mode and because raster data often requires more data storage for a comparable resolution in representation. Data capture techniques are based on digitising for vector data (the tracing of map detail on an electronic tablet) or on scanning for raster data (the sampling of map detail on a fine grid).

When capturing Postcode information in area-based vector mode, the key issue is whether to capture the complete, closed boundaries of each Postcode or whether to use intersecting lines (as in figures 1.5 and 1.8). The first case uses more storage space and is slower in certain operations, but can be manipulated with much simpler software. In raster mode, the pixels can all hold the same value if the aim is simply to represent the area's identity i.e. a number of (probably adjacent) pixels might hold a value representing Postcode Sector 'AL6 9'. Otherwise, the range of possible values which the pixel can hold' will determine the description available.

Most of the differences in performance of spatial analysis procedures between different GIS depend upon the form of data structure they employ. In vector mode, systems which store and manipulate topological information describing the interrelationships of lines and areas offer the greatest potential for spatial analysis. This is because the topological relationships are predetermined by a structuring program and are sorted and indexed in such a way that some spatial analyses are reduced to little more than the straightforward extraction of information. A good example is the determination of adjacency, i.e. which Postcode Districts are adjacent to (or touch) SE8? A GIS which determines and stores such topological relationships can retrieve the answer very rapidly (see figure 5.3 to see how complex adjacency to SE8 is!). In raster mode, indexing mechanisms known as 'quadtrees' can be used to compress the number of pixels needed to represent an area, and help establish the relationships between 'clumps' of pixels and their neighbours.

An important function in any GIS is the capability for manipulation of the existing representations of geography so as to generate new forms of structuring or representation. Manipulation has been described earlier for list-based representations in databases (the creation of new variables and the like). In a specifically spatial context, manipulation encompasses coordinate transformations (needed to integrate maps referenced to different coordinate systems such as was once the case with OS and Bartholomew's maps before the latter transformed their maps onto the National Grid projection) and aggregation of areas. Vector-based GIS are more effective at transformations since the spatial resolution is not fixed (as in the raster case). They are also more effective in the aggregation of points, lines and areas since it is more difficult to maintain all the interrelationships between these geometric components in the raster environment.

A critical requirement from any GIS is the ability to retrieve data by specified geographical 'window' or by attribute or some combination of these criteria: this is sometimes referred to as 'clipping' – an example is given in Plate 1. Spatial search operations rely on the link between the spatial coordinate information and the associated attributes. Hence it is possible to look up either one of these by reference to the other: examples include searching for the names of the Postcodes falling in a specified zone or checking the location of some Postcoded addresses found by a search for the highest house-price valuations. Searches for distances between two places are often known as 'proximity analysis', and are easily and quickly carried out in a GIS. An extension of such searches, for example, to find the nearest postcode centroids to a census enumeration district centroid is known as 'nearest neighbour analysis' and is closely related to the procedure used to create Thiessen polygons above. These GIS search tools are often constructed on top of SQL with extensions to support spatial criteria such as 'nearness' or 'enclosure'.

'Buffering' is another form of spatial search which is easy to carry out in a GIS and which is useful in Postcode analysis. It is created by establishing a buffer or corridor of a fixed width around a class of features such as roads and then searching the contents of the area thus created. If it were important to find all Postcodes near to Oxford Street shopping area in London, the obvious way to proceed would be to create a buffer of, say, 300 metres width centred along a single line representing the road centre line then carry out a point-in-polygon search to ensure which Postcodes had grid references falling within the polygon resulting from the buffer operation. The last stage involved 'overlaying' the polygon on a set of points. These 'buffering' and 'overlay' capabilities can be generalised – they can obviously be applied to certain combinations of point and line and area data. Table 5.5 summarises the possible interrelationships in a matrix:

Table 5.5   Matrix of possible spatial interrelationships between different geometric representations.

	Point	*Line*	*Area*
Point	Centroid averaging	Point on line	Point-in-polygon tests
Line		Line connectivity	Lines assignment to areas
Area			Area on area overlay

In summary, genuine GIS can carry out most of the following forms of spatial analysis quickly and effectively:

- Centroid averaging is the process of averaging the x and y values for the positions of any number of points representing the centres of Postcodes. This can be implemented by most GIS in raster or vector mode;

- Point on line (or within a specified distance of) operations can be employed to relate Postcode centroids to routes e.g. which Unit Postcodes are near the line of a new sewer? This could be implemented as an overlay of centroids falling within a certain distance of the sewer. This is easy in both raster and vector;

- Point-in-polygon tests are a fundamental element of linkage from Postcode centroids to other area-based spatial units. It is implemented in raster mode as a set membership test and in vector mode using algorithms such as that shown in figure 5.13;

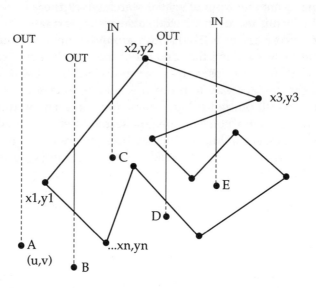

Figure 5.13 The principles of the crossings algorithm: an odd number of crossings indicates the point is IN, and an even number indicates it is OUT

- Line connectivity is little used in Postcode manipulation but is important for transport routing. It is implemented using topological information stored or calculated in vector mode only;

- Line assignment to areas is important so that transport, river flows or telecommunications can be linked to Postcode zones. It is implemented by the overlay of the lines onto the areas. In raster mode, this involves an overlay and an evaluation of all the combined pixel values in the new map (e.g. 'does this pixel contain both a road and a specified Postcode name?') In vector mode, it involves intersection of all the line segments within the area boundaries – the lines will then be sub-divided at area boundaries and coded with the attributes of the area each line crosses;

- Area on area overlay is a very common (indeed often unavoidable) means of linking area-based spatial units. Implementation is similar to the 'line assignment to areas' case except that, where an area carries a numerical value, the value in the one area must be apportioned to the other areas. GIS achieve this by computing the area of each of the new intersected areas and assigning numerical values accordingly. Few GIS yet have tools by which numerical values can be assigned to the target areas by using some form of spatially-varying function.

Finally, no list of GIS functionality should omit the potential for map display. GIS have a variety of tools by which cartographic symbolism may be adjusted to user needs or desires e.g. areas may be shaded or point symbols may be sized according to the value of the measured parameter. Hence it is common to display the location of cases of disease occurrence within Postcode zones at different levels of frequency of occurrence by shading the Postcodes according to the number of cases falling therein. GIS also have tools to display perspective view mesh surfaces to show (say) noise levels across a city; Postcode Sector or other boundaries can be draped on top of the mesh. Some GIS (such as GIMMS) also have the ability to draw mini-graphs, such as pie charts, positioned within each area for which there is data. It would, for instance, be possible to show the amount of Postcoded mail within the business segments outlined in chapter 3 for every Sector in a city. Such display is constrained not so much by the software, though that is important, but by the quality of the hardware on which it is displayed. For that reason, we now consider the more physical manifestations of a GIS.

The technological setting of GIS

A complete description of the components of a GIS should include not only software but also hardware, spatial data and the necessary human skills and management required to operate the system. Estimates of the typical lifetime costs of a GIS project indicate that staff and data associated with database development actually amount to 75% of the total, whereas hardware and software may account for around 25% of the total. This implies that the cost of the data and the expertise required to run a GIS are a key part of the project and that these are the most important assets for an organisation to protect in the long term. Figure 5.14 shows how the relative importance of these components has changed over the last 5 years and predicts that, in the UK at least, only data costs will remain of high importance over the next two decades.

The most rapid change in the technological setting for GIS has been in the hardware component. The price/performance of hardware has improved by huge amounts over the last few years, principally through the increase in performance and capacity of the processor chips in the computer. The development of powerful personal computers (PCs) from the late 1970s onwards revolutionised what was possible in handling geographical data. Most of these systems have run the single user MS-DOS operating system. From about 1988 onwards, however, the GIS scene has come to be dominated by Reduced Instruction Set Chips (RISC) as the processing engines within multi-user 'workstations' running the

UNIX operating system. These new systems have placed the cost-effectiveness of the traditional minicomputers and mainframes under severe examination, although they remain capable of large transaction throughputs. Table 5.6 compares the essential characteristics of different systems but the reality is somewhat more complicated than it portrays.

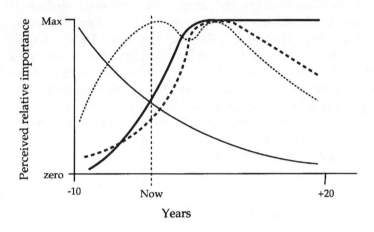

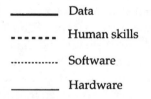

Data

Human skills

Software

Hardware

Figure 5.14 Changes in the relative importance of the costs of the components of GIS

Table 5.6 A simplified comparison of hardware platforms for GIS

Platform	Users	RAM	Hard disc space	Process speed	Transactions
PC	1	0.5-8Mb	2-200Mb	1-10 Mips	Low
Workstation	2-8	8-128Mb	200Mb-1Gb	5-200 Mips	Medium+
Mini	2-40	16/128Mb	Many Gigabytes	5-200 Mips	Medium
Mainframe	20-200	32Mb+	Many Gigabytes	20-800 Mips	High

Storage capacity and cost are important factors in dealing with geographical data which are typically voluminous. Fortunately for us, the capacity of Random Access Memory (RAM) chips and storage media has also grown whilst costs have fallen dramatically. Computers now use internal magnetic discs (known as 'hard' discs to contrast with 'floppy' discs which users carry around) as standard on-line interactive storage. They are favoured because they offer very fast 'seek' times (15-25 milliseconds) to any part of the data in store and can transfer it to the main memory (RAM) at high rates.

Table 5.7 shows the most common forms of data archiving available in early 1992 and gives details of their technical specification and the cost of the hardware unit (media costs for tapes, cartridges and discs are small in comparison). These forms of data storage are used for the exchange and back-up of the main data storage, and fall into three main types. The first is magnetic tape at various densities and sizes stored on reels or in cartridges (9 track, 3480, QIC 150; PAF is sold on this medium); secondly, digital tape in video and audio formats (Exabyte and Digital Audio Tape–DAT); and finally optical discs using analogue video forms (LV-ROM), digital storage (Compact Disc CD-ROM (e.g. PAF on CD), Write-Once-Read-Many times WORM) or hybrid optical and magnetic storage (erasable optical). Note that approximate costs at 1991 prices are more related to history and competition in the market than to technical specifications (CD-ROM is an international standard and a consumer product). Some parameters are less important for certain applications than for others: for CD-ROM, for instance, 'read time' is short but 'seek time' to find data is quite long so data is stored in such a way on it that most applications can be achieved by continuous reading of data.

Table 5.7 Forms of data archiving available in 1991 and their approximate costs

System	Medium	Capacity	Transfer speed	Cost of system to read data
9 Track tape	1600/6250bpi tape	25/300Mb	240 Kb/sec	£5000
IBM 3480	0.5" tape	200Mb	3 Mb/sec	£10000+
QIC 150	0.25" tape	150Mb	100 Kb/sec	£1500
Exabyte	8mm video	2.3Gb	246 Kb/sec	£3000
DAT (dds)	4mm DAT	1.3Gb	183 Kb/sec	£3500
LV-ROM	12" video disc	300Mb		£1000
CD-ROM (ISO)	5.25" optical disc	600Mb		£400
WORM	5.25" optical disc	~1Gb		£4000
Erasable optical	5.25" opt/mag disc	400Mb	620 Kb/sec	£2500

Given all these technical developments, workstations now offer the ideal platform for GIS with powerful RISC processors, large amounts of RAM, hard disc on-line data storage running into Gigabytes and high-resolution large colour screens. These systems are typically networked together to allow users to access spare processing power elsewhere and to read data stored in other locations. Such networks are now normally based on international standards for data transfer enshrined in the ISO networking Reference model (figure 5.15). These standards govern the type of physical wiring connection (typically 'ethernet', based on Institute of Electronics and Electrical Engineers [IEEE] standards 802.2-5); the means of data exchange and the network identification (an example is Transmission Control Protocol/Internet Protocol [TCP/IP] used on UNIX workstations); and the way in which computers are connected over the network. It is also now relatively easy to link dissimilar networks together using a variety of specialist hardware illustrated in the reference model (figure 5.15).

ISO-OSI Reference Model	TCP/IP	IEEE 802	Devices that connect networks together			
Application Layer 7						Gateway
Presentation Layer 6	FTP TELNET					
Session Layer 5						
Transport Layer 4	TCP				Router	
Network Layer 3	IP			Bridge		
Data Link Layer 2		802.2 802.3	Repeater			
Physical Layer 1		802.4 802.5				

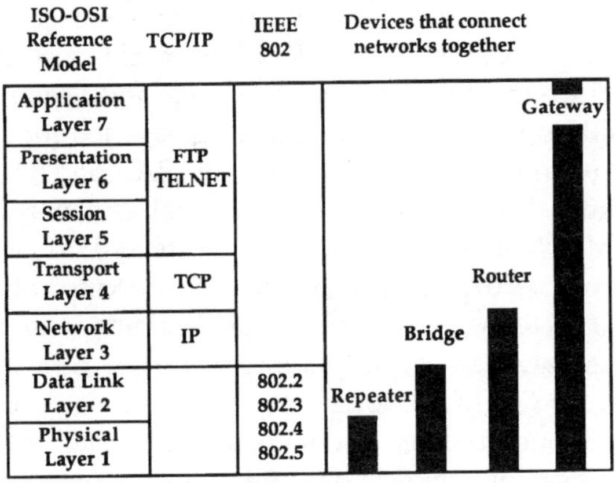

Figure 5.15 ISO Networking Reference model, with some example standards and their level

The technological setting of GIS has therefore changed radically in the last few years. Handling truly gigantic quantities of data in real time (i.e. immediately) is now not only feasible but routinely achieved. Hence, as a consequence of hardware and software development in parallel, the GIS market is now highly developed and there is a sophisticated market-place where over 200 commercial products compete. The last few years have seen an enormous investment in GIS world-wide, ranging from systems which cost less than $100 to those which are implemented on large mainframe computers and accessible across whole organisations. The largest users of GIS for Postcode applications in the UK in 1992 are probably the geodemographic consultancies, some of whom store and annually update the electoral roll and hold the complete Small Area

Statistics (SAS) for the census, linking these with Postcoded data for marketing and other purposes (see chapters 7, 8 and 9). However, at the other end of the scale, the small business user or researcher can gain equivalent benefit from manipulating the smaller amounts of data targeted on specific problems; both types of user are handling information more productively with Postcode referencing and GIS technology.

Commercially available packages for handling Postcodes

This chapter on the tools available for exploiting Postcode-based information has concentrated on the various choices that need to be made about representation and computer implementation in planning any system to achieve these ends. It seems appropriate to conclude by discussing the types of software packages which are already in use as a pointer to possible choices that the user might make. The systems available can be divided into several types for Postcode handling purposes. First, there are a range of both raster and vector systems which are primarily aimed at the handling of area-based data. The vector systems which fall into this category generally require that the areas are closed, and often involve the duplication rather than the interlocking of area boundaries.

An example of this is the PC-based package MapInfo, which is one means used by Kingswood Ltd. for distributing their European postal areas product (see figure 5.16; *cf* figure 1.6). MapInfo can read in coordinates for Postcodes boundaries in Autocad DXF or MapInfo Boundary Interchange format (MBI) and creates closed areas in a map display window known as a 'Mapper'. The areas each have a unique identifier (ID) which is used as a key into the associated relational table known in MapInfo as a 'Browser'. Once imported, these areas can be shaded by other attribute values in the associated browser. MapInfo also supports SQL, hence a query made on a browser which returns a number of records can also be displayed as a map. This opens up the possibility of mapping the output from a multiple attribute query, using SQL as a means of query and calculation. Other packages in this category include INFO-MAP and MapGrafix (which creates interlocking areas) which have been widely used for mapping health and crime statistics by Postcodes (see appendix 2).

Most raster systems are also primarily aimed at the handling of area-based data. SPANS is a quadtree-indexed raster package which can be used to analyse Postcodes on PC or workstation. SPANS is particularly suited for the overlay of Postcode boundaries onto other boundary data sets, since raster overlay is very rapid and efficient. As one example of its application to this type of data, SPANS was used to map the land cover changes in the National Parks in England in a recent study commissioned by the Countryside Commission. The land cover changes were summarised by administrative areas, so it would be relatively straightforward to assign the land cover areas to other (e.g. Postcode) spatial units for linkage to (say) population density. Since SPANS has the capability to convert boundary data into pixels, it is not important whether the source boundaries for the overlay operation are in raster or vector form. Another package in this category is ERDAS, which has excellent integration capabilities for remote sensing data from satellites.

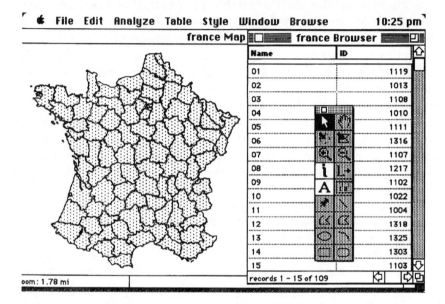

Figure 5.16   Postal codes 'mapper'/'browser' of France in MapInfo *(Source: Automobile Association; Kingswood Ltd)*

Beyond the systems which primarily handle area-based data, there are a range of more powerful GIS packages capable of handling topologically structured vector data. Of these packages, GIMMS is oriented towards mapping and overlaying Postcode boundaries with planning areas, census output areas and road networks and has excellent business graphics tools. Other packages which are available on PCs, workstations, minicomputers and mainframes and which also have excellent area handling are ARC/INFO, Genamap and MGE. These software systems can accept Postcode point or boundary representations and convert them into topologically structured areas using Thiessen polygons or the intersection of the boundaries. They also have facilities for adjacency checking, buffering, spatial querying based on map- or table-based selections and overlay of points, lines or areas on areas. These systems (and others like them which do not have PC versions such as Metropolis, System 9 and Smallworld GIS) are the most highly configured GIS currently available but they require the most training and the largest capital outlay (see appendix 2).

Finally, there are packages such as ProSpex produced by GeoMatrix (see plate 8) which have been produced specifically to handle Postcodes. ProSpex has the Postcode Sector boundaries 'hard coded' into it; hence it does not have general purpose mapping capabilities. It does, however, support links to geodemographic census 'profiles' and other related data.

Paradise or hell?

The technology for handling Postcoded and other geographical data is now in routine use. By the standards of only a few years ago it is highly effective and cheap. This does not, however, ensure that its use is always successful. Postcodes can be represented in a variety of ways inside a computer and can be manipulated by a range of sophisticated tools – especially GIS. However, all computer implementations rest on the underlying representation of the 'real world' chosen by human beings and all the results of operations on these representations should be assessed by users for the presence of inaccuracies. Errors are liable to accumulate throughout any process of spatial analysis and may undermine the validity of the end results. We urge you to exploit Postcode data using computer tools but *caveat emptor!*

Non-postal applications of Postcodes

CHAPTER 6   The Censuses and Postcodes

Introduction

The Census of Population – carried out separately for England and Wales, for Scotland and for Northern Ireland – provides the richest available sources of information on the number, characteristics and location of the population. The importance of the census is difficult to overstate and goes far beyond the substantial cost involved (£135 million for the 1991 Census). Results from our censuses form the corner-stone of many activities inside central and local government, in marketing (chapter 8) and business planning and in academic and private research (chapter 9). They form a critical part of the basic calculations of funds transferred from central government to the National Health Service and to local government. On a smaller scale, the location or closure of individual facilities like schools, clinics and hospitals may be based substantially upon the picture revealed by the census. Population projection figures needed for planning long-term constructions like reservoirs are 'calibrated' by use of the more detailed census statistics and road and rail transport modelling is completely dependent upon them.

Thus, almost no part of our daily lives is untouched by what comes out of the Population Census. Its value has long been recognised; the British censuses have been held since 1801. Indeed, the sequence of censuses is even longer in the US where the requirement that one be held is written into the Constitution and the statistics are used for both taxation and representation in Congress purposes.

A contributory factor in the growth of use of census information has been the huge changes in cost and ease of use of computer facilities for handling it (see chapter 5 and the Introduction to the book). Indeed, the effects of this general phenomenon have nowhere been more marked than in dealing with census data. When one of the authors of this book wrote another on the census some ten years ago (Rhind 1983), it was criticised in the press for containing too many references to computer methods. Now their use is almost ubiquitous. What was difficult for the average user in the early 1980s and nearly impossible in the 1970s is relatively trivial in the 1990s. The best way to illustrate this is to consider how the data might be stored: the entirety of all the questionnaire response data arising from the 1991 census data, for instance, could be stored on one CD in a fashion analogous to that of the PAF. Such a CD could not of course be made publicly available for reasons of confidentiality (see below).

The role of Postcodes in the UK censuses is basically two-fold: they can help in the planning and conduct of a census and they can provide the essential link between the riches of census data and other sorts of information such as that relating to clients and customers. The small size of the Unit Postcode when considered as an area facilitates both of these operations. This chapter describes the principles involved and introduces the potential of integrating census data more closely with Postcodes. In order to understand why this is so important it is necessary to know something of the nature of census data.

The nature and value of the Population Census

The significance of the population censuses in relation to other sources of information derives from five main characteristics:

- they are nationally comprehensive, every household in the country must, by law, fill in a census form. Census data thus cover the whole country;

- the census survey is synchronous, i.e. all respondents fill in the questionnaire relating to the same moment in time, thereby providing data comparable from place to place;

- censuses are held regularly every ten years (with only two exceptions: there was no census in 1941 and a 'mid-term' census was held in 1966), thus giving a regular time series of data;

- the questions asked in the census are basically comparable between censuses (though new questions are carefully introduced at each census to meet new policy-related issues), thus making intercensual comparisons possible;

- census results are made available for quite small areas (until 1981 the smallest unit for all censuses was the ED which build up in a hierarchical non-overlapping way to comprise many different sizes and types of area, ranging from an electoral ward to a health region.

Conducting the census

A census form is delivered by hand to every household in the country (some 23 million existing in Great Britain in 1991) and collected again after the census date. Extensive checks are made on the quality of the responses; all of the person-specific information gleaned is held confidential for 100 years though it is subsequently made available as part of the aggregate statistics for EDs and other areas, suitably treated so that no details of any one person can be obtained.

Census questions are of two kinds: those relating to the household as a unit and those relating to individuals within households. In 1991, for example, some 37 items of information could be derived from a completed census form: 16 relating to households and 21 relating to individuals. The content of the 1991 Census questionnaire is shown in table 6.1.

Table 6.1 Content of questions in the 1991 Census questionnaire *(Source: OPCS)*

Individual level	Household level
Whereabouts on census night	Geographical location
Usual whereabouts	Housing tenure
Age	Type of dwelling
Sex	Number of rooms
Marital status	Sole or shared toilet
Relationship to head	Sole or shared bath
Economic activity status	Central heating
Hours of work*	Cars or vans in household
Means of journey to work	Number of households in dwelling
Address of workplace/college	Number of vacant household spaces*
Occupation	Permanence of accommodation
Industry	Household composition variables
Higher educational goals	Family composition
Address one year ago	Life cycle

Table 6.1 *(cont.)*

Individual level	Household level
Limiting long-term illness*	Overcrowding
Country of birth	Multi-occupancy
Ethnicity*	
Language (Scotland and Wales)	
Status in communal establishment	
Permanence of accommodation	
Type of communal establishment	

* New questions in 1991

From the 23 million or so responses to these questions, the three census agencies have to produce tables of statistics describing the characteristics of the population and of its housing. These tables are created under the authorisation of the 1920 Census Act and are laid before Parliament. In addition, however, a huge variety of other tables are produced under the sanction of the Act for use by government and others. In essence, the way this is done is simply to exploit geography: the total numbers of people or households meeting specified criteria are added to a register; an analogy to this process is of pouring wine (the census questionnaire) into various bottles (the registers). Thus each person in the country will be allocated to one age category or other (typically in five year groups). The classifications used may be quite complicated; for example, the numbers of people in a given area may be recorded in a single table not only by age but also by gender and by the nature of their employment. Naturally, the analogy breaks down because the same people will be counted several times, once per table if they match the criteria on which it is based.

As a consequence of this operation, any desired number of tables of statistics may be produced by combining the answers to the basic questions. As an example, table 6.2 is a census table containing hypothetical information for an area but in a form used in the 1981 Census. As computer technology has improved, the number of such tables and the number of 'cells' (the numbers in each table) have been allowed to rise: in 1971, the standard and most widely used census statistics comprised 1,571 cells for each area. In 1981 that number rose to around 4,400 but, from the 1991 Census, it is (depending on the areas chosen) either over 8,000 or 14,000. This provides the user with a greater range of information and hence permits him or her to carry out a wider range of tasks with it. Such tables are normally produced by area of residence, i.e. the questionnaire respondents' home addresses. In addition, a complementary set of statistics is produced for area of workplace, but it contains considerably less detail than the widely available SAS. As we point out in chapter 8, the results between these two sets of data may vary considerably: for the Holborn area of London, they differ by a factor of ten!

Table 6.2 Example of a census table containing results for a hypothetical area

1. All persons present; plus absent residents in private households

	TOTAL PERSONS	In private households		Not in private households	
		Males	*Females*	*Males*	*Females*
1. All present residents	257	102	121	18	16
2. All absent residents	21	11	10	0	0
3. All visitors	96	35	46	6	9
Res. in UK	41	15	18	4	4
Res. outside UK	55	20	28	2	5
ALL PRESENT 1981					
1971 BASE (1+3)	353	137	167	24	25
ALL RESIDENT 1981					
1981 BASE (1+2)	278	113	131	18	16

In principle, the most flexible form in which to distribute the census data is not to distribute the data on such an area-by-area basis but actually as the totality of each and every household and individual's responses to the questionnaire. From these, the user could produce any tabulation he or she preferred. In practice, however, this is not feasible for reasons of keeping the census results secure: no information on individuals or their homes must be released singly or in a form where it can be interpreted from information for an area (even by buying two sets of data for overlapping areas, 'overlaying' them (chapter 5) and subtracting one from the other). Thus providing the data in a form summarised by area is not only convenient but also enables the census agencies to check by computer each and every cell value. Where these areas are very small – in practice if the total population therein falls below a specified threshold value – then much of the information is simply suppressed as being too confidential to release. Even where the population is large enough to retain and publish all the statistics, some statistical manipulation is still done to ensure that sophisticated analyses cannot disentangle the records of any one person.

Census geography

It will be obvious from all of this that the size of the area for which data are made available is critical to both the user and the census agencies. If the area is very small, much of the information is liable to be suppressed and hence unavailable. Even if it is made available (i.e. is just above the population threshold used), the reliability of it (particularly if it is one of the census questions coded up on a sample basis – see Rhind 1983) may well be suspect. Yet if the area is *too* large, it smooths out much geographical variation and the results may not adequately answer the needs of users interested in a particular area of different shape to that for which the standard statistics are produced.

The Postcode is, in general, too small as an output area: the median value of 12 delivery points quoted in chapter 2 suggests an average population of about 30 people in each (but see chapter 7). In 1981, the cut-off threshold used below which information was suppressed was 25 but in 1991 the corresponding figure is 50. Thus most census information would be suppressed in the majority of Postcodes if the agencies agreed to publish it at this level of detail. The Postcode plays rather a different role: in Scotland at least, it is the building block from which other, larger areas can be assembled to meet the users' needs and desires. On this basis, immense flexibility is built in. Even where areas mutate over time (as most electoral and administrative ones do), the use of Postcodes enables consistent areas to be built up for a time period covering multiple censuses, and hence comparisons to be made.

Moreover, the advantages do not solely occur at the output end of the process: Postcodes can play an important role at the stage of planning how a census is to be carried out. Before 1981, the territorial basis for carrying out the census in Scotland was essentially the same as that for England and Wales. The deployment of the census enumerators, armed with the census questionnaire to be filled in by each household, was arranged on the basis of one enumerator per ED. In Scotland in 1971 the average number of households per ED was 120 persons, though this figure was rather higher in densely populated areas where accessibility to the population to be counted was much easier and often significantly lower in remote rural areas (e.g. the Highlands) where accessibility was more difficult. The ED was also the smallest 'output unit' for which the results of the census were reported. EDs were thus, in a sense, the foundation on which the entire census was built, their boundaries being carefully designed to fit neatly into a hierarchy of larger output units such as wards, local authority districts, counties and regions.

When the time came to plan the 1981 Census, however, the GRO(S) decided to make the transition to full integration between EDs and

Postcode zones. A similar Postcode basis for carrying out and reporting the census was used in the Census of 1991. The experience of Scotland in this respect is therefore useful in gaining an understanding of some of the practical issues that lie behind the collection of nation-wide demographic and social data as recommended by the Chorley Committee in 1987 (see the Preface and the Introduction to this book). The position in Scotland also provides an interesting contrast with the more cautious way in which Postcodes and census EDs are being brought together in the census for England and Wales. We now consider the approaches used by both agencies.

The Scottish approach

It is helpful to understand how the distinctive Scottish approach evolved so we describe the 1981 and 1991 census-taking separately.

The 1981 Census in Scotland

Although the ED remained the basic unit of data collection and output, the Postcode was used in carrying out the 1981 Census in Scotland in three ways. First, it was used to give a reliable estimate of the enumeration workload in each Postcode. This was done by using the Post Office's count of 'delivery points' within each Postcode. These delivery points were adjusted to give estimates of the workload taking account of non-residential premises and communal establishments. Using the maps described below Postcodes were then assembled into EDs containing the desired workload. The second use made of the Postcode was in editing and checking certain types of census data. Because an ED contained a unique set of Postcodes it was a simple matter to check that the householder or enumerator had put the correct Postcode on the census form. Thirdly, the Postcode was used as a building block for the aggregation of the statistics into areas such as wards which were not recognised in planning EDs.

The great advantage of this Postcode-ED relationship was the way it made possible the fit of Postcodes into the hierarchy of Output Areas (OAs) used for census (and other) purposes and hence to link census data to other information. Since 1973, GRO(S) has mapped the boundaries of Unit Postcodes, including any changes that are made to those boundaries. A boundary is drawn around all the addresses in a Unit Postcode (taking into account property boundaries and road-centre lines) so that the entire land surface of Scotland is covered. Once a boundary has been drawn in this way, it is a relatively easy matter to assign a Postcode to an electoral ward, a civil parish and about 15 other area types for which Scottish census results are given. Moreover, the codes for these 'area types' are stored on a Unit Postcode directory which is used within GRO(S) to assign other Postcoded data with which it is concerned (i.e. births, marriages and deaths) to larger reporting areas. This directory was also used by other organisations which generate Postcoded data (e.g. local authorities, utilities and market research organisations), enabling them to link their own data to the Small Area Statistics (SAS) produced by GRO(S) for each and every ED.

A further benefit of this approach came when records from the 1971 Census were retrospectively 'Postcoded', thus making it possible to aggregate this information to 1981 EDs and so produce detailed statistics of demographic and social change between 1971 and 1981.

Planning the 1991 Census in Scotland

The decision by GRO(S) to use the Postcode to create different areas for census data collection and output was taken on a number of grounds, many of them emerging after consultations with census data users. The considerations were:

- the need to make the collection of census data more cost-effective leading to larger EDs in 1991;

- the need to maintain continuity with the OAs adopted for 1971 and 1981;

- the need to increase flexibility over 1981 in the aggregation of census OAs to other *ad hoc* areas, and;

- the need to continue to capitalise on the facility for data linkage inherent in the Postcode system.

As a result, GRO(S) decided to abandon the ED as the main census OA – though it was the need to maintain geographical compatibility with OAs for 1971 and 1981 that loomed largest in this decision (Thomas 1991). In the creation of new OAs, two important criteria applied. The first was that, in order to preserve the confidentiality of the information given to the census-takers by individual households, no OA should contain fewer than 16 households or 50 residents. These thresholds (which also apply to the census in England and Wales) were double the equivalent levels for 1981 and were approved by Parliament in its debate on the form, content and output of the 1991 Census.

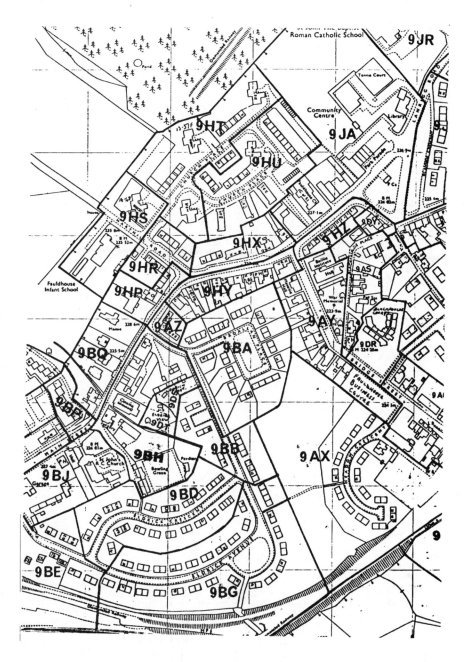

Figure 6.1   The source material for GRO(S) digitising of Postcode boundaries, consisting of Ordnance Survey maps on which the boundaries are drawn *(Source: GRO[S] and Ordnance Survey. © Crown Copyright)*.

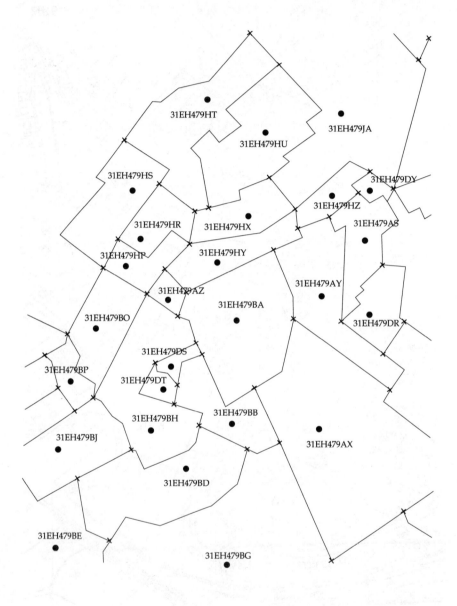

Figure 6.2   Output from the computer files of the digitised, checked and edited boundary data from figure 6.1 *(Source: GRO[S] and Ordnance Survey © Crown Copyright)*

There was an element of 'guess-work' involved since in the census-planning phase it was necessary to create Provisional Output Areas (POAs) based on the estimated household counts used in planning ED boundaries. Once the actual counts of households and residents were known (i.e. after the census was taken), then these provisional OAs could be accepted or rejected depending on whether they met the confidentiality criteria or not. Final OAs are created by merging below threshold POAs. Secondly, each POA was created from Postcodes belonging to a single 1981 ED. If the estimated threshold count was high enough, the Postcodes were split into several POAs, so that each POA had a count of at least 40. Each POA was given a seven character code comprising the six characters of the 1981 ED code plus a suffix.

In order to be able to assemble Postcodes into the POAs necessary for reporting the 1991 census results, GRO(S) decided to digitise the boundaries of all Unit Postcodes in Scotland. This was a costly and time-consuming business, involving the 'capture' of the boundaries of roughly 130,000 Postcodes on 5,500 maps. Figures 6.1 and 6.2 illustrate the source document and the resulting computer representation of the boundaries. It did, however, have a number of off-setting operational and commercial advantages:

- it produced a database from which neighbouring Postcodes could be identified directly and hence 'clumped together' to produce provisional OAs

- it provided a file of information that could be used directly and flexibly in devising 'quality checks' of output areas in relation to the Postcode directory and against the Postcodes used in planning POAs;

- it created boundary files for customer use (i.e. for location, mapping and analysis) with the SAS produced from the census, and;

- it created a product that could be used with customer-produced data (i.e. routine Postcoded information) either for mapping at Postcode level or for building into a range of other types of area.

SCOTTISH POSTCODE BOUNDARY PRODUCTS

A list of the various products that GRO(S) has derived from its use of Postcodes as the basic collecting unit for the 1991 Census and from digitising the Postcode boundaries is given in appendix 6. Depending on what kind of data handling tools are available to the user (see chapter 5), these products permit the carrying out of many different kinds of analyses on census data for geographically very small areas. Moreover, significant flexibility is maintained in relation to data from the previous census and other types of data. Analyses of change between censuses are facilitated by the structure of the OA code. The OA-Postcode Directory to be produced by GRO(S) will allow the linkage of Postcoded non-census data to OAs. Analyses of change between censuses (and the linkage of other data to these analyses) are thereby made significantly easier. It should be pointed out that some other changes between censuses still produce problems in making comparisons (e.g. change in the wording of questions and hence the definitions of variables; see Norris and Mounsey 1983); nevertheless, the use of Postcodes greatly reduces the problem of comparing census results for different dates.

Postcodes and the census in England and Wales

The 1981 Census in England and Wales was carried out in a fashion broadly similar to its predecessor in 1971 (though the innovative production of census statistics for 1km National Grid squares in that early census was not repeated). Thus EDs formed the basic 'building block' for both the data collection and publication stages of the 1981 Census in England and Wales. The 'typical' 1981 ED contained about 150 households though considerable variations occurred, i.e. it was about ten times as populated as the 'average' Postcode. OPCS, the England and Wales census agency, provided a different solution to coping with change of boundaries through time to that adopted by the Scots: they created a set of census tracts by aggregating both sets of EDs in such a way that the boundaries of these new, larger areas were identical for both 1971 and 1981. Clearly these were multiples of EDs in many cases: the boundaries of only 44% of EDs remained unchanged between 1971 and 1981 despite strenuous efforts by OPCS to maintain continuity where possible.

Between the 1981 and 1991 Censuses, OPCS studied the various options available to them for collecting and publishing the census information. They were urged to adopt a Postcode-based solution by the government's Committee of Enquiry on the Handling of Geographic Information in 1986 and 1987. However, the OPCS case to the Treasury for the funding for such a development fell foul of changes in Treasury rules regarding offsetting of expenditures and was abandoned. As a consequence, the 1991 Census in England and Wales shares many of the characteristics of its predecessors. It should be emphasised however that OPCS have set out to create an ED to Postcode Directory; this was made possible by recording the Postcode for each house on the census questionnaire. More details of this are given below but the Directory will certainly facilitate linkage of census and any other data which contains a Postcode as a geographical reference. It will obviate the error-prone linkage needed for 1981 data which involved computing the nearest ED centroid to each and every Postcode in an area of interest (chapter 7). Since the Grid References held in both PAF (chapter 4) and in the 1981 Census SAS were only at 100m resolution, the results of the process were frequently in error.

The ED to Postcode directory

Though the principles set out above are firmly established, the detailed situation in England and Wales regarding Postcode geography is only just becoming clear at the time of writing (late 1991). The account below therefore relies heavily on the work of Dr David Martin of the University of Southampton who has followed OPCS decision-making in relation to Postcodes closely (Martin 1991). It also draws upon the account published by Davies (1991) as we went to press.

Instead of digitising Unit Postcode boundaries, OPCS are providing a means of making a link between census data and Postcode geography through an ED to Postcode directory which will tell the user which Postcodes are located within or, more strictly, associated with, an ED. The reason it cannot be said that all Postcodes are contained within a particular ED is that in England and Wales (unlike Scotland) many Unit Postcodes fall across the boundaries of two or more EDs. Unit Postcodes falling entirely or partly within an ED are called, in OPCS terminology, a Part Postcode Unit or PPU. With the aid of the ED to Postcode directory, it is thus possible to build up a set of Postcodes into an approximation to an ED, in effect, a pseudo-ED.

The directory consists of a record for each PPU consisting of the Unit Postcode, the ED code, the pseudo-ED code, the OS 100m grid reference of the Postcode taken from the Central Postcode Directory (see chapter 4) and the number of usually resident households (including an allowance for persons resident in communal establishments). The pseudo-ED code represents the ED in which the majority of the current population of the Postcode falls. An illustration of the way this works is given below in table 6.3.

Table 6.3   Relationships between Postcodes and EDs in the new directory
(Source: OPCS)

DM1	1AA	WAED01	WAED01	01234	05678	23
DM1	1AB	WAED01	WAED01	01233	05677	18
DM1	1AB	WAED02	WAED01	01233	05677	9
DM1	1AC	WAED02	WAED02	01239	05679	31

In this example, Unit Postcode DM1 1AA is completely contained within the ED WAED01, its National Grid reference is given as Easting and Northing 01234 05678 and it contains 23 resident households. The pseudo-ED to which it is allocated is also WAED01. Postcode DM1 1AB, however, appears on two lines of the directory. This indicates that it lies across the boundary between EDs WAED01 and WAED02 and is divided into two PPUs : one consisting of 18 households, the other consisting of nine households. It is therefore assigned to pseudo-ED WAED01. Postcode DM1 1AC has all its 31 households in ED WAED02 and is therefore assigned to that as its pseudo-ED. In addition, the directory will also show the proportion of Postcodes that have had to be allocated to a particular pseudo-ED, the allocation depending on the number of households they contain.

Census Data and Postcoded Information

According to Martin (1991), the Postcode-based data for the 1991 Census in England and Wales will offer a number of improvements in data processing techniques and uses to which the census can be put. The technical advantages include:

- use of the ED to Postcode Directory as a 'gazetteer' file (e.g. with the SASPAC 91 software), to produce more refined geographical aggregations of census data;

- the provision (with appropriate software) for faster and more flexible linkage of user-generated data with census data.

The data analysis advantages include:

- a more accurate allocation of ED characteristics to Postcodes as used in the various neighbourhood classification schemes developed for market research and related purposes;

- a more accurate representation of the distribution of population within an ED, thus opening up the possibility for better spatial modelling of census data.

Conclusions

We now know that it is possible to organise and run a census based entirely on the Postcode system as an area base. At the time of writing, the potential advantages of this are very clear but the data (both in Scotland and England and Wales) are just becoming available. Thus we can not be certain how much take-up of the different types of data there will be. The comparison is in any case complicated by the fact that demand for census data is greatest where there is only a hybrid Postcode basis, i.e. in the more numerous affluent areas of England. All that said, OPCS recognise the merits of using Postcodes – indeed they have for many years maintained the CPD (see chapter 4) – and it seems likely that increasing use of the Postcode system will be made by them in future. This is, of course, subject to any additional 'start up' funding that may be necessary being made available by the Treasury or perhaps some other source!

CHAPTER 7

Applications of data linkage
through Postcodes

Introduction

In earlier chapters we have argued that linking geographical data sets together provides 'added value' since many more applications are possible with data sets that are linked together than when they are held separate from each other. We have pointed out that often the only things which the data sets share is the geography of the data collecting areas. Because of this, Postcodes can act as a conversion mechanism to link separately collected data sets together.

The problems involved in linking data sets together depend upon the combination which is under consideration. As we have seen in chapter 6, there is no difficulty in linking any kind of Postcoded data with Scottish census data since Postcodes are an integral part of that census and Postcode boundaries have been digitised. The concern of this chapter is not with such relatively straightforward tasks: under such conditions, linkage of geographical data sets becomes technically trivial and routine. Our concern here is in relation to where life is more difficult, where one or other of the data sets is not Postcoded and we have to resort to other strategies – exploiting all Postcode products and our knowledge of good methodologies – to produce a meaningful answer in linking the data sets together.

We do not need to go far to provide an example where linkage is not easy: in England and Wales prior to 1991, an equivalent census ED-to-Postcode linkage could only be made in one of two ways. The first was by painstakingly and manually locating Postcodes on maps of EDs. The second approach, essential for larger scale studies, was to create a Thiessen polygon around each ED centroid and 'capture' the grid-references of Postcodes within that zone (see chapter 5). The need for this approach arises because no boundaries of the Unit Postcodes or of all EDs exists in computer form south of the Scottish border (though, as we have seen in chapter 4, the ED boundaries, but not the Postcode ones, are now being digitised in England). As a result, many researchers in commerce (notably marketing; see chapter 8) and academia had to resort to a series of approximations to link their data together.

A particularly common problem is in the linkage of address-based data, such as that from sample surveys, to that from the Census of Population and other data. The difficulties encountered include translating Postcoded addresses of sample points to National Grid references and subsequently relating these spatial references to census EDs. As a result, this chapter evaluates three methods of coping with the 'worst case' when linking postal addresses in a large-scale sample survey to EDs and assesses the relative accuracy of each method. It is based upon detailed research work undertaken for a public sector body. Given the existence of the reliable ED to Postcode Directory now being produced by OPCS (see chapter 6), this project would soon become much simpler. Nevertheless, it still serves as an excellent worked example of how to carry out linkage between any two geographical data sets without a common key being explicitly recorded in each file. It also serves to emphasise the care that needs to be taken in establishing the 'genealogy' of a data set: if you do not know how data have been assembled and processed, it is very risky to proceed to link it to other data and analyse the new product. The results might simply be a reflection of the imperfections of the data rather than of reality.

Linkage of Postcoded addresses to Census Enumeration Districts

In order to undertake the above procedures two sources of information were used in this study:

- The OPCS/GRO(S) Central Postcode Directory (CPD);

- OPCS ED centroids derived from the 1981 Census of Population Small Area Statistics.

The character of CPD information has already been described (chapter 4). It is now necessary to describe the coordinate geography of the other half of the data-linkage equation, the EDs. For each of the 105,964 EDs in England in the 1981 Small Area Statistics, OPCS assigned centroids in the form of 100m resolution National Grid references, i.e. identical in level of detail to those in the PAF on CD and in the CPD. The principle underlying the positioning of these centroids was that they should be population-weighted (thus the density of population clusters within the ED influence the location of the centroid) and not geographical centres in the sense of being in the middle of the land area (Martin 1989).

In practice, two different procedures were employed to georeference EDs and some of the results obtained reflect this duality. Where Enumeration Districts in 1981 were unchanged from 1971 (44% of all EDs in England and Wales), 1971 Census centroids were re-used. These were originally allocated according to the following criteria:

- wherever possible, the National Grid reference should not relate to more than one ED (which could easily happen in urban areas since EDs there are often comparable in size or smaller than the 100m resolution used);

- the Grid reference should relate to a single building within the ED and should be the approximate centre of population of the ED;

- identification and referencing of an identifiable single building was more important than recognising the centre of population (but in some EDs, no central address could be identified and an arbitrary reference was allocated according to OPCS (1984).

For Enumeration Districts which were new in 1981, a centroid was selected so as to be as near as possible to the centre of population of that area. This was carried out by manual examination of the OS 1:10,000 and 1:10,560 scale maps used by OPCS for Enumeration District planning. The topographical information shown on these maps was supplemented by adding details of housing change obtained from district councils. Figures 7.1 and 7.2 illustrate the location of 100m ED centroids in relation to the boundaries of Enumeration Districts for the two contrasting London Boroughs of Bromley, and Hammersmith and Fulham. The population 'weighting' of ED centroids can be inferred from the positioning of centroids in the larger (generally more rural) EDs for Bromley.

Evaluation of the data linkage methodologies

The basics of data linkage were described in chapter 1 and the technical details were summarised in chapter 5. Here it suffices to say that the 'fuzzy matching' (see figure 1.1) type of data linkage demands that grid references exist both on the 'client' and in the census data files. To achieve this, the Postcodes of the (very large number of) addresses on the client

Figure 7.1   Enumeration District boundaries from the 1981 Census overlaid with ED centroids for the London Borough of Bromley

address file were assigned a 100m resolution National Grid reference and local authority code identifier by use of the CPD. From this data set, a subset of 800 sample point addresses covering six selected local authority areas was extracted for the purpose of evaluating various matching procedures.

The local authorities selected for study were: three London Boroughs, a Southern Coastal town, a city in the South West and a part of the West Midlands conurbation. This includes two highly urbanised London

Figure 7.2 Enumeration District boundaries from the 1981 Census overlaid with ED centroids for the London Borough of Hammersmith and Fulham

Boroughs with relatively high population densities and a substantial amount of older housing. These areas are of particular interest because of the high concentration of client sample points located within Inner London. The Outer London Borough included large areas of interwar and postwar suburban housing as well as some 'semi-rural' areas and extensive areas of Metropolitan Green Belt. The Southern Coastal town was selected to represent a large urban area in the outer part of the South East region. The West Midlands candidate was an example of a highly urbanised area with older housing and inter- and post-war peripheral housing estates outside the South East region. Finally, the South Western city is a major urban centre in a predominantly rural area.

Using client sample addresses in this subset of data, the following matching procedures were applied:

- Nearest Neighbour Analysis;

- the construction of Thiessen polygons followed by Point-in-Polygon (PIP) matching;

- Point-in-Polygon matching within digitised ED boundaries.

In the strict sense, there is no mathematical distinction between the first two methods, other than the fact that edge effects are liable to be significant in the Thiessen polygon-based method (see chapter 5). These can be seen in the maps and in the tables of results. We include both procedures because researchers have often used one or other without knowledge of their mathematical equivalence; our results show how sensitive any one method is to such factors as the size and shape of areal units at the edge of the map.

Nearest Neighbour Analysis

This involved the application of a distance algorithm to link Unit Postcode 'centroids' (UPCs) to the nearest ED centroid in each case. The distance was computed from each UPC for a client sample address to ED centroids within a specified area (in terms of the Easting and Northing coordinates of the grid references; see chapter 2 and appendix 5 for an explanation of the National Grid system). Addresses were then assigned to an ED on the basis of the nearest ED centroid.

Thiessen Polygons

Thiessen polygons are areas formed around geographically referenced data points; there is one polygon per data point (see figure 5.5). The polygons are created so as to ensure that every other part of space is allocated to its nearest data point. The entire set of Thiessen polygons for all the data points being considered is sometimes termed a Dirichlet tessellation. In practice, creating such a tessellation converts a data set from being based on points to being area-based. In this case, 'synthetic' ED boundaries were created using the ARC/INFO GIS software by constructing Thiessen polygons using ED centroids as the 'seeds' from which the polygons were 'grown'. Figures 7.3 and 7.4 illustrate the construction of Thiessen polygons for Bromley and for Hammersmith and Fulham. Note that polygon areas and shapes are determined by the spacing of the ED centroids.

A Point-in-Polygon (see chapter 5) search was then undertaken using these imputed ED boundaries. This involved the use of a computer method to determine which polygon (or synthetic ED) contains each UPC

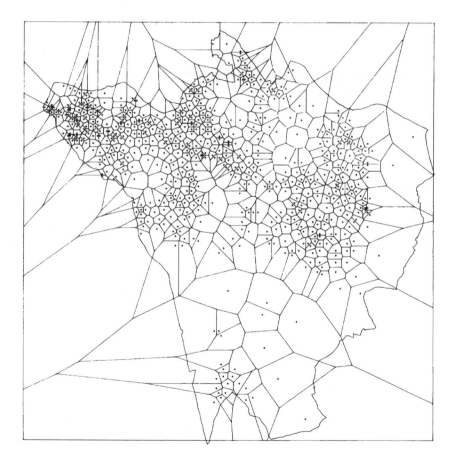

Figure 7.3   Thiessen polygons generated from the ED centroids in Bromley (*cf* figure 7.1). These form synthetic Enumeration Districts

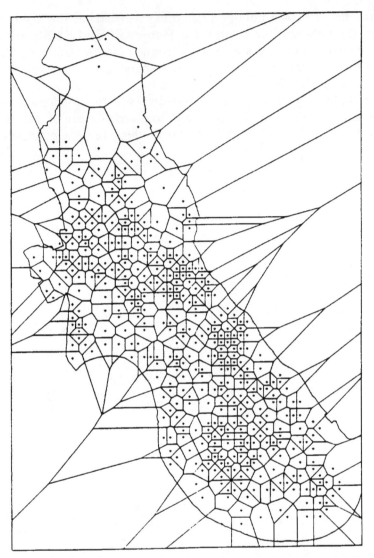

Figure 7.4   Thiessen polygons generated from the ED centroids in Hammersmith and Fulham (*cf* figure 7.2). These also form synthetic Enumeration Districts

in which lay a client sample address. In mathematical terms, there are obviously very close similarities between Nearest Neighbour Analysis and the application of Thiessen polygons. Unsurprisingly, therefore table 7.1 shows that similar allocations were obtained for these two methods. The lowest correspondence (circa 70%) was found in the Inner London areas where EDs are small and numerous; this stems from the edge effects mentioned above.

Table 7.1   Percentage of cases where Nearest Neighbour Analysis and use of Point-in-Polygon routines with Thiessen polygons allocate Postcoded addresses to the same ED

Selected Local Authority	% of correspondence	No. of Sample Addresses
South Coast town	80	65
London Borough 1	95	156
London Borough 2	71	223
Southwest City	85	53
London Borough 3	73	172
Midlands City	88	100

Point-in-Polygon matching within digitised ED Boundaries

The third method involved using a Point-in-Polygon routine to locate the UPC centroids within digitised ED boundaries. Digitised ED boundaries in computer-readable form have in the past rarely been available (though we report in chapter 4 on the progress being made towards a complete national set of these digitised ED boundaries). In this case, the boundaries were specially digitised for the purpose of the study, using 1:10,000 scale OS maps of EDs for four of the local authority areas selected for the study.

Manual Assignment of client sample addresses to EDs

For two London Boroughs (one in inner London, one in outer), a comprehensive accuracy check of some 328 client sample point addresses was undertaken. This involved locating each of the addresses on 1:1250 scale OS maps. For one London Borough, this was made easier by use of the local authority's ICL PLANES property information system: this stores accurate locational references for each address in the Borough based on previous manual assignments.

Assessment of the results

The information derived from these manual procedures provides a check on the validity of the three linkage methodologies. For the London Boroughs 1 and 3, the assignments derived from each method have been assessed against the correct location of sample points. The full results of this analysis are shown in Table 7.2. For linkages to individual EDs, margins of error are large. Nearest Neighbour Analysis and the use of Thiessen polygons are similar in their low level of accuracy, with only between 35% and 55% of addresses matched to the correct ED. Digitised boundaries do not necessarily produce a higher proportion of correct matches but, where mismatch occurs, errors tend to be smaller than for the other methods. The results suggest that marked geographical variations in the level of accuracy are likely to occur, with the highest errors in densely populated areas which often have many small, irregularly shaped EDs (see also 'Postcodes in sample surveys' in chapter 9).

Table 7.2. Allocation of Postcoded English House Condition Survey (EHCS) addresses to correct EDs using various matching methodologies in two selected local authority areas

London Borough 1

Level of Accuracy   **Matching Methodology**

| | | | | *Point-in-Polygon* | | | | | |
| | *Nearest Neighbour* | | | *Thiessen polygons* | | | *Digitised ED boundaries* | | |
	No	%	Cum. %	No	%	Cum. %	No	%	Cum. %
Direct Match	72	41.9	41.9	61	35.5	35.5	58	33.7	33.7
Adjoining ED	73	42.4	84.3	85	49.4	84.9	103	59.9	93.6
Next ED but 1	24	14.0	98.3	22	12.8	97.7	7	4.1	97.7
Next ED but 2	3	1.7	100.0	4	2.3	100.0	2	1.2	98.9
More than 2 EDs away	0	0	100.0	0	0	100.0	0	0	98.9
Other	0	0	100.0	0	0	100.0	2	1.2	100.0
TOTAL	**172**	**100.0**	**100.0**	**172**	**100.0**	**100.0**	**172**	**100.0**	**100.0**

London Borough 3

Level of Accuracy   **Matching Methodology**

| | | | | *Point-in-Polygon* | | | | | |
| | *Nearest Neighbour* | | | *Thiessen polygons* | | | *Digitised ED boundaries* | | |
	No	%	Cum. %	No	%	Cum. %	No	%	Cum. %
Direct Match	83	53.2	53.2	84	53.8	53.8	92	59.0	59.6
Adjoining ED	63	40.4	93.6	62	39.7	93.6	54	93.6	93.6
Next ED but 1	5	3.2	96.8	5	3.2	96.8	5	3.2	96.8
Next ED but 2	3	1.9	98.7	3	1.9	98.7	1	0.6	97.4
More than 2 EDs away	1	0.6	99.9	1	0.6	99.3	2	1.3	100.0
Other	1	0.6	99.3	1	0.6	99.3	2	1.3	100.0
TOTAL	**156**	**100.0**	**100.0**	**156**	**100.0**	**100.0**	**156**	**100.0**	**100.0**

The results also suggest that overall accuracy levels may be considerably improved if allocation is made on the basis of small clusters of EDs rather than a single ED. For example, in London Borough 1, the proportion of sample points allocated to either the correct or adjoining ED ranges from 84% to 94% according to the methodology used, whilst for London Borough 3 the corresponding figure is 94% for each of the methods. Clearly, however, whatever method is used, little reliance can be placed on the quality of address matches made to individual EDs. This is by no means an unanticipated result, other researchers have found similar levels of error using similar methods (Openshaw 1989). Nevertheless, it may be helpful to recount the principal sources of error in some detail here.

First, the CPD file was known to be prone to some error when this exercise was undertaken. Only 50% of grid references on the file are within 100m of the 'true' location of the first address in the Postcode; the overall accuracy of the National Grid references for any random sample of addresses will probably be worse than this figure. An estimated 2% of grid references are subject to gross error, being more than 900m from the 'true' location of the first address (Wilson and Elliot 1987), but see also the section on PAF accuracy in chapter 4). Each Postcode grid reference on the CPD, even when correct, is not in any real sense a centroid at all (see chapter 5 and figure 5.4). The first listed address could fall *anywhere* within the areal extent of the Postcode; at best, the grid reference is only intended to indicate the bottom left-hand corner of the 100m grid square containing this first address.

ED centroids may be less problematic but are by no means error-free. These centroids are also at best only accurate to within 100m. In practice, and despite attempts by OPCS to minimise the problem, this can mean that an ED population centroid falls outside the ED concerned. These problems are particularly acute in areas of high population density such as certain of the London Boroughs. Indeed, the total area covered by the target ED can be a statistically significant variable which helps to explain variations in the level of mismatch in some circumstances. The relationship between matching error and ED area was found to be weak where Nearest Neighbour and Thiessen polygon techniques had been used but was statistically significant where digitised ED boundaries were used and where mean ED areas exceeded a certain minimum threshold (e.g. in London Borough 3). In other words, the bigger the ED, the lower the rate of matching error. At the extreme case, where the area concerned is the whole of Britain, the extent of the mis-match must be zero so this result was to be expected. On the other hand, it is helpful to be able to establish that it still applies at the micro-scale and puzzling why it should not apply with certain approaches.

Where both ED and postal area geography are congested, additional problems can arise. Unless care is taken by filtering out all 'special EDs', the National Grid reference for a Postcode in the Central Postcode Directory may be matched to a special ED which contains no private households (e.g. a hospital or a prison). This happened in three matched cases in London Boroughs. More than one ED may also have centroids at the same 100m grid intersection. This occured eight times, for example, with EDs in the London Borough of Camden (Boyle and Dunn, 1990). The ED centroid clearly has an increased likelihood of falling outside the correct ED in congested areas. In Camden, for example, just 46% of OPCS centroids fall within their correct EDs (Boyle and Dunn 1990). Pinpoint Analysis Ltd have suggested that, for London as a whole, only 45% of ED centroids lie within their current ED.

Enumeration District shape is also a relevant factor in explaining the variations in the level of mismatch. Boundaries of these areas tend to follow significant topographic features such as roads and railways and, where possible, blocks of housing are grouped into reasonably compact shapes. However, many EDs in inner-city areas are linear, following road lines. Others extend beyond compact shapes to make up sufficient workloads for census enumerators or include large sections of relatively unpopulated land (Rhind 1983). Gross mismatch (e.g. linkage to a non-adjacent ED can easily occur in inner-city locations where small, linear EDs frequently occur in clusters.

These results demonstrate that, whilst a comprehensive set of digitised boundaries would facilitate linkage procedures, they would not solve all the problems involved in data linkage. The only way to reduce these errors to infinitesimal proportions is to have the boundaries of both Unit Postcodes and EDs accurately digitised at high spatial resolution (much better than 100m) or to have individual grid references for each and every house within the Postcode and match these to high quality ED boundaries. The same logic applies for any combination of Postcode and 'other area' data where the latter are no more than about ten to 20 times the size of the Postcodes; where the non-Postcode areas are 1000 times as large as the average Postcode, the errors are probably small, unless the areas involved are very long and thin!

Assignment of Postcodes to Clusters of EDs

If our ability to allocate Postcodes to EDs or like areas on the basis of the grid references of their centroids is very limited, can we get acceptable results by linking not to one ED but to groups of them? This seems likely to be a partial solution for in getting better matching of the data we pay the price in losing geographical detail. This may not matter if the areas concerned (e.g. EDs) all have the same characteristics but, if this is so, why do we need to use data of this level of detail?

In practice, accurate definition of groups of contiguous EDs is not possible from ED centroids alone: the boundaries of other areas might interdigitate but be unrecognised on the basis of the centroids alone. As an experiment, therefore, clusters were defined using fixed radii around an appropriate centroid. These clusters are considered to be more meaningful than a fixed number of contiguous EDs, particularly on the fringes of urban areas where ED size is highly variable. Such clusters can be formed by drawing radii either about the National Grid reference of the Postcode containing the client sample address or about the centroid of the ED in which the sample point is located. In this particular study, it was considered preferable to base clusters directly on Postcode grid references.

The basic procedure adopted to carry out validation tests for clusters was as follows. For each grid reference of a UPC which had been assigned to a client sample point in London Borough 1 and London Borough 2, radii at 250m and 500m were drawn using the 'Point Distance' function in the ARC/INFO GIS. This measured the distance to appropriate ED centroids falling within clusters defined using these radii. The results of this analysis are presented in Table 7.3. In the case of London Borough 1, just over 70% of ED centroids relating to client sample points fell within 150m of the UPC grid reference. Around 92% fell within 250m and 98% are within 500m. At 250m, the average size of the cluster was eight EDs whilst at 500m this figure increased to 23.

To put these figures in context, the average population size of EDs in London Borough 1 was about 320, with an average of 1.9 persons per household space. On this basis, 500 dwellings would encompass approximately three EDs and 3000 dwellings about 18 EDs. In London Borough 3, where the average area of an ED is about four times higher than is the case in London Borough 1, a somewhat different pattern emerges. For 72% of addresses the correct EDs fall within 250m of the CPD grid reference and 86% are within 500m. In 10% of cases, the 250m radius fails to include an ED centroid. The mean number of EDs per cluster is also about one-quarter of that for London Borough 1 at both 250m and 500m radii.

Conclusions

As we noted previously, the production of an ED to Postcode Directory by OPCS means that we shall no longer have to undertake exercises like that described here in the future. However, a number of principles of data linkage that will be of value in other exercises do emerge from this exercise. Thus, it follows from all that has been said above that, where

Table 7.3 Clusters of EDs based on fixed radii about English House Condition Survey (EHCS) sample points represented by UPC in selected local authority areas

London Borough 1

Radial distance	% of correct EHCS sample point EDs	Cumulative %
0 (tied)	20.3	20.3
1–150m	50.0	70.3
150–250m	21.6	91.9
250–500m	6.4	98.3
500m+	1.7	100.0

n = 172

Cluster size (no. of EDs)	Mean	Min	Max	Median
at 250m	8.1	1	15	8
at 500m	23.5	5	39	25

London Borough 2

Radial distance	% of correct EHCS sample point EDs	Cumulative %
0 (tied)	5.8	5.8
1–150m	45.5	51.3
150–250m	21.2	72.5
250–500m	13.5	86.0
500m+	14.1	100.0 (rounded)

n = 156

Cluster size (no. of EDs)	Mean	Min	Max	Median
at 250m	2.2	0	7	3
at 500m	6.3	0	15	7

data records in two data files do not pertain to the same areas, the accuracy of linking the data together is wholly dependent on at least four factors:

- the ratio of the sizes of areas being matched. It is much easier matching small areas approximated by centroids to a few large areas approximated by centroids. It is even easier if the boundaries of the large areas are in computer form and Point-in-Polygon processing can take place;

- the shape of the areas. Compact rather than elongated areas give the best results;

- the resolution and accuracy of digitising of the geographical data, whether these are centroids or boundaries. The grid references on the CPD (and now the PAF on CD) and in the 1981 England and Wales census data encouraged many people (including ourselves) to carry out data linkage which contained high error rates. The moral is that, if data are made available, they will be exploited and misused!

- the quality of the computer methods used within the software. Accuracy of methods is not easily checked by most users and no independent evaluation of particular software has been carried out but differences are known to exist between packages.

The linkage of formerly quite disparate data sets is now quite common, made possible by geographic referencing and the availability of data handling tools such as those described in chapter 5. The extent of data linkage operations as long as five years ago can be seen in a survey carried out for Royal Mail, the results of which are given in appendix 7. In addition to the sheer range of applications what is significant about this appendix is how many could have important policy implications for health, housing, education, employment and the like. In such circumstances it is especially important that there is some understanding of the advantages and disadvantages (and geographical variation in these) of the data linkage methods used.

It is especially important that the user be very careful indeed when using 'black box' GIS tools to link geographical data sets together. So far as the Postcode is concerned, we have to realise that, even though it is very small, linkage using its name and/or the grid references at present attached to the PAF on CD or the CPD is liable to significant error. Unfortunately, no general statement on the magnitude of this error is possible; each case must be judged in relation to the factors involved. The only consolation is that linkage using many other data sets will be much worse! We suspect that many users of PAF on CD and of CPD do not understand these constraints on the use of the data. It seems that at a time when the handling of geographic information in very large amounts has never been easier there is an even greater need for some understanding of basic geography!

CHAPTER 8 Applications of Postcodes in marketing[2]

Introduction

Contemporary society takes the marketing of goods and services as normal activities. The matching of supply and demand is assumed to be part of the way an efficient market society works. Given this, the role of the Postcode is an important one since Postcodes describe (in effect) where businesses and consumers are located and where they can be contacted. Moreover, they are part of the channel of communications to them. That said, Postcodes and the whole postal system is nothing more than a means to an end so far as marketeers are concerned, rather than an end in themselves.

The crux of the Postcode for the marketeer is that it is a label for an area. Only if this area can be 'typed' or categorised in marketing terms is this of value. The 'typing' must be in terms of the inherent propensity and ability of the businesses and consumers in that area to consume goods and services of different kinds and prices. An alternative which is potentially more efficient is to hold details of the individuals concerned, rather than some aggregate profile of the people in the area as a whole. This alternative has several disadvantages: the data files are much larger and more difficult to maintain up-to-date, notably since government does not provide a single comprehensive data set for individuals as it does for populations in small areas through the Census of Population (see chapter 6). Moreover, holding such personal information introduces the need to register under the Data Protection Act and be subject to the strict guidelines on privacy of personal information which it enforces.

[2]This chapter was largely written by Professor John R Beaumont of the School of Management at the University of Bath

Postcodes have obvious advantages for marketeers because they are geographically small and can be used to create almost any larger areas. In addition, they are familiar to the general public and some marketing-related information (e.g., questionnaire responses) is often collected for confidentiality reasons, with only the Postcode to identify the respondent. For these and other reasons Postcodes are one of the most important means by which marketeers reach their particular goal of assessing and influencing the buying budget of both businesses and consumers. Before considering the specific applications of the Postcode in this field, however, we need to understand the principles and practice of contemporary marketing. This will serve to show what stringent demands we make on Postcoded information in this important sphere of business life.

Marketing as a process

Marketing is a function that exists in most organisations, in both the public and the private sectors. There has been a tendency in the past to link its activities only to sales (and indirectly to production). Now there is a growing appreciation that a business approach is necessary, viewing marketing as a corporate activity involving not only the production of products and services but also their design, distribution and ultimate consumption. Marketing is not about products and services *per se*; the focus of attention must be on consumers (or potential consumers) and how their needs can be satisfied in the context of market dynamics and changing tastes and fashions. The consumer is 'king' in the sense that he or she should start and finish the marketing process. It is also necessary to understand (local) markets and to be able to appreciate and avoid competition.

For marketing in general, the 1950s and 1960s were characterised by 'mass' marketing, and the 1970s and 1980s were characterised increasingly by 'niche' marketing. This differentiation trend will continue through a focus on individual consumers, particularly through the growing establishment and maintenance of customer databases. Rapp and Collins (1987), for instance, have introduced the concept of 'MaxiMarketing' and there is a growing interest in so-called 'relationship marketing'. Organisations are developing concerns for service and quality with a mosaic of desired individual consumption patterns now in existence. (For an overview of marketing concepts and strategies, see Dibb *et al* 1991).

Marketing maturity obviously varies by market sector (particularly the basic categorisation by industrial and consumer marketing) and by organisation. The need for this external orientation, however, is increasingly a competitive necessity, as more and better competition is found in all industries.

Simply stated, marketing objectives are concerned with combinations of existing and new products/services and markets, that is:

- existing products/services in existing markets;
- existing products/services in new markets;
- new products/services in existing markets;
- new products/services in new markets.

Baker (1990, page 8) suggested that

'*real* marketing has four essential features:

- start with the customer;
- long-term perspective;
- full use of *all* the company's resources;
- innovation.'

Behind all this, however, is one important component. The basic argument in this chapter is that information is a key strategic resource which needs to be managed for 'successful' marketing. Christopher *et al* (1980) summarised this view by saying:

> 'Good information is a facilitator of successful marketing, and indeed, seen in this light, marketing management becomes first and foremost an information processing activity.'

The traditional 'four Ps' of marketing illustrate the function's responsibility for managing the marketing mix. Marketing strategies are based conventionally on:

- Products;
- Price;
- Promotion;
- Place

Given the nature of the marketing function and assuming Christopher *et al* and many others to be correct, the availability of useful and actionable information is very important. Furthermore, it will become even more significant for organisations in the future. In fact, it is not unreasonable to suggest a fifth P, (data) Processing, that comprises data collection, data analysis and data presentation (see figure 8.1). Taking the argument further, a sixth P could be People, not only as end-consumers but also, in many services, as an integral part of the production/delivery process. Finally, it is relevant to note that retailing, which can be thought of as the marketing of products and services, is normally deemed by practitioners to be about 'location, location and location'.

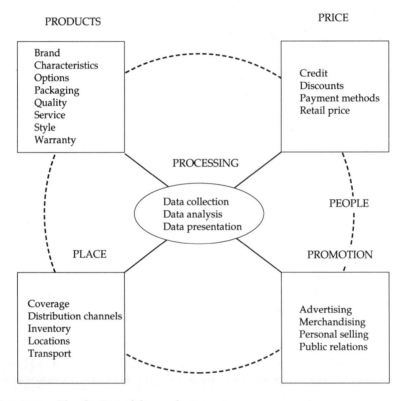

Figure 8.1   The 'Six P's' of the marketing mix

In this chapter, particular attention is concentrated on 'market analysis' (which is sometimes referred to as 'geodemographic' analysis; see Beaumont 1991 and Brown 1991 for introductory overviews), with illustrations taken from consumer marketing rather than industrial marketing. Geographically disaggregated market analysis has become increasingly important for organisations in order to be able to plan both tactically and strategically with regard to customers' needs and competitive threats. Yet, while much progress has been made since the initial, 1970s handling and repackaging of British Census of Population and market research data, the majority of the applications remain of a tactical nature. Few realise their potential business benefits. Such criticisms are not unique to the particular field of marketing: they could with justice be made more generally about many investments in computer-based information systems and their associated analyses. As a consequence of the specific shortcoming however, some consideration is given in this chapter to the nature of management decision-making and market analysis applications are described briefly to illustrate different systems. Existing shortcomings, specifically the focus on the demand side, are highlighted and possible future developments are explored. Throughout the discussion, the necessary spatial scale of analysis is highlighted, with particular reference being given to postal geography. Indeed, in the next section, a brief discussion of the context of Postcodes in marketing is provided. It should be stressed yet again that, for a marketeer, Postcodes are only a means to an end, rather than an end in themselves.

Spatial referencing

This topic has already been covered elsewhere in this book (see, for instance, chapters 2 and 5). Here it is addressed specifically from the viewpoint of marketing. In Britain, geographical referencing is founded on the OS's National Grid system. The available linkage between Postcodes and this reference system means that Postcodes become locationally flexible. This is vital, since, for marketing purposes, addresses and their Postcodes are the most appropriate spatial referencing system. While the OS system can provide a comprehensive coverage of the country, identifying a full range of features (such as houses, lakes, . . .), Postcodes are collections of delivery points addresses – the locations to which most goods and services are delivered and at which most are consumed. The success of Royal Mail's promotional activities about use of Postcodes (see, for instance, plate 4) ensures that most consumers know both their address and its Postcode. Despite its value, few people know, or can remember, a twelve figure OS coordinate of the middle of their home!

The OPCS/GRO(S) Central Postcode Directory (CPD) provides the main intermediate database for the locational linkages though the recent enhancements to the Postcode Address File may ensure that it becomes more widely used by marketeers. In terms of the locational referencing, the CPD provides the OS National Grid reference for the first address in each Postcode (see chapter 4). This is to a supposed accuracy of 100m resolution in England and Wales and of ten metres resolution in Scotland). With the advent of the Pinpoint Address Code (PAC; see chapter 4), supposed accuracy of one metre grid references are now available for over half of the postal addresses in England and Wales, primarily the South East and urban areas which are the areas likely to be of most value to marketeers.

Thus, if each Postcode is referenced by a National Grid coordinate, Census of Population EDs and Postcodes can be linked by simple proximity analyses. Hence it is possible to know approximately which Postcode is in which ED. While this linkage is derived computationally and some inaccuracies inherently result (see OPCS 1987 for a commentary on CPD inaccuracies and Openshaw (1989) for the shortcomings of proximity analyses), data collection enhancements are being undertaken to provide greater accuracy. For the 1991 Census of Population in England and Wales, returned questionnaires from the households in each ED are tagged with Postcodes. As a result, a Directory of Postcodes wholly or partly within each ED is being constructed and this will be much superior to that created by proximity analysis. The situation is more advanced still in Scotland where the individual Postcode boundaries are available in a digital form. A relevant development is that the ED boundaries for England and Wales are being digitised at the time of writing by two competing organisations, Graphical Data Capture Limited and by a joint group involving MVA Systematica and the London Research Centre, with the involvement of OS.

These geographical or spatial units are fundamental 'building blocks'. They are important for marketing purposes because it is necessary to be able to *describe* and to *locate* the target market of both existing and potential consumers. Typically, a range of fundamental questions must be answered by marketing management, including:

- who?
  - are our customers?
  - should our customers be?
  - are our competitors?

- what?
  - new/existing products and services should we develop?
  - new/existing market should we enter?

- where?
    - should we develop?
    - are our customers?
    - should we distribute our products and services?
    - are our competitors?

- why?
    - should consumers buy our products and services?
    - should we develop new products and services and/or enter new markets?
    - should we remain in existing markets?

The most desirable marketing information would measure 'disposable income'. Unhappily this is unavailable in Britain. In its absence, the Census of Population, which offers a comprehensive description of the socio-economic and demographic profile of households, has provided the foundation for assessing local market demand for different products and services by household type for the last 15 years.

As described in chapter 6, the geography of the Census of Population comprises approximately 130,000 EDs, each consisting of approximately 150 households. However, the geography of the business world is not EDs, which were determined for data collection purposes and linked to local government administration. Postal geography, which was devised to enable Royal Mail to automatically sort mail in the UK (see chapter 6), is more relevant and useful for market analysis. Table 8.1 presents average household and population sizes for different spatial units in the postal geography system (the example given below the table can be seen as a map in figure 5.4).

Table 8.1 A summary of Small User Postcodes in terms of national totals and averages *(Source: PAF on CD 1991/4)*

	Areas	Districts	Sectors	Units
Number	120	2,679	8,820	1,397,754
Households	183,000	8197	2490	15.71
Population	466,000	20,873	6,340	40.0
Example	MK	MK42	MK42 9	MK42 9LG

Though the Postcode is thus of considerable importance to marketeers, the use of a National Grid reference-based spatial linkage mechanism is necessary in practice because other types of geographies are also important in market analysis. For historical and structural reasons, for instance, many organisations have their own sales and administration territories. Unless these were built from the outset in terms of Postcodes, the only simple and low-effort way of achieving such a conversion is through use of the National Grid. The boundaries of any defined area of interest can be digitised by reference to the Grid; once this is done, census-based market analysis can then be undertaken through the allocation of EDs to describe the households' socio-economic and demographic profile and the market potential in the different territories.

In addition to the derivation of bespoke geographies as described above for individual organisations, a range of standard (digitised) geographies are available from the companies offering market analysis services (see appendix 2). These sets of areas include not only postal geography Areas, Districts and Sectors, but also:

- public sector/planning geographies;
  - local authorities;
  - health authority regions and districts;
  - (standard) economic planning regions;
  - urban areas as defined by the Office of Population Censuses and Surveys (OPCS) and the Department of the Environment;
  - travel-to-work areas;

- media geographies:
  - Independent Local Radio Station areas;
  - Incorporated Society of British Advertisers regions;
  - Broadcasters' Audience Research Board regions;
  - 'Plumby Brick' system for sales and distribution;

- retail geographies:
  - CACI's Local Expenditure Zones;
  - CACI's Shopping Centre Planner's 'primary', 'secondary' and 'tertiary' catchment areas;
  - Pinpoint's SHOPPIN boundaries;
  - drive time isochrones.

Computer-based information systems and management decision-making

The nature of management decisions affects the type of information required and thus also impacts upon the design and specification of a computer-based information system. The solution is not solely technological: it is primarily dependent on management's awareness of the real potential. Recent British research (for example, by Oasis 1989) indicates that the handling of marketing information is relatively poorly developed. This confirms the findings of a survey of US marketeers which found that a relatively unsophisticated tool, the Lotus 1-2-3 spreadsheet software, is the most frequently used (Higby and Farah 1991). Indeed, it is far from clear that information systems have been necessarily useful and relevant for management's decision-making in marketing, thus far at least. While it is straightforward to argue that particular information is, or should be, helpful for management's decision-making, it is much more complicated to know how and why a manager makes use of information provided by a computer-based system.

The manager and information

More generally, Mintzberg (1989, page 9) characterises much of his management writing as 'celebrating intuition'.

> 'If you ask managers what they do, they will most likely tell you that they plan, organise, coordinate and control. Then watch what they do. Don't be surprised if you can't relate what you see to those four words.'

He goes on (Mintzberg 1989, page 12) to highlight four myths, of which one is:

> 'Folklore: The senior manager needs aggregated information, which a formal management information system best provides.
>
> In keeping with the classical view of the manager as that individual perched on the apex of a regulated, hierarchical system, the literature's manager is to receive all important information from a giant, comprehensive MIS (Management Information System). But a look at how managers actually process information reveals a very

different picture. Managers have five media at their command: documents, telephone calls, scheduled and unscheduled meetings and observational tours.

Fact: Managers strongly favour the oral media, namely telephone calls and meetings'.

The capabilities of an individual manager's brain to receive, process, store, retrieve and apply effectively data varies enormously. Moreover, with the advances in both information and communications technologies and automatic data capture (for instance, retailers' Electronic Point of Sales (EPOS) data), it is becoming more important to recognise the brain's severe limitations to handle complicated decision-making tasks and dynamic business environments. Cognitive psychologists have demonstrated that more information is not necessarily helpful; in fact, in times of information 'overload', managers use less information in their decision-making than when having a near 'optimum' amount of information. For the distribution of free newspapers, for example, lists of addresses and Postcodes are probably too detailed; maps indicating Postcode Sectors or other areas for distribution are sufficient.

On-going research on human-computer interactions should allow the development of more 'user friendly' systems (Raper 1991). This will be a necessary, albeit not a sufficient, condition for enhanced information resources management. However, while some researchers have started to explore decision-making in relation to the use of information, the real relevance of this work to practising managers is unclear. Current efforts to research decision-making are overly academic, attempting to 'program it', seemingly not aligning academic interest in analysis with the manager's tasks of synthesis, understanding and of reduction of uncertainty. 'Successful' information systems, for instance, often succeed by making the specification of alternative decision options and their implications much clearer. Evidence is beginning to demonstrate that the resulting information can be deemed threatening (and sometimes unacceptable) to some managers. In considering future developments of computer-based information systems, therefore, it is important not to neglect the necessary investments in human capital and the requirements to explore new ways of working.

Because of all these factors, the failure fully to exploit (marketing) information systems is increasingly a non-technical issue. The 'information literacy' of managers and the 'information culture' of their organisations are key determinants. Piercy (1990, page 254), for instance, in his consideration of marketing information systems, suggests that

'• managers seek information to justify what has already been decided;

• marketing information may be used to make sales people 'properly optimistic';

• managers may seek information as a way of delaying decisions;

• marketing information may serve an 'organisational' function, for example, providing common ground or a shared frame of reference, acting as a collective memory, functioning as a stabilising factor or even providing reassurance.'

Marketing managers' knowledge and experience of the potential of information systems (particularly as more relevant data become available) are thus important constraints on their exploitation. Despite valiant efforts to eradicate them, there remain two opposing problems:

• the development of user expectations that are much greater than can be delivered (at least at a reasonable cost);

• the lack of user awareness about the effective and efficient use of information in marketing.

Types of management function

In the 'classic' work of Anthony (1965), managerial activities were classified into one of three categories. These have been influential in the subsequent development of thinking on management of information systems:

• strategic planning (goals, strategies and policies);

• management control (implementation of strategies);

• operational control (efficient and effective performance of individual tasks).

Examples of activities under these categories are given in Table 8.2.

In terms of the general development of business applications using information and communications technologies, the overall historical trend is from operational activities towards more strategic applications. Moreover, within an organisation, the stage of growth can vary by

Table 8.2   Typical planning, control and operational systems

Planning systems	capacity planning
	operating plans
	profits/earnings forecasts
	sales forecasting
Control systems	budgetary control
	inventory management
	management accounting
	sales analysis
Operational systems	order-entry processing
	purchase orders
	shop floor scheduling
	tracking shipping documents

function (with the accounting/finance function usually ahead, at least of the marketing function).

Using Anthony's classification, a useful framework is offered by Gorry and Scott Morton's (1989) differentiation between management planning and control activities, each with their different information requirements. Figure 8.2 summarises the relationships between different types of decisions and their information characteristics. Marketing planning and strategy decisions, for example, are relatively unstructured and require qualitative as well as quantitative information. By contrast, many market control activities, such as monitoring sales and inventories, require simple structured decisions based on quantitative data. Further differentiation with regard to information requirements relates to the time horizon, a future, rather than a current/historical perspective. Moreover, the required spatial resolution also varies by application. For instance, targeted direct mail campaigns based on secondary data are usually undertaken at the Postcode level; this situation is likely to change as more customer databases are established and maintained, allowing targeting at an individual address level. More general targeting, such as via coupons or 'free' newspapers, is likely to be at a Postcode Sector level or at a broader level.

Table 8.3 is illustrative of some of the information requirements for some marketing tasks, many of which need to be disaggregated geographically.

While many organisations have benefited from investments in information and communications technologies to support marketing, many other organisations have made costly errors or, at least, have not realised the true business potential of these investments. Certainly there

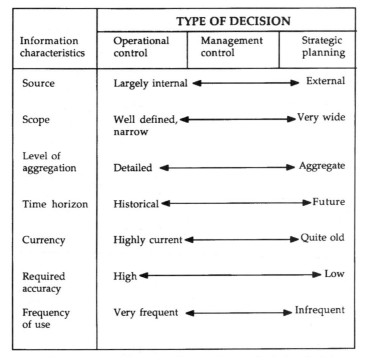

	TYPE OF DECISION		
Information characteristics	Operational control	Management control	Strategic planning
Source	Largely internal ◄――――――► External		
Scope	Well defined, narrow ◄――――――► Very wide		
Level of aggregation	Detailed ◄――――――► Aggregate		
Time horizon	Historical ◄――――――► Future		
Currency	Highly current ◄――――――► Quite old		
Required accuracy	High ◄――――――► Low		
Frequency of use	Very frequent ◄――――――► Infrequent		

Figure 8.2 Information requirements for market analysis by decision category *(Source: Gorry and Scott Morton 1989)*

Table 8.3 Information and marketing tasks *(Source: L K Parkinson and S T Parkinson 1987)*

Task	*Information Requirements*
Analysing the market	Sales/profit: - total - by products, area client - market rates of growth - cash flows by each segment Client attitudes: - brand awareness - brand loyalty Number of customers: - by product - by area - by purchasing patterns

Table 8.3 *(cont.)*

Task	Information Requirements
	Units sold per unit input:
	- advertising to sales ratio
	- personal selling effort to sales
	- shelf space to sales
Defining marketing	Sales/profit performance
objectives	Market Share
	Cash flows
	Competitive strengths/weaknesses
	Technical, legal, political and social influences on the market
	Resources and skills in the organisation
	Buyer loyalty
	Channel loyalty
	Customer needs and buying power
	Financial position
	Manufacturing competencies, capacity and flexibility
	Research and development strengths
Developing appropriate	Data on current strategies:
marketing strategies	- cost
	- effectiveness
	Identification of strategic options:
	- cost
	- potential effectiveness
	Targets
	Budgets
Controlling performance	Units sold per unit inputs:
	- advertising to sales ratios
	- personal selling effort to sales ratios
	- shelf space to sales ratios

are real practical difficulties in investment appraisal; all too frequently, however, abdication of responsibility occurs by saying such evaluations are too difficult or even impossible. Another perspective is that information has value, and the value of the same information varies by organisation, manager, application and over time. An associated difficulty is that marketing management often views information systems and their associated data as an administrative/business expense, rather than as a business investment. Much market analysis is thus carried out as 'one-off' projects which can be covered within the budgetary control of a junior/middle manager . The necessary re-orientation of management approaches, with positioning more at a strategic rather than an operational level, may well require the involvement of more senior management than typically occurs at present.

Databases, information and added value

Databases and information systems do not possess value from their existence *per se*, but from their application in different decision-making domains. Value should be measured against the 'productivity' of management as it feeds into their decision-making. The value of information could be seen as linking means and ends (with their ratio being often defined as 'productivity'). An enhanced definition of the organisation's customers should enable more efficient and effective targeting. A real difficulty exists, however, because the value of information for the decision-making process has to be anticipated when information systems and databases are specified, often long before they become operational. Yet value can only be really known after the impacts of the decisions can be assessed. Moreover, 'added value' can be created in a number of ways, including:

- the ability automatically, rather than manually, to search large databases (such as of customers' historical purchasing patterns);
- the creation of new information by the linkage of different databases (which is the essence of much market or geodemographic, analysis; chapter 5 describes the tools for doing such linkage);
- multiple different applications exploiting the same database(s) (which can result in shared construction costs).

As one example, consider the transaction processing of accounts of regular customers. Many organisations now provide their own company credit cards. The associated billing means that, as a minimum, the organisation holds customers' names, addresses and Postcodes. This large-scale, automatic processing has been necessary for the growth and development of many businesses. However, particularly as the databases are established over time, analysis of the records for marketing purposes provides an opportunity to 'cross-sell' additional products and services to existing, 'satisfied' customers and to promote these efficiently to potential customers. Linkage with other databases, such as market research data, can also assist in understanding of an organisation's positioning within an overall market.

Applications of market analysis systems

It is stressed that many of the different analyses completed under 'market analysis' do not have firm theoretical underpinnings and many research issues certainly exist which need to be addressed if the subject is to be founded more solidly in understanding rather than preconception. Another shortcoming is that no cost-benefit analysis has been completed of the use of management information systems and, specifically, no real examination has been made of the business impacts of data quality, such as inaccuracies in spatial referencing. However, marketeers *do* have real problems with regard to understanding their markets, their competitors and their customers (and potential customers) for their products and services; despite its imperfections, market analysis is proving relevant and useful to them. In practice, there are a range of generic application types that are applied across the different vertical markets, such as retailing, financial services and local government. While necessarily selective, a description of three application types is now presented:

- customer profiling;
- branch location analysis;
- direct mail.

In considering each one of these, attention is focused on the marketing aspects rather than technical issues *per se*.

Customer Profiling

While it may appear surprising, in practice, many organisations are unable to describe their existing customer base, let alone define their potential target. Through market analysis, it is possible to provide simple summaries of similar and different neighbourhood areas and make inferences about the households in a particular area.

There is no such thing as a single, ideal classification for a particular database, set of areas or set of phenomena of interest. Different purposes, for instance, are best met by purpose-specific classifications. However, the derivation of general-purpose so-called 'geodemographic discriminators' has been very useful (see Beaumont 1991 and Brown 1991 for more details). These classifications give descriptions of neighbourhoods based upon multiple input variables; the result is a consistent summary of residential areas in terms of their households' socio-economic and demographic profiles. Moreover, their linkage with market research data, such as the Target Group Index (TGI) and the National Readership Survey (NRS), means that expenditure estimates can be made for specific products and services.

As each address can be linked to a specific geodemographic category, customers' Postcodes can be used to provide a profile of an organisation's existing customer base. For example, CACI's ACORN ('A Classification Of Residential Neighbourhoods') was the first geodemographic discriminator to be developed, and figure 8.3 provides a summary profile of customers from two competing retailers, Miss Selfridge and Principles, based on TGI data. The latter has a relatively significant customer base in ACORN Group J, 'Affluent Suburban Housing'.

It should be stressed that such geodemographic discriminators are aggregate descriptions. The degree of homogeneity within a particular category varies enormously. In principle, the smaller the area, the more homogeneous it is likely to be though the constraint that census data are generally only available as far 'down' as EDs limits the level of market targeting (some firms have inferred the socio-economic characteristics of Postcodes from the census ED in which they lie and other information). This within-area variation can affect the efficiency of a marketing effort. If an area is highly varied, targeting is less likely to be successful than in one which is entirely homogeneous. Fortunately, the standard geodemographic discriminators are relatively cheap to use and *do* provide a consistent coverage of the country. To reduce the shortcomings of the standard area-based discriminators, attempts have been made (in mail order, for example) which use in-company data to provide greater precision than that provided by the consumers'/potential consumers' neighbourhood level: target marketing approaches have been developed to produce an individual level classification of the agents (see Brown and Batey 1990 for more details). The first-time availability of a Sample of Anonymised Records from the 1991 Census of Population should permit micro-(household) level analyses to be undertaken (see chapters 6 and 9). Such analyses should permit further examination of neighbourhood heterogeneity, although no individual household or even Postcoded data will be identifiable since this would contravene the legal basis on which census data are collected.

Branch Location Analysis

The ability to describe or estimate the catchment area of an existing or new branch is the basis of any branch location analysis, whether this is for hospitals, leisure facilities, schools or shops. Once the catchment area has been defined, it is possible to:

```
                     ANALYSIS BY ACORN FROM THE TARGET GROUP INDEX
 PRODUCT:   Shopped in Miss Selfridge last 12 mnths      BASE:        ADULTS
```

ACORN GROUP	PRODUCT (x1000)	%	BASE (x1000)	%	PENET. %	INDEX	0 50 100 150 200 225+
A Agricultural Areas	43	1.8	1400	3.1	3.1	57	AAAAAAAAAAA
B Modern Family Housing, Higher Incomes	404	16.7	7426	16.5	5.4	102	BBBBBBBBBBBBBBBBBBBB
C Older Housing of Intermediate Status	478	19.8	8027	17.8	6.0	111	CCCCCCCCCCCCCCCCCCCCCC
D Older Terraced Housing	107	4.4	1904	4.2	5.6	105	DDDDDDDDDDDDDDDDDDDDD
E Council Estates - Category I	266	11.0	5858	13.0	4.5	85	EEEEEEEEEEEEEEEEE
F Council Estates - Category II	149	6.2	4136	9.2	3.6	67	FFFFFFFFFFFFF
G Council Estates - Category III	130	5.4	2912	6.5	4.5	83	GGGGGGGGGGGGGGGGG
H Mixed Inner Metropolitan Areas	119	4.9	1598	3.5	7.4	139	HHHHHHHHHHHHHHHHHHHHHHHHHHHH
I High Status Non-family Areas	208	8.6	2068	4.6	10.0	187	IIIIIIIIIIIIIIIIIIIIIIIIIIIIIIIIIIIII
J Affluent Suburban Housing	374	15.5	7904	17.5	4.7	88	JJJJJJJJJJJJJJJJJJ
K Better-off Retirement Areas	140	5.8	1888	4.2	7.4	138	KKKKKKKKKKKKKKKKKKKKKKKKKKKK

ACORN TYPE	PRODUCT (x1000)	%	BASE (x1000)	%	PENET. %	INDEX	0 50 100 150 200 225+
A01 Agricultural Villages	32	1.3	1070	2.4	3.0	57	AAAAAAAAAAA
A02 Areas of Farms and Smallholdings	11	0.4	331	0.7	3.2	60	AAAAAAAAAAAA
B03 Post-war Functional Private Housing	112	4.6	1946	4.3	5.7	107	BBBBBBBBBBBBBBBBBBBBB
B04 Modern Private Housing, Young Families	98	4.1	1373	3.0	7.2	134	BBBBBBBBBBBBBBBBBBBBBBBBBBB
B05 Established Private Family Housing	108	4.5	2689	6.0	4.0	75	BBBBBBBBBBBBBBB
B06 New Detached Houses, Young Families	67	2.8	1274	2.8	5.3	98	BBBBBBBBBBBBBBBBBBBB
B07 Military Bases	19	0.8	143	0.3	13.5	252	BBBBBBBBBBBBBBBBBBBBBBBBBBBBBBBBBBBBBBBBBBBBBBB
C08 Mixed Owner-occupied & Council Estates	108	4.5	1620	3.6	6.7	124	CCCCCCCCCCCCCCCCCCCCCCCCC
C09 Small Town Centres & Flats above Shops	117	4.8	1738	3.9	6.7	126	CCCCCCCCCCCCCCCCCCCCCCCCC
C10 Villages with Non-farm Employment	104	4.3	2193	4.9	4.7	88	CCCCCCCCCCCCCCCCCC
C11 Older Private Housing, Skilled Workers	150	6.2	2477	5.5	6.0	113	CCCCCCCCCCCCCCCCCCCCCCC
D12 Unmodernised Terraces, Older People	76	3.1	1211	2.7	6.3	117	DDDDDDDDDDDDDDDDDDDDDDD
D13 Older Terraces, Lower Income Families	27	1.1	531	1.2	5.1	94	DDDDDDDDDDDDDDDDDDD
D14 Tenement Flats Lacking Amenities	5	0.2	162	0.4	2.9	54	DDDDDDDDDDD
E15 Council Estates, Well-off Older Workers	53	2.2	1756	3.9	3.0	56	EEEEEEEEEEE
E16 Recent Council Estates	79	3.2	1158	2.6	6.8	127	EEEEEEEEEEEEEEEEEEEEEEEEE
E17 Better Council Estates, Younger Workers	88	3.6	2121	4.7	4.1	77	EEEEEEEEEEEEEEE
E18 Small Council Houses, often Scottish	47	1.9	823	1.8	5.7	106	EEEEEEEEEEEEEEEEEEEEE
F19 Low Rise Estates in Industrial Towns	63	2.6	2086	4.6	3.0	57	FFFFFFFFFFF
F20 Inter-war Council Estates, Older People	51	2.1	1340	3.0	3.8	71	FFFFFFFFFFFFFF
F21 Council Housing, Elderly People	35	1.5	709	1.6	5.0	93	FFFFFFFFFFFFFFFFFFF
G22 New Council Estates in Inner Cities	52	2.1	795	1.8	6.5	121	GGGGGGGGGGGGGGGGGGGGGGGG
G23 Overspill Estates, Higher Unemployment	35	1.4	1149	2.5	3.0	57	GGGGGGGGGGG
G24 Council Estates with Some Overcrowding	24	1.0	641	1.4	3.7	68	GGGGGGGGGGGGGG
G25 Council Estates with Greatest Hardship	20	0.8	326	0.7	6.1	113	GGGGGGGGGGGGGGGGGGGGGGG
H26 Multi-occupied Older Housing	4	0.2	49	0.1	8.9	166	HHHHHHHHHHHHHHHHHHHHHHHHHHHHHHHHH
H27 Cosmopolitan Owner-occupied Terraces	42	1.7	464	1.0	9.0	169	HHHHHHHHHHHHHHHHHHHHHHHHHHHHHHHHHH
H28 Multi-let Housing in Cosmopolitan Areas	8	0.3	228	0.5	3.1	58	HHHHHHHHHHHH
H29 Better-off Cosmopolitan Areas	62	2.6	760	1.7	8.2	153	HHHHHHHHHHHHHHHHHHHHHHHHHHHHHHH
I30 High Status Non-family Areas	79	3.3	1037	2.3	7.6	142	IIIIIIIIIIIIIIIIIIIIIIIIIIIII
I31 Multi-let Big Old Houses and Flats	121	5.0	803	1.8	15.1	281	IIIIIIIIIIIIIIIIIIIIIIIIIIIIIIIIIIIIIIIIIIIIIII
I32 Furnished Flats, Mostly Single People	8	0.3	228	0.5	3.5	65	IIIIIIIIIIIII
J33 Inter-war Semis, White Collar Workers	133	5.5	2938	6.5	4.5	85	JJJJJJJJJJJJJJJJJ
J34 Spacious Inter-war Semis, Big Gardens	137	5.7	2529	5.6	5.4	101	JJJJJJJJJJJJJJJJJJJJ
J35 Villages with Wealthy Older Commuters	102	4.8	2529	5.6	1.9	40	JJJJJJJJ
J36 Detached Houses, Exclusive Suburbs	56	2.3	1077	2.4	5.2	96	JJJJJJJJJJJJJJJJJJJ
K37 Private Houses, Well-off Older Resident	62	2.6	1117	2.5	5.6	104	KKKKKKKKKKKKKKKKKKKKK
K38 Private Flats, Older Single People	78	3.2	771	1.7	10.1	188	KKKKKKKKKKKKKKKKKKKKKKKKKKKKKKKKKKKKKK
U39 Unclassified and Unmatched Respondents	0	0.0	0	0.0	0.0	0	U
TOTALS	2418	100.0	45122	100.0	5.4	100	

```
CACI COPYRIGHT RESERVED     CACI MARKET ANALYSIS DIVISION     (01) 404-0834
SURVEY PERIOD APR 1988 TO MAR 1989
```

```
                     ANALYSIS BY ACORN FROM THE TARGET GROUP INDEX
 PRODUCT:   Shopped in Principles in last 12 mnths       BASE:        ADULTS
```

ACORN GROUP	PRODUCT (x1000)	%	BASE (x1000)	%	PENET. %	INDEX	0 50 100 150 200 225+
A Agricultural Areas	57	2.7	1400	3.1	4.1	86	AAAAAAAAAAAAAAAAA
B Modern Family Housing, Higher Incomes	469	22.0	7426	16.5	6.3	133	BBBBBBBBBBBBBBBBBBBBBBBBBBB
C Older Housing of Intermediate Status	357	16.7	8027	17.8	4.4	94	CCCCCCCCCCCCCCCCCCC
D Older Terraced Housing	87	4.0	1904	4.2	4.5	96	DDDDDDDDDDDDDDDDDDD
E Council Estates - Category I	183	8.6	5858	13.0	3.1	66	EEEEEEEEEEEEE
F Council Estates - Category II	79	3.7	4136	9.2	1.9	40	FFFFFFFF
G Council Estates - Category III	77	3.6	2912	6.5	2.6	56	GGGGGGGGGGG
H Mixed Inner Metropolitan Areas	67	3.1	1598	3.5	4.2	89	HHHHHHHHHHHHHHHHHH
I High Status Non-family Areas	144	6.8	2068	4.6	7.0	147	IIIIIIIIIIIIIIIIIIIIIIIIIIIIII
J Affluent Suburban Housing	505	23.6	7904	17.5	6.4	135	JJJJJJJJJJJJJJJJJJJJJJJJJJJ
K Better-off Retirement Areas	112	5.2	1888	4.2	5.9	125	KKKKKKKKKKKKKKKKKKKKKKKKK

ACORN TYPE	PRODUCT (x1000)	%	BASE (x1000)	%	PENET. %	INDEX	0 50 100 150 200 225+
A01 Agricultural Villages	39	1.8	1070	2.4	3.6	77	AAAAAAAAAAAAAAA
A02 Areas of Farms and Smallholdings	18	0.8	331	0.7	5.4	115	AAAAAAAAAAAAAAAAAAAAAAA
B03 Post-war Functional Private Housing	104	4.9	1946	4.3	5.3	113	BBBBBBBBBBBBBBBBBBBBBBB
B04 Modern Private Housing, Young Families	89	4.1	1373	3.0	6.5	136	BBBBBBBBBBBBBBBBBBBBBBBBBBB
B05 Established Private Family Housing	162	7.6	2689	6.0	6.0	127	BBBBBBBBBBBBBBBBBBBBBBBBB
B06 New Detached Houses, Young Families	102	4.8	1274	2.8	8.0	168	BBBBBBBBBBBBBBBBBBBBBBBBBBBBBBBBBB
B07 Military Bases	13	0.6	143	0.3	9.0	189	BBBBBBBBBBBBBBBBBBBBBBBBBBBBBBBBBBBBBB
C08 Mixed Owner-occupied & Council Estates	65	3.1	1620	3.6	4.0	85	CCCCCCCCCCCCCCCCC
C09 Small Town Centres & Flats above Shops	93	4.3	1738	3.9	5.3	113	CCCCCCCCCCCCCCCCCCCCCCC
C10 Villages with Non-farm Employment	110	5.2	2193	4.9	5.0	106	CCCCCCCCCCCCCCCCCCCCC
C11 Older Private Housing, Skilled Workers	88	4.1	2477	5.5	3.6	75	CCCCCCCCCCCCCCC
D12 Unmodernised Terraces, Older People	58	2.7	1211	2.7	4.8	101	DDDDDDDDDDDDDDDDDDDD
D13 Older Terraces, Lower Income Families	11	0.5	531	1.2	2.0	43	DDDDDDDD
D14 Tenement Flats Lacking Amenities	18	0.8	162	0.4	11.2	236	DDDDDDDDDDDDDDDDDDDDDDDDDDDDDDDDDDDDDDDDDDDDDDDDD
E15 Council Estates, Well-off Older Workers	47	2.2	1756	3.9	2.7	56	EEEEEEEEEEE
E16 Recent Council Estates	43	2.0	1158	2.6	3.7	79	EEEEEEEEEEEEEEEE
E17 Better Council Estates, Younger Workers	63	2.9	2121	4.7	3.0	63	EEEEEEEEEEEEE
E18 Small Council Houses, often Scottish	30	1.4	823	1.8	3.6	76	EEEEEEEEEEEEEEE
F19 Low Rise Estates in Industrial Towns	27	1.3	2086	4.6	1.3	27	FFFFFF
F20 Inter-war Council Estates, Older People	16	0.7	1340	3.0	2.7	56	FFFFFFFFFFF
F21 Council Housing, Elderly People	16	0.7	709	1.6	2.2	47	FFFFFFFFF
G22 New Council Estates in Inner Cities	35	1.6	795	1.8	4.4	93	GGGGGGGGGGGGGGGGGGG
G23 Overspill Estates, Higher Unemployment	32	1.0	1149	2.5	1.9	40	GGGGGGGG
G24 Council Estates with Some Overcrowding	15	0.7	641	1.4	2.4	50	GGGGGGGGGG
G25 Council Estates with Greatest Hardship	15	0.7	326	0.7	1.5	33	GGGGGGG
H26 Multi-occupied Older Housing	1	0.0	49	0.1	2.0	44	HHHHHHHH
H27 Cosmopolitan Owner-occupied Terraces	18	0.8	464	1.0	3.8	80	HHHHHHHHHHHHHHHH
H28 Multi-let Housing in Cosmopolitan Areas	21	1.0	325	0.7	6.4	135	HHHHHHHHHHHHHHHHHHHHHHHHHHH
H29 Better-off Cosmopolitan Areas	28	1.3	760	1.7	3.7	79	HHHHHHHHHHHHHHHH
I30 High Status Non-family Areas	46	2.1	1037	2.3	4.4	93	IIIIIIIIIIIIIIIIIII
I31 Multi-let Big Old Houses and Flats	78	3.7	803	1.8	9.7	206	IIIIIIIIIIIIIIIIIIIIIIIIIIIIIIIIIIIIIIIIII
I32 Furnished Flats, Mostly Single People	21	1.0	228	0.5	9.0	191	IIIIIIIIIIIIIIIIIIIIIIIIIIIIIIIIIIIIII
J33 Inter-war Semis, White Collar Workers	190	8.9	2938	6.5	6.5	137	JJJJJJJJJJJJJJJJJJJJJJJJJJJ
J34 Spacious Inter-war Semis, Big Gardens	160	7.5	2529	5.6	6.3	133	JJJJJJJJJJJJJJJJJJJJJJJJJJJ
J35 Villages with Wealthy Older Commuters	72	3.4	1359	3.0	5.3	112	JJJJJJJJJJJJJJJJJJJJJJ
J36 Detached Houses, Exclusive Suburbs	83	3.9	1077	2.4	7.7	162	JJJJJJJJJJJJJJJJJJJJJJJJJJJJJJJJ
K37 Private Houses, Well-off Older Resident	57	2.7	1117	2.5	5.1	108	KKKKKKKKKKKKKKKKKKKKK
K38 Private Flats, Older Single People	55	2.6	771	1.7	7.1	151	KKKKKKKKKKKKKKKKKKKKKKKKKKKKKK
U39 Unclassified and Unmatched Respondents	0	0.0	0	0.0	0.0	0	U
TOTALS	2136	100.0	45122	100.0	4.7	100	

```
CACI COPYRIGHT RESERVED     CACI MARKET ANALYSIS DIVISION     (01) 404-0834
SURVEY PERIOD APR 1988 TO MAR 1989
```

Figure 8.3 ACORN geodemographic discriminators in the customer profiles of two competing retailers *(Source: CACI Ltd)*

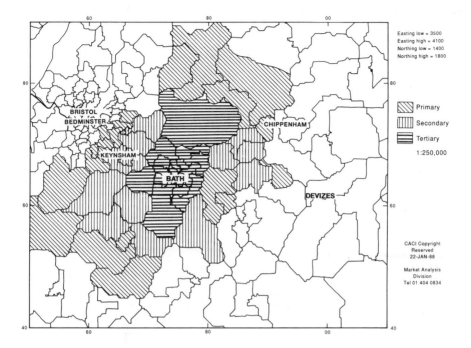

Figure 8.4   The Bath catchment area for customers of stores in different locations, showing primary, secondary and tertiary zones of catchment. *(Source: CACI Ltd)*

- describe the profile of the households in the catchment area;
- estimate the local market demand of the catchment area for the specific products and services of interest;
- estimate local market share (or branch sales) for the particular products and services given the competitive position.

With a knowledge of a sample of customers' Postcodes from, say, the customer origin surveys undertaken by many organisations, proximity analyses can be completed to indicate the mean distance which customers travel to patronise a branch (see figure 8.4 describing the pattern of patronage of different branches, based on individual Postcodes of the customers; while the Postcode level is very helpful graphically, the analysis is usually undertaken at a Postcode Sector level). Such proximity analyses are necessary to examine the extent to which convenience/accessibility to a branch determines patronage. For example, in addition to looking at the distances which customers travel to a branch, it is straightforward and valuable to examine whether customers go to their nearest source of service or whether there is some customer loyalty. Results indicate that, for many applications, straight-line or road network distances are inappropriate and it is necessary to use travel time distances. Another factor is the timing of journey flows. Most analyses are founded on spatial interactions between a household's residential location and the branch network; the standard and most widely-used census data are population statistics based on area of residence. However, work-based rather than home-based trips are significant for many services and must be considered explicitly. CACI's WORKFORCE database, for example, shows that the approximately 10,000 permanent residents in the Holborn district of London are increased by about ten times through the daily influx of office workers.

A relatively new development so far as management support is concerned are the so-called Spatial Decision Support Systems, which have grown out of the Decision Support Systems (DSSs) available for a number of years (Densham 1991). So far as the practice is concerned, Beaumont and Clarke (1992) provide two anonymised case studies which show the business power of DSS for strategic marketing planning. Their examples are a major high street retailer and a vehicle importer and distributor. In the context of this discussion, it is appropriate to note that the DSSs had two main components, a national information system and a predictive modelling capability. Data collection, interrogation and analyses are completed at different spatial scales, with customer accounts founded on the Postcode of residence and the local demand estimates generated for Postcode Districts.

It is important to note that a description and understanding of catchment areas and customers' profiles for existing branches not only provides a consistent and operational basis for evaluating existing performance, especially the mix of products and services. It also offers a foundation from which to rank potential new locations. Key indicators can be derived to monitor progress, and 'under performers' with regard to both their relative and absolute potential, disaggregated by products and services, can be highlighted directly. Branch performance analysis and site evaluation can now be completed with the rigour used for other investment decisions that involve millions of pounds. In some aspects of this, Postcodes play a critical role.

Direct Marketing

Direct marketing has lost its 'Cinderella-image' of the early 1980s and is now recognised as an important tool in the marketeers' armoury in its own right. As the name suggests, direct marketing involves selling goods or services to consumers without the conventional involvement of a retailer or a wholesaler. It can be subdivided as:

- direct mail;
- telephone selling;
- direct response advertising ('off-the-page');
- direct personal selling;
- door to door distribution.

These approaches can be employed separately or in combination. For example, direct mail or the telephone can be used to generate leads for salesmen to follow up; British Telecom's Phone Disc CD which provides telephone numbers based on retrieval keys such as the Postcode is important in this respect and is described in chapter 4. Direct mail is the most important medium and attention here is restricted to it. It is estimated to be just under 10% of total advertising expenditure. Over 60% of this expenditure can be attributed to four business sectors:

- mail order companies;
- manufacturing companies;
- financial services;
- retailers.

The rapid growth in direct mail can be related to the effective handling of databases of customers which are organised in terms of their addresses plus the developments in geodemographic analyses to assist marketing management. Perhaps understandably, consumer resistance to direct mail solicitation is greater in the UK than it is in the US. The scale of activity in the UK does not reach that in the US, in part because of the geography of its market, the nature of business and cultural differences. But households in Britain also receive a significantly lower number of direct mail items than do households in other European countries. The scope for further expansion may therefore still be considerable. In passing, the growth of direct mail has greater relevance for Royal Mail than simply the use of the Postcode: a significant fraction of the increase in mail volume shown in figure 3.1 is attributable to direct mailing.

The influence of market analysis on mailing is exemplified by Royal Mail's award of a contract to CACI to develop an advanced sorting system for its Mailsort range of services, a discount scheme for large mail users (see chapter 4). Mailsort, which has been developed to enhance the quality of Royal Mail's delivery mechanism, has three options:

- Mailsort 1: for delivery the next working day;

- Mailsort 2: for delivery within three working days;

- Mailsort 3: for delivery within seven working days
  (plus a deferred delivery option).

As every domestic address in the country has a geodemographic description, it is straightforward to complete a direct mail campaign once the target market has been defined. It is obviously important for the cost-effective success of any direct marketing campaign that the medium is directed towards those households most likely to become customers. Direct mail costs for a mailshot of a specified quantity are virtually fixed whatever the take-up rate and thus any improvement in the conversion rate is directly beneficial to the business. It is, of course, important to note that market analysis will never be successful if the product/service offered or the associated creative promotion material does not appeal! One way of improving take-up is to personalise the letter. Mailings can be personalised (e.g. by adding names) through linkage with the Electoral Register. Added value can also be provided by using geodemographic discriminators to enhance existing customer lists: the British Investors Database, for instance, is available cross-referenced by the SUPER PROFILE geodemographic categories.

For direct mail, success or failure is measured primarily by the response rate, whether it is in terms of expressed interest or actual client conversion. To extend the market penetration, it is necessary to be as efficient as possible in the targeting. For instance, CACI's SPECTRA system is designed to maximise response rates and involves two stages:

- an expanded customer profiling system, using the addresses of post respondents from either previous mailing campaigns or a test mailing, to identify discriminators that most influence response;

- a prospect scoring system, which combines these discriminators, to predict the potential responsiveness of any address to future mailings.

Industry expectations of a 'successful' direct mail campaign are for a response rate of between one and three %, although the break-even point is the key factor and this varies according to the industry and the specific promotional campaign. The use of geodemographic discriminators has however helped companies to achieve significant success beyond these levels in reaching the identified target audience. For example, to promote an Autumn 1984 'Lets Go' brochure for weekend breaks, the English Tourist Board mailed to the following specified ACORN categories:

- B5 - 'Modern private housing, older children';

- B6 - 'New detached houses, young families';

- I30- 'High status areas, few children';

- J34- 'Spacious inter-war semis, big gardens';

- J36- 'detached houses, exclusive suburbs'.

A 13.5% response was achieved for this mailing campaign. On average, each response cost £1.51, which was significantly cheaper than 'off-the-page' advertising or inserts which ranged between £2.68 and £6.75 per response.

We pointed out at the start of this section that well-designed special-purpose classifications would normally be more efficient than general-purpose ones. To illustrate this, we can demonstrate the relative efficacy of Pinpoint Analysis Limited's market-specific FiNPiN over its general-purpose discriminator, the Wealth Indicator. The anonymised results from a 100,000 mailout promoting home loans are summarised in two tables below. For the original campaign, the target market was defined in terms of specified bands of Pinpoint's Wealth Indicator. In aggregate and at the time of the response analysis, the response was slightly above 1.5%; by financial direct marketing standards, this campaign was viewed as a success (see table 8.4 below).

Table 8.4 Wealth Indicator Profile of the Response Analysis *(Source: Pinpoint Analysis)*

	Frequency	*Frequency*	
Wealth Band	Distribution of mailout	Distribution of response	Response rate
65.1–70.0	39,601	585	1.47
70.1–75.0	29,498	445	1.50
75.1–80.0	16,763	259	1.55
80.1–85.0	8,985	150	1.67

This campaign was re-profiled using FiNPiN, and it is summarised for the main neighbourhood categories in table 8.5.

Table 8.5 FiNPiN Profile of the Response Analysis *(Source: Pinpoint Analysis)*

FiNPiN	Response Rate	Percentage of UK households
Four-level classification		
Active	4.0	20.1
Informed	2.6	25.9
Conscious	0.2	27.1
Passive	0.0	26.9
Forty-level classification		
1 'Wealthy' families with older children	6.3	2.0
2 'Wealthy' families	7.8	2.2
3 'Families' with young children and two working adults	4.8	1.9
4 'Wealthy' families with students and older children	3.1	2.7
5 'Families' with growing children and two working adults	9.3	2.8
6 'Wealthy' empty-nesters	1.7	2.6
7 'Wealthy' retired	0.3	5.9

At the four-level classification, the direct relationship between interest in the products and the degree of financial activity is clear. The finer discriminatory power of FiNPiN, however, is demonstrated at the forty-level within the 'Financially Active' category. Not surprisingly, the financially secure savers are relatively less interested in the new home loans products, particularly so for the 'wealthy retired'. Indeed, there were eight FiNPiN types (accounting in total for approximately 21.8% of Great Britain's households) in which the response rate was more than twice the original average response.

For completeness, it is important to comment on direct mail's apparent bad name in some quarters. 'Junk' mail is highlighted when companies send mail to people who have moved away months or years ago, or worse, to those who have died and left relatives at the same site. The Mailing Preference Service (MPS) exists as a central body to register individuals who do not want to receive any unsolicited mail. While there are time lapses in its updating process, the files from the MPS are available to member organisations to clear mailing lists. Individuals may also elect to receive more direct mail about specific topics. More generally, some positive action is required to enhance the perceived professionalism of this growing industry. A key issue relates to the ability of list brokers to update their systems. In this, there already exist real opportunities for better and more informed practice. As an example, we consider the two issues of 'gone-aways' and 'deaths' separately. Because the Electoral Roll is the only current database with a supposed national (names and address) coverage, we also need to examine some of its characteristics.

The scale of household movement prior to the recession which began in 1990/91 was approximately two million or 10% of households moving each year. This means that the 'gone-aways' are a real practical problem, although some companies endeavour to clear their lists using the MPS or returned items. However, no central database exists currently that is explicitly concerned with household movement. The annual Electoral Roll does permit some updating, but neither comprehensively nor on, say, a monthly basis. Moreover, up to 20% of the electorate in some parts of the country is believed to have absented themselves from the Roll because of their fear that the record will be used to locate non-payers of the Community (or Poll) Tax. One alternative would be to exploit Royal Mail service for redirecting mail but this would require 'movers' to permit their names to be passed onto the direct mail industry. In some other countries in Europe, this redirection service is available free of charge and the majority of 'movers' use it (compared with approximately a quarter of all movers in Britain). After a mailing campaign 'gone-away' returns are sometimes pooled by some computer bureaux operating so-called Nixie banks; however, this up-dating process is directly dependent on the coverage of the original mailing and the actual returns.

At the time of writing, the best means of cleaning a general mailing list is to use the annually up-dated Electoral Roll, with all its known weaknesses. This register is collected by local authorities and at least four different companies enter the data into their computers (although inevitably, there are delays of months before completion). De-duplication is an important process in maximising the utility of such lists. Without it, addressees sometimes receive a single mailout two or three times because their name is stored in different formats, such as:

- Professor John R Beaumont;

- Professor John Beaumont;

- Professor J R Beaumont;

- Professor J Beaumont;

- Professor Beaumont.

Using computer processing power to match names and addresses on a probabilistic basis, it is possible to suggest that this is the same person and to send him only one mailing!

Ultimately, the attention paid to the accuracy of mailing lists will be driven only by market forces or political factors. Improvements in lists *should* enhance response (and also reduce annoyance), thereby reducing overall costs. Once the economics involved in this and large-scale cleaning process become attractive, a single company will take the lead and their mailing list will become the new *de facto* standard. There is a case for government encouraging such a situation to come about either by financial or legislative mechanisms.

Finally, will address lists become available from national companies with a large coverage of consumers' names and addresses? After the divestiture of American Telephone and Telegraph in 1984, the AT&T Consumer Connection was established to explore the opportunities to use the company's database as a new revenue stream. British Telecom's Yellow Pages are already available for business-to-business direct marketing; notwithstanding regulatory constraints, British Telecom, British Gas, and other companies all have personal data that would help establish up-to-date consumer databases for marketing, although note that direct mailing by third parties is already carried out in billings. They are, of course, in competition with Royal Mail, since that organisation already holds an address database which can be manipulated to produce address labels or enhance a company's address database (see chapter 4).

Concluding comments : future outlook

To date, applications of market analysis have been concerned primarily

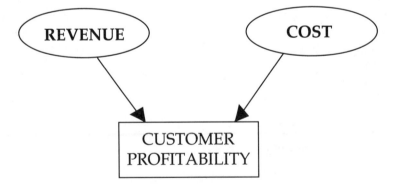

Figure 8.5 The components of profitability; GIS is often used to maximise revenue but is less frequently used by marketeers to predict the likely profitability of new initiatives

with the demand side. This has been founded on geodemographic and market research data, estimating aggregate expenditure on specific goods and services for defined local catchment areas. However (as is illustrated by figure 8.5), if we can estimate expenditure, why should we not attempt to estimate the profitability of the target customer market?

The recurrent failure to incorporate costs in market analysis is very surprising, not only because they also have an explicit geographical dimension but also because much of the data needed is available. The demand/supply interface must be explored explicitly; indeed, a broad definition of marketing should recognise it as mutually beneficial and reciprocal exchange relationships. A sensible business extension to current market analysis would therefore be to provide information on 'target customer profitability'. The argument is developed here through reference to retailers' recent interest in Direct Product Profitability (DPP). Gross margin profit is an inadequate business performance measure and, in practice, it is often estimated rather than actual. As Table 8.6 shows, other direct costs can be included in any analysis.

Table 8.6   Derivation of Direct Product Profitability

	Sales	
-	Cost of Goods Sold	
=	Gross margin	
+	Discounts and Allowances	
=	Realised margin	
-	Warehouse costs	*Direct*
-	Transport costs	*Product*
-	Store operations costs	*Costs*
-	Inventory holding costs	
=	Direct Product Profitability	

For long-term success, vision and management are necessary. Successful organisations in the future will be those that provide an added value, quality service to customers. Marketing is critical to commercial success in many fields and is hence an important corporate activity, dependent increasingly on the management of information. The (marketing) information systems must support not only management's decision-making but, increasingly in the future, also relationships with customers, suppliers and possibly 'collaborating competitors'. As information and communications technologies are used increasingly for supply chain management by electronic linkage of customers and suppliers, the resulting data collected in 'real-time' and suitably summarised will provide new applications opportunities. This is particularly true of those which can enhance an organisation's customer service quality.

It seems highly likely that, as marketing managers learn about the benefits of and needs for information for their decision-making, strategic information management for marketing is likely to develop further. The technology platform for the next decade (in the form of GIS) is already available and proven, although its full exploitation remains elusive for the majority of organisations because of their failure to align such investments with their overall business strategy. With more information-literate managers and enhanced information products, much of the standard market analyses will in future be undertaken in-house by organisations. The systems and some of the data, such as Census of Population data, address files and Postcodes, will be viewed increasingly as commodities. The 'added value' will be provided through applications which improve management decision-making. Current Postcode-based analyses may be superseded by some applications with address-level matching in organisations' customer databases, say in teleshopping but, as we have indicated above, the confidentiality and privacy considerations are not trivial.

Figure 8.6 'Alouette' wine label with addressing in UK and French Postcodes only!

As any information system's power is dependent directly on data, it is important to plan tomorrow's information systems in the appreciation that data availability and quality will be enhanced greatly. (In actual fact, many organisations design their information systems for today's business environment!)   Both the quantity and quality of data from within organisations will increase enormously; as the 'tradeable information' sector is developed by the government (see appendix 3), secondary data sources will also increase and Royal Mail can play an important role in this evolution.

The problems for management in marketing can be classified as:

- the definition and analysis of (local) markets;
- the integration of marketing with other business functions within the organisation and as a component of organisational change;
- the trade-off between short-term revenue requirements and longer-term (local) market share considerations; (see Brownlie 1991 for more details).

Ultimately, however, such developments will only provide real business benefits if the management of (marketing) information is seen as a strategic, corporate issue which is driven by senior executives. 'Marketing' as a concept is linked inextricably to economic demand/supply conditions which differ geographically; it has developed with a clear and strong normative element under an 'analysis-planning-control' framework. Based on what is postulated above, there is no longer the need for decision-makers in marketing to do without access to the information they require to perform their duties.   None of their problems are new, but the risks associated with their decision-making are heightened in today's competitive business environment. The important roles of Postcodes in all of this are as a framework for describing different parts of a market and as a means of delivering certain types of goods to consumers (see figure 8.6 for an esoteric example). In the longer term, however, Royal Mail's address database may become as critical to marketeers as are the Postcodes at present!

CHAPTER 9

A gallery of Postcode
applications

Introduction

A Postcode begins life as a means to speeding the sorting and delivery of
mail. That is what it was designed for and is its primary purpose. As we
have seen, however, the Postcode system has a number of attributes which
raise intriguing questions as to whether it can be put to use in areas for
which it was not originally intended. Such questions may be raised in a
research context, in which case researchers are exploring the
characteristics and accuracy of Postcodes against other data sets; or they
may be raised in relation to applied work in which case practitioners are
probably using some aspect of Postcodes as a surrogate measure for data
that do not exist in a more appropriate form. More often it is a mixture of
these two that motivates those working with Postcodes.

The main attributes of Postcodes which are attractive to researchers and
practitioners alike are:

- they are part of a clear hierarchy of geographic areas, some of which
  are quite accurately mapped;

- they relate, at the lowest level in the hierarchy (the Unit Postcode), to
  very small and hence highly adaptable areas;

- they are geographically referenced to quite a high degree of
  resolution and these grid references are computer readable;

- they relate to the well defined notion of a 'delivery point' which may
  be a residential unit or a large (i.e. commercial) user.

In Scotland, of course, these attributes are enhanced to a very considerable degree by the fact that the Postcode system is integrated into the census data collecting and reporting system.

In this chapter, the aim is to describe a selection of ways in which Postcodes have been used by practitioners in various fields: town planners, geographers, educationists, market analysts, statisticians and others. Rather than review a large number of applications of Postcodes in brief, we have chosen to present shortened accounts, mainly in the words of the original authors, in order to give an idea of the research context in which the application is embedded. Some of the sections are based upon more than one source and this is indicated appropriately at the head of each section. We have chosen accounts which seem to us to be excellent of their kind and have, within the bounds of considerably shortening each account, basically used the authors' own words. We are most grateful that the authors agreed to this modest plagiarism! This process of maintaining the research or applications context of each account serves to underline the point that whatever assessment is made of the attributes of Postcodes is in relation to an application for which Postcodes were not originally intended. This may be unfair in one sense. In another it highlights areas where modifications or improvements to Postcodes might have very considerable benefits.

A final point: this chapter is by no means exhaustive of the possible applications to which Postcodes can be put (see Harrison 1986 for an early bibliography). Our suspicion is that this is limited only by the ingenuity of the researcher or information manager who needs to use this source of data. The chapter does not include, for example, the use of Postcodes in customer advice on retail branch locations, or store catchment area definitions, or in ascertaining the geographical range (in terms of client base), for communications systems, or the many variants of their use in market research (see chapter 8). No doubt some readers know of even more ingenious applications for georeferenced Postcodes. We would be pleased to hear about them.

Postcodes in Geodemographics

Title: Exploring Geodemographics
Author: **Peter Brown**
Source: I Masser and M Blakemore (eds) *Handling Geographical Information*, Longman, 1991

Title: *DEFINE User Manual*
Author: **Susan Squires**
Source: Infolink Limited, Croydon, 1988

The field of market analysis known as 'geodemographics' saw its most rapid development in the early 1980s. It derived from recognition of the enormous commercial value of area or neighbourhood classification schemes in distinguishing variations in consumer behaviour and as a tool for use in target marketing and related marketing activities. The ability of commercial concerns to exploit this market potential derived essentially from four things: the spread of cheaper computing power, the publication (usually in computer readable form) of census Small Area Statistics (SAS) for Enumeration Districts, the availability of the PAF and the ability to make the link between SAS and Postcodes via georeferencing. Today, the applications of geodemographics are legion and include, in the private sector, market research and segmentation, target advertising, credit scoring, store location planning, site finding and optimisation of store catchment area ranging. In the public sector geodemographics are used by central and local government, the National Health Service, the police and emergency planning services and many others (see chapter 8).

In fact, the principles lying behind geodemographics date back to the early part of the century when geographers and sociologists in the US examined patterns present in urban census tract data (see, for example, Park *et al* 1925). In the 1950s more systematic methods were employed in analysing census area data in an effort to develop theories about the social structure of cities. In the UK, the appearance of 'SAS' data from the census for the first time in 1966, the improvements to them in the 1971 and 1981 censuses and vastly improved data handling capabilities meant that geodemographic-type studies could embrace the country as a whole, not just the cities.

Gradually, however, the social theoretical side to this work fell away and it came to be dominated by empirical, more practical, concerns. Even so, geographers and others continued to sound a note of caution over aspects of the interpretation of geodemographic products both as regards the underlying theory (Knox, 1978) and the statistical techniques utilised.

In particular, it should be recognised that the use of census data and sophisticated statistical methods does not mean that geodemographics is a completely objective methodology. It involves making subjective choices in several areas including the number and type of input variables, the way these variables are 'clustered' together and the cut-off points used in mapping the resulting clusters. In relation to the 1981 Census for England and Wales there was, as we have seen, an element of error involved in allocating Postcodes to EDs, though this should be significantly reduced when the geodemographic systems are revised using 1991 Census data (see chapter 6). Also of importance is the fact that, because geodemographics are area based, it cannot be assumed that the characteristics of individuals exactly match the characteristics of the areas in which they reside. Amongst geographers this is known as the 'ecological fallacy' (Openshaw 1984).

As might be expected, the firms in the geodemographic field have successfully turned the flexibility of the methodology to their advantage and offer a varying range of products based on different input variables and area groupings. Most offer a census ED to Unit Postcode linkage capability and hence can be used to incorporate other data of various kinds, including the client's own customer data. First in the field and still the market leaders were CACI with their ACORN (A Classification Of Residential Neighbourhoods) system, which developed into a number of associated specialist products such as INSITE, MONICA and WORKFORCE. Other firms with variants of geodemographic systems are CCN with MOSAIC, PINPOINT with PiN and CDMS with SUPERPROFILES and Infolink with DEFINE.

The Infolink DEFINE system provides a typical example of how geodemographics works, with a significant 'add-on' brought about via data linkage. First, an assignment is made of Unit Postcodes to EDs using one of the methods described previously. Then some 90 variables from the 1981 Census are statistically grouped together using a technique known as principle components analysis. This results in a number of census types which are further classified into census groups. On this basis Infolink assigns a three-digit code to every residential address in the UK (some 24 million in all). The first code (two characters) provides the census based demographic information. This comprises ten broadly tenure-based categories ranging from 'Affluent Owner Occupiers' through to 'Military Personnel', which are in turn broken down into 47 neighbourhood types such as 'high income, high status owner occupiers' and 'semi-skilled and un-skilled workers with young families.' Two examples of census groups are mapped at Unit Postcode level for the Norwich urban area in Figures 9.1 and 9.2. The first shows the pattern of DEFINE Group '0' ('Affluent Owner Occupiers') and the second DEFINE

Group '2' ('Poorest Owner Occupiers'). The geographical distinctions between the two groups in 1981 are quite clear. The third digit in the DEFINE code is a classification of financial and Electoral Registration data for Postcodes based on Infolink's own databases.

Infolink claims that DEFINE 'lets you learn more about your existing customers and enables you to recruit relevant new ones. It offers greater accuracy, flexibility and efficiency in the world of Direct Marketing'. Even so, the DEFINE User Manual takes care to point out that DEFINE codes are an area classification, not a classification of individuals and it cannot be assumed that all individuals in a particular area share the characteristics of the demographic code for that area.

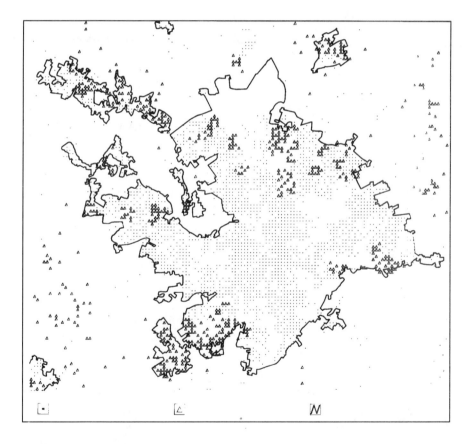

Figure 9.1   DEFINE code '0' for Norwich urban area: Affluent Owner Occupiers *(Source: Infolink)*

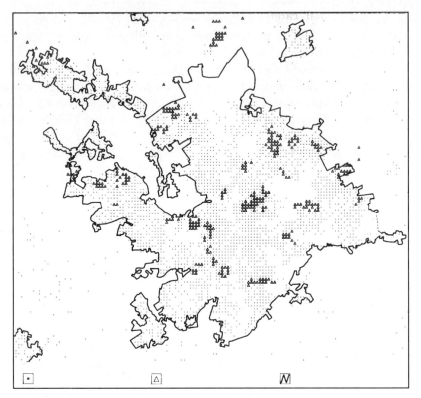

Figure 9.2 DEFINE code '2' for Norwich urban area: Poorest Owner Occupiers
(Source: Infolink)

Postcodes in Community Health Care

Title: GIS and Community Health Care: a case study of geriatric service provision
Authors: **Paul Dowie, Susan Koval, Peter Burnhill and Richard Healey**.
Source: *Proceedings, European Geographical Information Systems Conference EGIS '91, Vol I, pp 267-277.* Utrecht.

Over the past five years there have been several reviews of health and social service provision carried out by the government. Two dealt in particular with aspects of care in the community rather than in institutions: *Community Care, Agenda for Action* (Griffiths 1988) and *Caring for People* (Department of Health 1989). The former, the Griffiths Report, identified two principal objectives of community care: to enable an individual to remain in his/her own home wherever possible, rather than be cared for in a hospital or residential home, and to provide more support to 'informal' carers such as family, friends and neighbours. The broader aim of community care was to 'integrate all the resources of a geographical area in order to support the individuals within it'. Such resources might include informal carers, NHS and personal social services and organised voluntary effort as well as sheltered housing, the local social security office, the church, local clubs and so on (Griffiths 1988, p.5-6).

The ESRC Regional Research Laboratory (RRL) for Scotland based in the University of Edinburgh collaborated with the Lothian Health Board, Edinburgh District Council Community Services and Planning Department and Lothian Regional Council Social Work Department to assess the geography of the administration of community care services in Edinburgh and to make recommendations on the information needed to administer these services more efficiently. The study was basically concerned with inter-agency collaboration and sought answers to the following questions:

- how far do existing service area boundaries in the three organisations overlap?
- what other area boundaries are relevant to the three organisations?
- what is the smallest most appropriate geographical unit for information collection and dissemination between organisations?

The local and regional government organisations involved in the study organised their service area boundaries around either electoral ward boundaries or Postcode boundaries. As we have seen, the latter were particularly important as since 1981 they had been an integral part of the geography of the census in Scotland. The availability of digitised boundaries for Unit Postcodes which related to small area population statistics from the 1991 Census meant that an approach based in Geographical Information Systems could be used in the analysis. It also provided an opportunity to introduce this new technology into the organisations concerned.

Building Service Areas

A GIS database was therefore assembled by the RRL Scotland group. This contained the topologically structured boundaries of the 62 wards and 90 Postcode Sectors into which Edinburgh is divided, the road and railway network and extensive land uses such as parks and various demographic variables from the census associated with wards and Unit Postcodes. Two analyses using the GIS were carried out: one designed to produce a more appropriate set of service area boundaries, the other to examine the accessiblity of services to a population 'in need'.

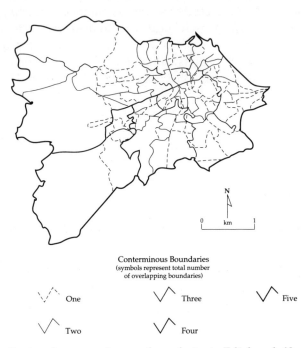

Conterminous Boundaries
(symbols represent total number
of overlapping boundaries)

One   Three   Five

Two   Four

Figure 9.3   Conterminous service area boundaries in Edinburgh *(Source: Dowie et al 1991)*

An 'overlay' of boundaries and their digital integration made it possible to establish 'membership tables' for both boundaries and areas. As figure 9.3 shows, there are few boundaries that are 'conterminous'. However, what emerged from the map when the road and rail network was introduced into the analysis was that there were some well-defined boundaries in the City, which were common both to the ward and Postcode Sectors as well as the derivative service areas. Moreover, Unit Postcodes, given their size (around 15 households), were found to be largely conterminous with ward boundaries (more so than EDs with wards). They thus turned out to be the most flexible building block on which to construct a set of boundaries shared by all the organisations. It was therefore recommended that the Unit Postcode should be the basic unit for population/client data collection, whilst the electoral ward should become the unit for 'higher level information exchange' (Burnhill *et al* 1991).

The final pattern of service areas recommended is shown in figure 9.4.

According to the researchers 'the adoption of this model ensures that local organisations will aim to design service areas which do not cross these main boundaries. If they do cross these boundaries then the boundaries of the underlying building blocks (wards and Postcodes) will be followed. Such a mechanism for service area definition should reduce the likelihood of incompatible aggregations of population and client statistics between organisations'.

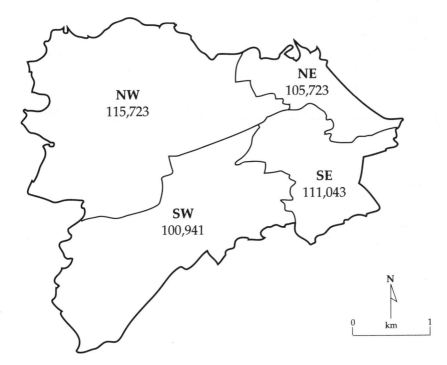

Figure 9.4   Final service area boundaries in Edinburgh *(Source: Dowie et al 1991)*

Matching services and needs

A second study used demographic data at ward and Postcode Sector level and the address-finding and grid referencing capabilities of the Postcode Directory for Scotland (GRO(S)) to relate the distribution of a population in need to the provision of services. Alzheimer's Scotland is a voluntary organisation concerned with sufferers from a specific form of dementia, a condition which increases markedly with age. It is concerned to support both sufferers and carers. Because many of the services required are basic (i.e., house cleaning, shopping etc.), many of the resources required, if properly organised, can be met from within the local community.

However, within the Lothian Region (as in other parts of the country), the distribution of services for dementia sufferers does not match the distribution of the current or potential client populations. Using data from the common service areas project it was possible to calculate the proportion of potential dementia sufferers within each ward or Postcode Sector. Then, the location of existing centres serving the needs of dementia sufferers was extracted from a database maintained by Alzheimer's Scotland and the Postcode used to obtain its National Grid coordinate from the Central Postcode Directory. Service centre locations were then stored within the GIS along with various attributes describing them, i.e., address, capacity, constraints etc.

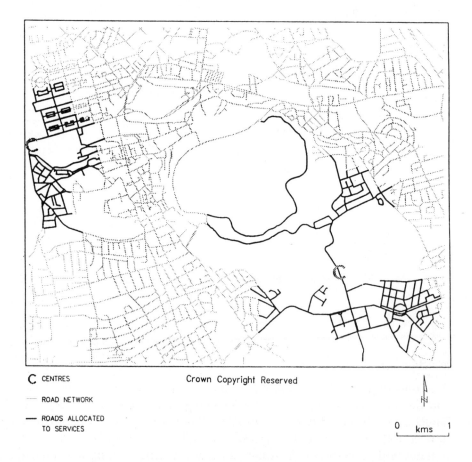

C CENTRES   Crown Copyright Reserved

···· ROAD NETWORK

— ROADS ALLOCATED
  TO SERVICES

0   kms   1

Figure 9.5   Geriatric service areas derived from GIS *(Source: Dowie et al 1991)*

Service centres were then located within the road network with their capacity defined from the Alzheimer's database. Using network analysis software embedded in the GIS it was possible to examine various 'scenarios' of allocations of the population in need to the provision of services (figure 9.5). Although these analyses were not able to give any perspective on the quality of services provided (though the information, if available, could be incorporated in the research design), they provided graphic evidence of the pattern of service over-provision and shortfall.

Postcodes and Geographical Interpolation: a case study of house prices

Title: Analysing local house price variations with GIS
Authors: **Robin Flowerdew, Mick Green and Susan Lucas**
Source: *Proceedings, Association for Geographic Information Conference 1991*, Birmingham

By now, it will be apparent that one of the most important attributes of geographical data is their ability to be integrated together but that one of the key problems in data integration is the diversity of areal units used for different purposes. Often we wish to compare two or more sets of data for some area (a country or region) but they are only available for different (within country or within region) zoning schemes. This is the case, for example, with administrative areas used for data collection by national censuses, government departments and local authorities, health authorities, Postcodes which are frequently used for commercial purposes, such as records of sales or client contacts. In order to compare data collected on a different zonal basis some method must be found for estimating what one set of data would look like if it were available for the other zonal system. In geography, this is known as the areal interpolation problem (Goodchild and Lam 1980). The North West Regional Research Laboratory (NWRRL), at Lancaster University has been working on problems of this type for some time. Their most recent work relates to local variations in house prices and the way these relate to the characteristics of the houses themselves and of the neighbourhoods in which they are located. Their study area is Preston.

There are essentially two practical approaches to this problem. One is to assume that data collected for discrete zones are really the statistical manifestation of some underlying continuous surface. In this case, if a surface can be specified from data for one set of zones, it is possible to calculate the same data for any other set of zones by mathematically integrating the surface over the new zones (Tobler 1979). This approach works well for data that do approximate to a continuous surface such as crop or soil types. However, for many types of data with social or economic interest (and these are invariably the types of data to which postal geographies relate), we find that there are usually abrupt discontinuities in the distribution. This is often the case, for example, in the change from rural to urban land use or in neighbourhood characteristics.

An alternative approach, the one adopted by the NWRRL team, assumes only that the data are likely to be uniformly distributed within the zones for which they are available. Referring to the zonal system for which the data are available as the source zones and the zonal system into which the data are to be 'transferred' as the target zones, then the data for the target zones are estimated as a weighted average of data for the source zones with which they intersect. This is called the 'areal weighting' method and is based on the assumption that the values for the data are evenly distributed within the source zone. Clearly this is a more realistic assumption, for social and economic data, than that which says the variable of interest is distributed evenly over the whole surface (and the extent to which it is better depends on the size of the data zones), but it still relates uneasily to what we perceive to be the geography of the real world. The NWRRL team have therefore developed a variant of the basic approach which takes into account the pattern of other variables which are known to vary over space with the variable which is being redistributed. This they call 'intelligent areal interpolation' and uses a variant of regression analysis to incorporate an additional set of weights into the estimation procedure (Flowerdew and Green 1991).

How well does the method work? House price data were collected for the borough of Preston during January to March 1990 by sampling property advertisements in local newspapers. The 759 properties in the sample were assigned to wards on the basis of address (figure 9.6(a)). Wards were taken as source zones and Postcode Sectors (figure 9.6(b)) were the target zones. Ancillary information was taken from the CPD, including the number of large user Postcodes (figure 9.6(c)). It was argued that, because the latter were likely to be common in central, inner city and commercially developed areas, these would have a negative relationship with house prices.

The NWRRL team used two approaches in developing ancillary information based on large postal users. One created a 'binary' variable from the data (Postcode Sectors with more than 10% large users and Sectors with less than 10% large users) and a continuous variable i.e. the actual percentage of large users. Unfortunately, the authors did not have information about the true values of house prices for the target zones so it

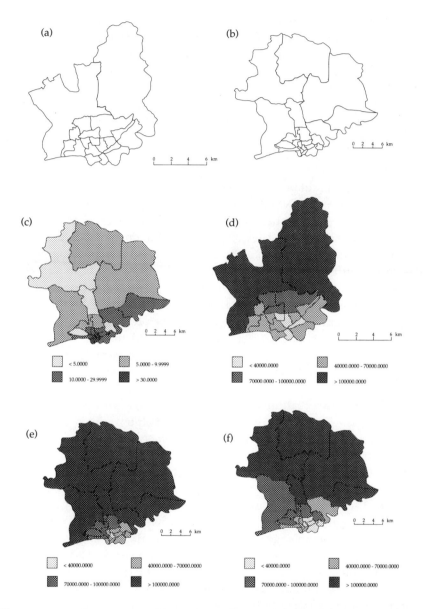

Figure 9.6 Preston, ward boundaries *(Source: Flowerdew, Green and Lucas 1991) (b)*; Preston, Postcode Sector boundaries *(Source: Flowerdew, Green and Lucas 1991); (c)* Percent of delivery points which are large users in the Preston Postcode Sectors *(Source: Flowerdew, Green and Lucas 1991); (d)* Preston, mean house prices by ward *(Source: Flowerdew, Green and Lucas 1991); (e)* Interpolated house prices, areal weighted solution *(Source: Flowerdew, Green and Lucas); (f)* Interpolated house prices, ancillary information solution *(Source: Flowerdew, Green and Lucas 1991)*

was not possible to evaluate the success of the methods directly. A perusal of figures 9.6(d) and 9.6(e) suggest that, on the basis of a visual evaluation, the method works reasonably well. However, closer inspection of the results of the areal weighted method and the estimates made using ancillary information suggests that there are some puzzling discrepancies. For example, when using the ancillary variable (figure 9.6(f)), in continuous form (which, theoretically uses more of the information available), the method produced un-realistically low house prices for the more suburban Postcode Sectors. The authors suggest, therefore, that different forms of statistical relationships between the variables used should be considered.

In conclusion, the NWRRL team also suggest that other ancillary variables such as residential densities derived from Unit Postcodes might also improve the results. They also reiterate the developmental nature of their work and its general contribution to the areal interpolation problem. The latter will be a useful line geographical analysis in social and economic studies until either we have a standard set of basic data collecting units (based on Unit Postcodes?) for all data collection or until we can order aggregates of address-based data 'off the shelf'.

Postcodes in Town Planning

Title: *Development Density and the Measurement of Urban Areas*
Author: **P Bibby**
Source: Halcrow Fox and Associates (unpublished, 1991)

Much of the activity of town planners, associated with guiding the development process and in securing the provision of infrastructure relies upon a detailed knowledge and understanding of the changing geography of population, economic activity and of the use of land. Most planners in a broader sense are concerned to provide infrastructure such as roads, sewers, water supply and other facilities. It is therefore vitally important that information relating to these should be as manipulable and as up-to-date as possible (Green and Shepherd *et al* 1988; Shepherd 1991). In fact, both the extent and accuracy of easily manipulable data can prove problematic. Despite the long term commitment to some form of town and country planning in the UK, there is relatively little manipulable information available about the use of land. Moreover, while there is an abundance of information concerned with demographic and social characteristics of the population of small areas, this derives primarily from the decennial census. Thus at the time of writing such data reflect conditions ten years ago.

Although the Postcode Address File on Compact Disc (PAF on CD) provides very limited information about population and land use, the coarse measures it does provide may be calculated for very small areas thus bringing flexibility to the planner's researcher design. In principle, accuracy of data is also ensured by quarterly update. As an example of a use of PAF we may note that the number of residential delivery points recorded for each Postcode on PAF, may serve as a proxy for the number of households. Thus in practical planning work, Halcrow Fox and Associates have found it valuable to compare for the water area of Kent the number of residential delivery points in water supply zones as of 1991 with the number of households indicated for the same areas from the 1981 Census. This provides a crude indicator of the shift in the distribution of population over the inter-censal period.

Estimating Urban Areas

The PAF may also be used, though in a less obvious manner, to monitor the extent of the urban area. The measurement of land in urban use is a matter of concern for at least two distinct reasons. At the strategic level, the pace of urban growth has been a hotly contested matter of concern for much of this century (Best 1981; Bibby and Shepherd 1991). Apart from such strategic concerns, land use is also of practical importance in the planning of infrastructure provision. Drainage planning, for example, makes use of quite different forms of hydrological model when examining paved and sewered areas than in analysis of rural environments. It is therefore important to have information about urban extent that is as up-to-date as possible.

However, the measurement of urban area is less straightforward than might at first appear, and it is for this reason that the PAF is of particular value. Characteristically the urban area is measured from maps, but this in fact is a problem of some complexity. This is because the area that a map-user measures depends upon the scale of the map. As the scale of the map increases say from a 1:250,000 road atlas to a 1:10,000 scale plan it becomes possible to separate parks and major open spaces from the surrounding urban areas, and with further increases in scale – up to the 1:1250 scale – to separate homes from gardens and so on. In other words, the measured area is described by geographers as being 'scale dependent'. Just as the recent surge of interest in fractals has intensified an awareness that the length of line shown on a map is scale dependent (Longley *et al* 1991), then it should be recognised that the measurement of the area under different types of land use is also scale dependent, although for quite different reasons. There is another problem associated with land use measurement: the recognition of particular land-uses is itself dependent upon the spatial units used. Identification of coarser land use zones depends upon recognising the functional association of house and garden, school and playing field and so on. Indeed, recent advances in the classification of urban land uses using satellite imagery actually depend upon identifying characteristic mixtures of land cover types (Barnsley *et al* 1991).

The use of the PAF allows estimates of urban extent to be made rapidly, and moreover, provides an indication of the impact of scale dependence upon estimates of area. Rather than attempting to measure areas, we may superimpose a square grid of cells of a particular size upon the coordinates of the Postcodes held within the computer. The number of delivery points within each cell may then be aggregated. As the grid references held on PAF are recorded only to 100m resolution, this places a limitation on the fineness of the mesh of cells. So for example if a square grid of side 100m is superimposed upon the PAF data (a 'raster' representation, see chapter 5), the number of delivery points may be aggregated to yield directly a density measure per hectare. This lattice of cells may be thought of as representing a delivery point density surface, which may be used in a number of ways; for investigation of development densities, estimation of urban area, and simple mapping etc. The lattice may be overlaid on the digitised boundary of a study area and the relevant cells extracted. The calculation of development densities is thus quick and simple.

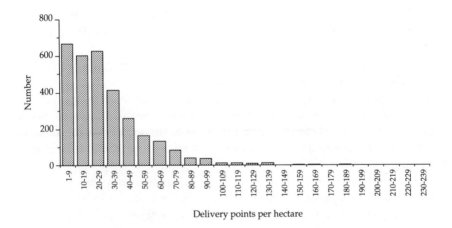

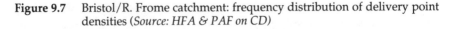

Figure 9.7 Bristol/R. Frome catchment: frequency distribution of delivery point densities (*Source: HFA & PAF on CD*)

This procedure was recently used in calculating the impact of urban growth on the catchment area of the river Frome near Bristol. Figure 9.7 shows the frequency distribution of delivery point densities for this catchment, which stretches from open farmland through the rapidly expanding northern fringe of the city to the area of Bristol itself. It appears that this is a secondary mode in the distribution at 20–30 delivery points per hectare, reflecting the large portion of the catchment area that is covered by fairly low density residential development. By selecting solely residential delivery points it is, of course, possible to use the same simple technique to make rapid assessments of dwelling densities characteristic of particular cities and localities.

An estimate of the total urban area may be made swiftly and directly by imposing a cut-off on the delivery point density distribution, and defining every cell with more than say five delivery points per hectare as 'urban'. Applying this cut-off in the case represented in figure 9.7 it appears that the urban area of the Frome catchment is about 19.6 square kilometres, around 12% of the total area. Overlaying the delivery point density surface on the mosaic of sub-catchments defined for hydrological modelling purposes, it is then possible to examine the percentage of each which is in urban use (figure 9.8).

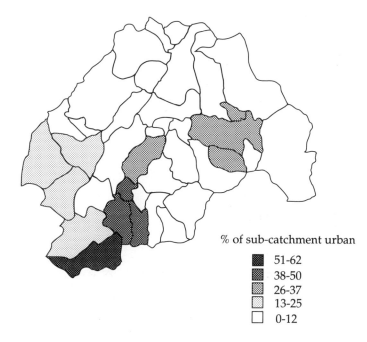

% of sub-catchment urban

■ 51-62
▨ 38-50
▧ 26-37
▢ 13-25
☐ 0-12

Figure 9.8   Bristol/R. Frome catchment: intensity of urban use by sub-catchment *(Source: HFA & PAF on CD)*

It can be objected that the cut-off is entirely arbitrary, and this is true. It is equally true, however, that the identification of urban areas from maps depends upon an arbitrary level of generalisation. Thus the definition of urban areas used in work for Department of Environment and OPCS (OPCS 1984), relies upon a rule that a building is added to an urban area if the distance to the nearest point included in that area is less than 50 metres. Using PAF, an arbitrary distance cut-off is replaced by an arbitrary density cut-off. There is, however, a major difference between the two approaches. While the digitising of urban areas is slow and tedious, the aggregation of elements of the delivery point density surface can be carried out very quickly. Hence, it is easy to measure the urban area using all possible density cut-offs and to compare the results. Figure 9.9 shows the effect of changing the cut-off on the measured urban area. If a maximum possible estimate were to be made by including all cells with one or more delivery points then the estimated urban area would increase correspondingly.

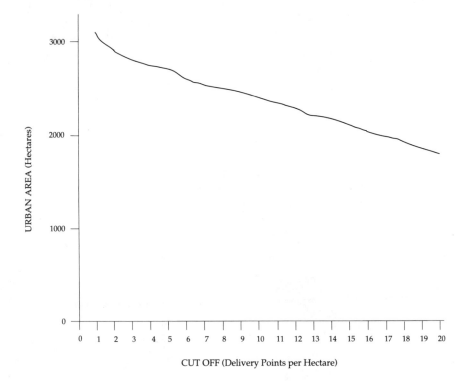

Figure 9.9   Bristol/R. Frome catchment: relationship between measured and selected density cut-off *(Source: HFA & PAF on CD)*

Having produced a delivery point density surface from what is basically a list, it is a small step to map the urban area. By showing each cell where the density of delivery points exceeds the cut-off by a square to scale, a convincing image of the urban area can be generated (figure 9.10). Alternatively, a contour might be threaded through the density surface at the level of the chosen cut-off to generate an urban 'edge' in vector form. It should be compared with the limit of the urban area generalised by the cartographer. The map generalised by the cartographer fails to exclude large areas of parks and open spaces from within the urban area yielding a substantially larger urban area. Note also that this sort of approach can be developed further by using changes in delivery point densities to try to measure urban growth, or to analyse the Postcode data alongside other data sets such as the Land Use Change Statistics collected by OS for the Department of the Environment (see Sellwood 1987). The practical limitations of such work depend primarily on the accuracy of the grid references assigned to the Postcodes (see chapter 7).

This brief exploration of the use of Postcodes in the measurement of urban land use leads us to three main conclusions. First, it is easy and quick to produce coarse measures of population distribution, development density and urban extent from PAF and to map them. Second, by changing the cell size of the grid, and by adjusting the cut-offs it allows the estimates of urban area to be explored. The classification of areas as urban or rural will, as in the example here, affect the choice of hydrological model and may ultimately affect the assessment of the scale of infrastructural investment required. Finally, it underscores the fact that holding data in machine-readable form may allow a range of analytic applications far beyond that originally envisaged by the data owners.

Postcodes in Local Economic Analysis

Title: *Notes on applications of PAF on CD with business databases*
Author: **P Bibby**
Source: *Halcrow Fox and Associates (unpublished report)*

One of the main advantages of the Postcode system is that it provides a means of identifying location fairly precisely. The success of the system has been such that there now exists a very large volume of machine-readable data referenced by Unit Postcodes. By means of PAF on CD, it becomes possible to provide National Grid coordinates for entries in a very large number of data sets. This section is concerned with the use of

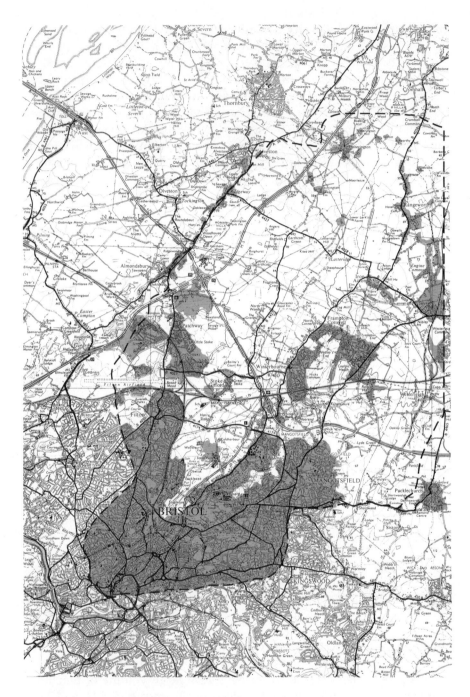

Figure 9.10(a)   Bristol/R. Frome urban areas (western side) generated by a)
approximating the urban area boundaries from the Ordnance
Survey 1:50,000 map (© *Crown Copyright*)

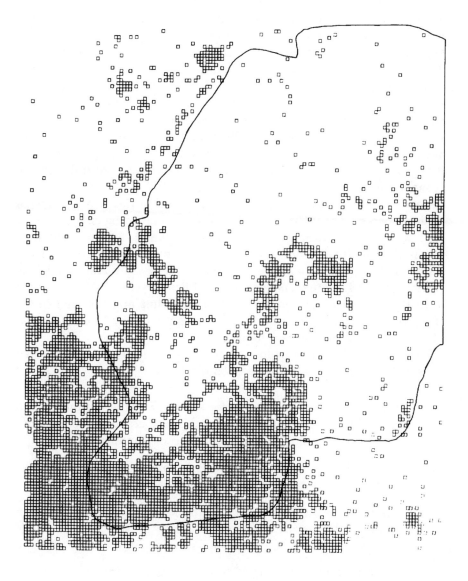

Figure 9.10(b)   b) plotting the location of the Unit Postcodes using grid
references from PAF on CD *(Source: HFA, PAF on CD and
Ordnance Survey. © Crown Copyright)*

Postcodes to build geography into business information and hence provide a basis for small area economic analysis in town planning.

The town planning system in the UK aims to ensure that there is an adequate supply of land to allow the development of sufficient   housing to meet the needs of the population and to ensure an adequate supply of land to meet the needs of economic activity.   At the same time, the planning system seeks to enhance amenity and to protect the environment.   To underpin this planning activity, it is frequently necessary to undertake economic analyses of areas which are small or which bear no relationship to the standard administrative units for which statistics are available.   For example, comparison of change within cities and at the urban fringe is of particular interest.   A noticeable feature of the geography of economic change over recent years has been the shift of economic activity from the cities to greenfield sites at the urban fringe or beyond.   In the 1980s this has expressed itself in the development of business parks.   The urban to rural shift in manufacturing employment is well documented (Fothergill and Gudgin 1982) and the impact on land use is demonstrated by on-going work for the Department of the Environment.   This tendency is a major challenge to planners.   In the worst case, market preferences for out-of-town greenfield sites may lead to further encroachment on the countryside while areas of land in the cities remain vacant or under-used.   It is thus very important that planners can gauge the pace of local economic change.

There are at least three main ways in which the use of postcodes can assist in this monitoring of local economic activity:

- by generating sampling frames for surveys designed to understand more fully the underpinnings of small-area economic change and land-use change, and assessing the impact of planning policy;

- by monitoring the rate of growth of economic activity away from the conurbations and major urban areas;

- by assisting in the assessment of the need for further release of building land to service economic growth.

All these applications depend either upon the definition of digital boundaries for small areas, or the identification of clusters of employment uses. Where digital boundaries are defined, a Point-in-Polygon algorithm can be used to ascertain which Unit Postcodes from PAF fall within the area of interest on the basis of their grid references (see chapters 5 and 7). The selected Postcodes may then be matched with business data, to generate lists of hit companies, or provide a basis for more complex analyses. For these purposes the availability of Postcode-referenced business data is of fundamental importance. Here we consider three principal sources with very different characteristics:

- the Census of Employment;
- private sector sources such as Kompass CD;
- British Telecom's 'Connections in Business' database.

Census of Employment

The Census of Employment collects for units approximating employing establishments (paypoints) information showing the Standard Industrial Classification (SIC) of a workplace and the number of employees cross-classified according to gender and hours worked (full-time or part-time). Surveys were undertaken annually from 1971 to 1978. Since then censuses have been undertaken in 1981, 1984, 1987 and 1989. Prior to the 1984 survey, complete coverage was attempted, though from 1984 onwards full coverage has only been attempted for those employing more than 25, with sampling arrangements for smaller employers. The strengths and weaknesses of these data are well-known (England 1985; Healey 1991) Establishment (i.e. factory or office) level records are Postcoded, though these data are protected by the provisions of the 1947 Statistics of Trade Act and not generally available. Most users must rely on aggregated data made available through the Department of Employment, usually through the NOMIS system (Blakemore 1991). Local authority planners, however, may have access to the establishment-level data (subject to restrictions on use) for the discharge of their statutory functions. Allied to the Postcode these data will support a wide variety of applications such as estimating the sectoral mix of employment in *ad hoc* urban priority areas and aggregating retailing employment into a mosaic of zones as an input to a shopping model.

Kompass CD

There exist a wide range of standard business directories and reference works, one of the best known of which is Kompass. This familiar reference work is organised on a locality by locality basis, providing information about products, turnover, ownership, key staff and employment. Kompass is not comprehensive, with companies being self-selected for inclusion, though it is frequently thought of as representing 'leading' companies, with a particular emphasis on manufacturing, industrial and producer services businesses. The CD version of this product provides information on 280,000 companies (including 43,000 in the UK) indexed by Postcode among other items. This source can be difficult to use because of its partial nature but provides for many included companies a range of detail that cannot be rivalled by other sources. Use of the Postcode provides the means by which, given due caution, such data can be brought to bear on small area analyses.

'Connections in Business'[3] Database

The 'Connections in Business' database maintained by British Telecom (BT) is updated weekly and holds alongside the Unit Postcode such items as names, addresses, telephone numbers and certain other information about business establishments with entries in YELLOW PAGES or BUSINESS PAGES. The other information includes the YELLOW PAGES category code (a numeric code corresponding to the headings used in the published YELLOW PAGES directory), coarser groupings of activities, an assigned SIC based on the YELLOW PAGES category code, and now an employee size band indicator. The YELLOW PAGES code provides an extremely fine classification of service activity, particularly for consumer services. Thus while the Census of Employment provides better data about employment levels, the 'Connections in Business' database has the advantage of virtually continuous update, and easy access. The assignment of establishments to YELLOW PAGES categories is good, but the 'translation' of these categories to SICs available from the 'Connections in Business' database is not completely satisfactory. Frequently, YELLOW PAGES categories refer to a class of goods but do not indicate whether the entrant is a manufacturer, say, or a wholesaler. 'Translation' cannot be satisfactory because entrants with the same YELLOW PAGES code can have very different SICs.

The most generally useful application of Postcoded business data in local economic analysis is the construction of sampling frames for surveys (see the next section). Thus faced with a requirement to ascertain the likely economic impact of a proposed new road upon existing businesses, it is possible to acquire the data for target groups of businesses from BT at Postcode District level, and then to extract the data for the particular small

[3]YELLOW PAGES and BUSINESS PAGES are registered trade marks and service marks of British Telecommunications plc in the UK.
[4]'Connections in Business' is a trade mark and service mark of British Telecommunications plc in the UK. 'Connections in Business' has recently been re-branded as 'The Business Database' from YELLOW PAGES.

area, on the basis of the digital version of the study area boundary. In this example, the extracted data were assembled as a design for a stratified random sample of businesses, the industrial sector forming the basis of stratification. It is possible, to use Postcoded business data more directly in local analyses. One use is to apply Postcoded business information such as the 'Connections in Business' database to overcome some of the difficulties of the official Census of Employment. Typically, two years will elapse between the employment census and the publication of the detailed results, and even when the data do arrive they are always subject to errors induced by the rather complex process used to assign Census of Employment data to establishments and hence administrative areas.

Typically, in local economic forecasting, the base data themselves must be a forecast. Recourse must frequently be made to Census of Employment data for earlier years with short-run employment growth factors being used to estimate the base. In preparing such base data it is important to take as many checks as possible, attempting to prepare estimates of base year employment using a range of methods. Thus, for example in preparing the base data for an assessment of the appropriate scale of employment land release in Warwick District in the period between 1989 and 2001, alternative estimates of the employment base were made using:

- short-term growth factors applied to 1981 and 1987 Census of Employment estimates checked against Census of Population and Census of Production estimates as available;

- application of employment density estimates to the area of land developed between 1987 and 1989 as indicated by the local planning authority's data;

- examination of levels of in-situ employment change in major employers over the period 1987–1989;

- estimation of 1989 employment levels on the basis of the stock of Postcoded businesses in the 'Connections in Business' database.

It is this last check that deserves comment here. In April 1989, there were rather more than 1.5 million entries in the 'Connections in Business' database (see table 9.1). By assigning them to broad economic sectors such as SIC divisions and comparing the number of units with total estimated employment nationally in each sector, it is possible to estimate a mean number of employees per entry for different types of operation. By applying these means to the numbers of Postcoded Units lying within the digital version of the District boundary, a further check on employment levels may be made. Table 9.2 draws a comparison between the estimates of 1989 employment levels in Warwick District based on growth factors and those based on the 'Connections in Business' database. The Postcoded business data are most useful as a check in sectors where most of the employment is in small establishments.

Table 9.1 'Connections in Business' database, April 1989 (*Source: BT*)

	SIC Division	Number of live database entries ('000s)
0	Agriculture	101.5
1	Energy and Water Supply	2.3
2	Metals, Chemicals	8.7
3	Metal Goods, Engineering , Vehicles	98.6
4	Other Manufacturing	103.8
5	Construction	115.2
6	Distribution	577.6
7	Transport and Communication	71.4
8	Business Services	210.2
9	Other Services	266.1
	Total	**1555.5**

The availability of a range of Postcoded business information thus enables some consistency checks to be made on local economic data, and enables the planner to benefit from the respective strengths of each of the sources. In stark contrast to the coarse analyses referred to above, Postcodes also prove an excellent device for identifying at a level of fine detail industrial estates, employment areas and urban land use zones. Thus in the context of the Warwick study referred to above, it proved possible to use Postcode geography and 'Connections in Business' data to define the detailed composition of land uses in business parks and fringe employment developments, and also to assess the types of land use which were being accommodated in converted property in the sensitive historic cores of Warwick and Leamington Spa. The detailed geographical base provided by the Unit Postcode system also allowed an estimate to be made of the extent to which the very rapid growth in the business services sector could be accommodated within the existing urban fabric rather than demanding the development of green-field sites. In this case almost one fifth of new employment floorspace in the second half of the 1980s was accommodated within the existing urban frame.

Table 9.2   Comparison of employment estimates: Warwick District 1989 *(Source: HFA, BT and Department of Employment)*

	1981 – 1987 Growth Factor Base	1989 'Connections in Business ' Base
Agriculture	500	480
Mining	0	0
Manufacturing	13400	14640
Construction	1700	2100
Services	40000	37800
Total	**55600**	**55020**

This brief review has highlighted both the significance of local economic analyses in the physical planning process and some of the characteristic difficulties with local economic data. The increasing availability of Postcoded machine-readable business data has the potential for improving data quality and informing urban analysis. At the present stage such data sets tend to be considered as lists or marketing tools and the work of exploiting their potential for planning analysis has hardly begun.

Postcodes in Sample Surveys

Title: An evaluation of the Postcode Address File as a Sampling Frame and its use within OPCS
Authors: **P R Wilson and D J Elliot**
Source: *Journal of Royal Statistical Society, Series A (General)*, Vol **150**, Part 3, 1987, pp 230-40

Title: The Use of the Postcode Address File as a Sampling Frame
Author: **R Butcher**
Source: *The Statistician*, **37**, 1988, pp 15-24

In addition to its responsibilities for the national census, the Office of Population Censuses and Surveys (OPCS) also plans and executes most of the major government household surveys and various special *ad hoc* surveys. These surveys, carried out by the Social Survey Division of OPCS are of considerable importance in helping to shape government policy on various matters. Among the major surveys are the General Household Survey (GHS), the Family Expenditure Survey (FES) and the Labour Force Survey (LFS); whilst the *ad hoc* surveys may cover such matters as the use of leisure time, the smoking habits of teenagers or the mobility problems of disabled people. In the course of a year, OPCS may interview up to 200,000 households. The development of efficient, rigorous and cost-effective ways of drawing samples of households and contacting them is thus an important part of the work of OPCS.

Although most of the OPCS survey work is targeted on households, no comprehensive national list of households actually exists as such. However, various list of addresses do exist and these can be used for sampling purposes since, in the great majority of cases, each address is inhabited by a single household. The address list (or sampling frame) most frequently used by survey organisations was the Register of Electors, a list of individuals eligible to vote. Although comprehensive in scope this was not, in the mid 1980s, available centrally in computerised form and also it tended to under-represent some groups in the population such as ethnic minorities and frequent movers. These were serious drawbacks for many government policy studies. It was in these circumstances that OPCS felt there was a need for a sampling frame of private addresses which was at least as good as the electoral Register in terms of coverage, but also lent itself to the rapid, cost-effective and accurate drawing of samples of the type most frequently used in general population surveys. In the late 1970s, the OPCS made a rigorous study of the possibility of using PAF as a sampling frame (Lievesley *et al* 1978) and in 1982 it developed a system for sampling from PAF.

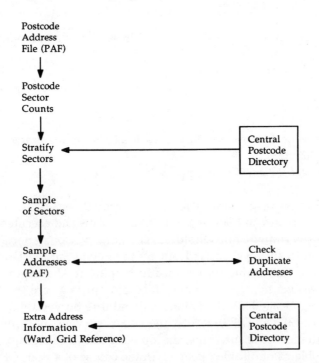

Figure 9.11   The OPCS PAF Sampling System *(Source: Wilson & Elliot 1987)*

The OPCS System for Sampling from PAF

The PAF sampling system used by OPCS is outlined in figure 9.11. It very closely resembles the procedures used in conducting the GHS. This is a multi-purpose survey designed to collect background information for social policy on a range of topics including household structure, housing, education, health and employment. Interviews are conducted with about 10,000 households each year.

POSTCODE SECTOR COUNTS

Previous research on sample design effects had shown that the use of electoral wards as primary sample units represented a reasonable balance between field economy and statistical efficiency. In a national interview survey it is essential for the quota of addresses to be clustered in a small geographical area so as to limit the amount of travelling between interviews. However, this area should not be too small since people who live in the same neighbourhood tend to have similar social and economic circumstances. This means that the sample of households is best selected in two stages: the first consisting of the selection of Primary Sampling Units (PSUs) or geographical units, the second consisting of the selection of addresses within the sampled area. Under the 'pre-PAF' system electoral wards gave the best balance between interviewer accessibility and requisite variety. It was therefore decided to base the PAF sampling system on Postcode Sectors since that is the level in the Postcode hierarchy that best corresponds to wards (see figure 1.1).

The main differences between wards and Postcode Sectors is that the latter are, on average, slightly larger than wards in terms of the number of addresses they contain. There are also rather fewer very small Sectors than very small wards and conversely more large Sectors. In the OPCS PAF sampling system the smallest Postcode Sectors are grouped with adjacent Sectors to form PSUs with a minimum size of 500 delivery points or addresses. The GHS involves an interview lasting up to an hour and allowing for the time each (part-time) interviewer spends travelling, contacting addresses and dealing with non-response; the maximum number of addresses an interviewer can deal with in a survey month is 20 – 25. The total number of PSUs selected each month is 48.

STRATIFYING POSTCODE SECTORS

Stratification is the statistical technique for ensuring that the sample accurately reflects the population on chosen factors. The system of stratification for the GHS divides the sample into 22 major 'strata'. One set of strata are derived from a regional and metropolitan/non-metropolitan area division of the country. The number of PSU selections taken from each stratum is set in proportion to the size of that stratum and since 1984 this has been based on the number of delivery points in the PAF, i.e., the Northern metropolitan stratum contains about 2.2% of the delivery points in Britain and so gets 2.2% of the PSUs or 13 out of the 576 taken per year. The overall distribution of the set sample allocation to strata changed slightly between the 'pre-' and 'post-' PAF versions of the GHS due to regional variations in ineligibility rates (see below).

Within these 22 major strata, the PSUs are further stratified using other factors, an important set of which are census variables. In order to use census variables for stratifying PSUs it is first necessary to make the link between census area units and Postcode Sectors. This was carried out by using a variant of the 'Nearest Neighbour' method of data linkage (see chapter 7). The grid reference of the Unit Postcode was linked to its nearest Enumeration District (ED) and then each ED was allocated to the Postcode Sector which contained the largest number of Unit Postcodes from the ED. Totals for census variables were then allocated to Sectors by aggregating the totals of the associated EDs. The range of PAF Postcode Sector stratifiers available to OPCS as a result of this exercise is shown in table 9.3.

Table 9.3 PAF Sector Stratifiers Available in OPCS *(Source: Wilson & Elliot 1987)*

% Owner-occupied households

% Local authority renting households

% Private renting households

% Households with no car

% Persons not in private households

% Persons moved in past year

% Persons born in New Commonwealth

% Persons who are pensioners

% Persons aged 75 and over

% Persons in private households aged 16 and over

% Persons aged 16 or over who are economically active

% Females aged 16 or over who are economically active

% Persons who are unemployed

% Males who are unemployed

% Females who are unemployed

% Employed persons who travel to work by car

Population Density

This stratification system allows up to three variables to be used in addition to region, hence Postcode Sectors can be ordered by the third variable in groups of the first two. Also, the stratifiers may be different for different regions. This makes the system general, i.e., it can be used to suit the purposes of different surveys. In a housing survey, for example, Sectors could be ordered according to proportion of households renting privately within the four groups containing combinations of high and low proportions of owner-occupied housing and council housing.

OTHER POSTCODE STRATIFIERS

The numeric order of Postcode Sectors can be used by itself to give some form of stratification because the lowest Postcode numbers tend to be in the centre of cities or large towns and the highest numbers in rural areas. Similarly, within Postcode Sectors the ordering of Postcodes has been allocated to some extent on a geographical basis so that Royal Mail can group them to form a delivery route. This provides an additional stratification when samples are selected systematically within Sectors, although the exact order of a delivery route cannot be obtained from information on PAF. Also, although the OPCS sampling system is based on sampling Postcode Sectors it can be adapted to larger sized PSUs. For example, PSUs approximating to local authority districts can be obtained by treating Postcode Sectors as lying within the local authority in which the highest number of the Sector's addresses lie. With further slight modification the system can be used to select samples which are restricted to particular local authorities or which have different sampling fractions in different authorities.

COMPLETING THE SAMPLE

When the frame of Postcode Sectors has been stratified, a systematic sample of PSUs is drawn, usually with probabilities of being selected proportional to Sector size (the number of delivery points). A fixed number of addresses is then sampled from each of the selected Sectors so as to give an equal-probability sample of addresses. Addresses are then automatically checked (using PAF) to make sure they are not duplicates of ones recently sampled. Geographical information on the sample is then added from the CPD since the ward code and the grid reference are used as ways of helping interviewers to trace addresses. The resulting sampled addresses can then either be made available to interviewers as computer listings, or they can be printed on labels if the survey is to be carried out by post.

INELIGIBLE ADDRESSES

As we have already seen, one area where there are some disadvantages to using PAF for sampling households compared with other sources is in the extent to which 'ineligible' units may be sampled (see chapter 4). Of the addresses in the 'small user' PAF when the OPCS system was set up, approximately 11% did not contain a resident household. One of the main reasons for PAF 'addresses' being ineligible is that they are vacant, others are that they are non-residential, under conversion or have been demolished. In addition, and potentially more seriously for geographically stratified sampling, there is considerable regional variation in PAF ineligibility rates. The extremes range from North London with 15% of addresses ineligible and Wales with 14% to the South East and East Midlands with 8% and 7% respectively ineligible (see table 4.2). Translated into differences between Sectors within regions these discrepancies cause some slight statistical problems, but, more significantly, add to the costs of carrying out surveys.

Other Survey Uses of PAF

The PAF is used in other important surveys carried out by OPCS Survey Division. In fact, the first OPCS survey to use the PAF sampling system was the LFS in 1983. It is important in LFS to ensure that all groups in the population are covered and electoral registers are inappropriate for this purpose. From 1971 to 1981 the LFS was therefore based on the Rating Valuation lists prepared for local authority districts. This entailed interviewers visiting Rating Officers throughout the country. Automated sampling using PAF is much cheaper and easier to control statistically since the sample can be based on areas smaller than local authorities. In the case of the National Food Survey (NFS), however, the use of PAF meant an increase in the size of geographical sampling unit since in the case of the NFS this was the electoral polling district. However, even here, the increase in fieldwork costs entailed in moving to the larger Postcode Sector as the geographical unit, was outweighed by the greater precision, greater control of sampling, greater speed of selection and better coverage given by PAF. Finally, the FES has used PAF since 1986. Here the considerations in converting to PAF were very similar to those for the GHS although in addition it brought new flexibility in geographical stratification.

Summary

The Postcode Address File has now become the standard address sampling frame used by OPCS when drawing samples of households in the population at large. It replaced the Electoral Register and the Valuation Lists for OPCS household surveys, although not for all surveys, i.e., those focused on individuals rather than households. In terms of sample design involving Postcode Sectors the use of PAF has brought:

- improved coverage of the population compared with the Electoral Register;

- reduced sampling costs;

- greater control of sampling procedures;

- greater choice of geographical clustering units.

On the debit side, PAF has a higher proportion of ineligible addresses – i.e., addresses that do not contain a private household – than alternative sampling frames. In addition these ineligible addresses are spread unevenly across Postcode Sectors which has a small impact on statistical precision and on the workload of interviewers. Also, because PAF does not provide the names of people living at an address this can make the task of locating addresses and contacting households more difficult in certain circumstances. Overall, however, there has been a significant net benefit in using PAF in the OPCS sample survey context. For GHS there has been a reduction in sampling costs and an improvement in coverage. For LFS and NFS there have been improvements in sample design.

Postcodes in Education Research

Title: Monitoring the social and spatial impact of educational reform
Authors: **C L Garner, B M Gittings and Tolgu K E A**
Source: *Regional Research Laboratory for Scotland, Working Paper No.9,* February 1990

Introduction

One of the enduring debates in the sociology of education is the extent to which educational performance is related to the natural ability of the pupil, the social character of the school and the neighbourhood in which it is located, and the resources that are put in to education at the school and local educational authority level. Disentangling all these effects requires, among other things, accurate geographical coding of pupils' addresses and the schools they attend as well as social and economic data at an appropriate level of aggregation and disaggregation. It is also extremely helpful in this form of research, especially if data sets are large, to have a convenient means for storing, structuring and manipulating data. GIS provides just such a tool.

The background to the research undertaken by the team led by Cathy Garner is the educational reforms carried out in Scotland since 1979. These reforms include the introduction of open enrolments (i.e., greater parental choice), the National Curriculum, the local management of schools and the 'opting out' of schools into grant-maintained status. In all of these developments geographically encoded data managed in a GIS have a potentially important role to play in monitoring the effects of change.

Open Enrolment

Open enrolment is a reform that has been in place for a sufficient length of time in Scotland to make detailed evaluative research worthwhile. Introduced in 1981 and extended in 1988, open enrolment means that parents are entitled to choose a school other than the one to which their child is allocated by the Local Education Authority (LEA). Prior to open enrolment LEAs typically operated a system of school catchment zones which, with the exception of denominational schools, formed non-overlapping, contiguous geographical units. Under this system pupils are allocated to schools on the basis of home address: primary school allocations being made on the basis of minimising distance travelled and secondary school allocations being made on the basis of a system of primary 'feeder' schools. The nomination of 'feeder' schools enabled the LEA, if it wished, to manipulate the social composition of secondary schools. In some LEAs the political will to see socially mixed schools led to a geographically complex pattern of secondary school catchment areas (Petch, 1988). Many LEAs had a liberal attitude to school catchment zoning systems but some, particularly those with a commitment to socially mixed schools, vigorously enforced these *de jure* (global) zoning systems at both primary and secondary school level.

The freedom to choose schools in Scotland proved very popular. Placement requests rose from just over 10,000 in 1982 to over 24,000 in 1987/88 (Scottish Education Department 1989). In Scotland as a whole in 1987/88 some 13% of primary (age five) pupils had placement requests made on their behalf compared with 10% of secondary (age 12) pupils. Parents in rural areas make many more placement requests than those in urban areas. Given this volume of requests (not all of which are met), it is not surprising that many school catchments are now different spatially and socially from those based on the LEA *de jure* catchment system. In Edinburgh and Dundee, for example, requests for secondary schools were towards schools with higher attainment measures, higher social class, previously selective schools and larger schools, and away from schools serving local authority housing schemes with catchment areas characterised by unemployment and low income (Adler and Raab 1988).

In these circumstances (which are compounded by the impact of the other reforms mentioned above and, in the cities especially, by the decline of the school-age population), it becomes increasingly difficult for the LEAs to plan the distribution of educational resources. As Coopers and Lybrand, in a report to the Department of Education and Science noted:

> ...open enrolment will limit schools' and the LEAs' ability to predict enrolment numbers and will increase the need for flexible planning. (Coopers and Lybrand 1988 p. 39).

The need for information systems to provide socio-economic details on pupils and their catchment areas is thus self-evident. Open enrolment means that such information must be related to the *de facto* or actual catchment of the school and not necessarily to the planned *de jure* catchment. The need for flexibility in the definition of catchments and the ability to link external data sources such as social surveys and the Census of Population for measures of deprivation, becomes crucial for the LEA and for individual schools. GIS technology provides the potential for data integration and linkage in a spatial framework and could provide a vital adjunct to existing LEA and/or school information systems.

School performance

Another reason why LEAs may wish to resort to more accurate means of locating pupils in relation to both school and residential neighbourhood is in the area of educational testing. The process of publishing school examination results and the accompanying debate over 'league tables for schools' is an area of great concern to LEAs and educational specialists alike. School-effectiveness studies have shown that to judge a school's performance in terms of unadjusted attainment scores, ignoring the wider socio-economic structure from which that school's pupils are drawn is grossly misleading (Goldstein and Cuttance 1988). The Coopers and Lybrand report to DES made the same point:

> ...great care is needed with any such comparisons of performance as the differences between schools and their socio-economic environments are such that superficiality can be misleading if not dangerous. (Coopers and Lybrand 1988, p. 42).

A GIS for Education Planning

At the RRL for Scotland a prototype GIS was established to fulfil many of the monitoring and evaluation functions to which the new legislation on education gave rise. Postcodes played an important part in the database both as an automated source of addresses and for data linkage. The study area was an LEA in Scotland for which there were four main types of spatial data:

- *de jure* school catchment boundaries for primary and secondary schools taken from OS 1:50,000 scale maps;

- 1981 Census of Population ED boundaries digitised from 1:10000 OS maps;

- infrastructure and physical features such as roads, railways and rivers, etc.;

- point locations for primary and secondary schools derived from the Scottish Postcode Directory (SPD) from GRO(S).

Data describing these features and the characteristics of the school population came from a wide variety of sources: details of school membership, pupil attainment, family background and post-school destinations from surveys carried out by the Centre for Educational Sociology at the University of Edinburgh; selected variables indicating area deprivation came from the Census of Population SAS for 1981; links between individual and school level data were made via the SPD and Postcoded directory listings provided other information on schools. Using these data in conjunction with the GIS, the researchers were able to delineate the *de facto* school catchments based on Postcoded addresses and construct the *de jure* secondary school catchments from the primary school feeder catchments. Given the delineation of both types of catchment, comparisons could be made of the geographical and social characteristics of the planned and actual school catchment areas. Various analyses could then be made on this basis of such administrative matters as pupil travel costs and the allocation of resources under formula funding and also of pupil attainments adjusted for the social composition of the catchment area. The system as a whole gave the potential for monitoring social and spatial change on a school by school basis.

An integral part of an educational monitoring system is the Postcoded information and the Postcode Directory which makes it possible to relate individual level data to school and catchment area data with relatively little difficulty. Further expansion of the system will incorporate further information in which Postcodes will play an important part including the site, size and type of new house building, Health Authority data on birth rates and NHS data on migration (via General Practitioner registers).

Conclusions

The aim of this chapter has been to give an idea of how the attributes of Postcodes have been used in a small number of specific applications. Because our sample of applications is so small we cannot justifiably draw from it any broad conclusions about Postcode applications. However, the examples are sufficient in number and breadth to make possible some general observations.

The first thing that these examples show, which confirms a point made at the very start of this book, is that the geography inherent in the Postcode system confers some significant advantages on researchers and users from different disciplines and application areas. This is represented by, for example, the carefully constructed hierarchy of postal zones, the georeferencing of Postcodes and the inclusion of the numbers and type of delivery points. In other words, the geography of Postcodes is by no means the domain of professional geographers. What this means in turn, however, is that all users of Postcodes for research and managerial purposes should have some idea of the 'real' geography that Postcodes contain. This real geography includes such things as the underlying distribution of population and employment and the way these and their land use characteristics are changing. Users should also have some knowledge of the basic principles of georeferencing and the way geocoded data are used with computers. These are, in the main, the reasons this book has been written and why we hope that the teaching of the principles underlying the Postcode system will soon find its way into the geography curriculum.

A second point confirmed in this chapter is that, in addition to representing a new data set in geography – a feature brought out most ingeniously in the example on the use of postcodes in town planning – the most important use of Postcodes is as a means of linking data sets together. This is clearly brought out in the two examples from RRL Scotland but is also inherent in the sections on geodemographics and local economic analysis. This aspect of Postcode use will become even more significant in England and Wales when the census ED to Postcode Directory and its associated computer software for handling 1991 Census information becomes widely available. These developments will also make it imperative that organisations ensure that a detailed and accurate Postcode is appended to information on the things, people and places with which they or their businesses are concerned. Postcoding is a comparatively trivial operation in itself, but one which can play significant dividends in terms of data integration and analysis and hence lead to better business decisions.

Thirdly, the Scottish examples in this chapter also bring out the value that can be added by authoritative and accurately digitised boundaries of Unit Postcodes. As we have seen here and also in chapter 6, digitised Postcode boundaries greatly facilitate data linkage and also make it possible to produce accurate, small-scale maps of Postcoded information. In addition, however, Postcode boundaries information in computerised form is useful in its own right insofar as it is an aid to the better management and coordination of the services provided by a business or public body. This was shown in the first of the Scottish examples. Finally, what also emerges from this chapter is the need for some sort of wide-ranging and detailed review of the use of Postcodes for non-postal purposes (see also chapter 10). This would be of value to both existing and new users of Postcoded data and would also indicate where improvements and/or additions to the geography of Postcodes would be most beneficial.

SECTION 4 The future

CHAPTER 10   Postcoding and the future

The history of the future

The title of this book *'Postcodes: the New Geography'* was chosen very deliberately to reflect the impact which Postcodes have already had on organisations of all kinds. Postcode referencing is now literally 'big business', and is playing an important role in geodemographic profiling, health planning and service delivery, the allocation of insurance premium levels, transportation surveys and planning, monitoring of crime levels, mapping of sales in various industries, retail planning, the provision of emergency vehicle responses and many more activities which are detailed in this book. In this final chapter, it seems appropriate to look ahead to the future of the Postcode. There are two kinds of future: one is the kind which has already started and which seems likely to continue. The other is the kind that has yet to be thought of but which we might bring about with luck, skill and effort. This chapter will try to explore both.

First, however, it is worthwhile looking back at what the UK government's Committee of Enquiry on the Handling of Geographic Information recommended in 1987 and what government itself accepted. The Committee was chaired by Lord Chorley (see the Preface) and reviewed almost the whole field of geographical data handling problems and opportunities; its Report (DoE 1987) proved a classic, requiring at least one reprint and selling around the world – highly unusual for a government publication produced by a Committee of Enquiry! So far as geographical referencing and the use of Postcodes was concerned, six recommendations are relevant. All but one of them came under the heading of data linkage. They were:

25   Unaggregated spatial data held by Government Departments should be made available to other users provided that the costs of doing so are borne by the users and that there are no overriding security, privacy or commercial considerations;

37   As far as practicable, all geographic information, including remotely sensed data, relating to the land areas of the United Kingdom should be referenced directly or indirectly to the National Grid or Irish Grid as appropriate;

38   Data suppliers should both keep and release their data in as disaggregated a form as possible;

39   The preferred bases for holding and/or releasing socio-economic data should be addresses and unit postcodes. Wherever possible, the boundaries of administrative and electoral areas should not split whole unit postcodes;

40   All addresses and unit postcodes should be grid referenced. For addresses, the proposed provision of point references should meet most requirements (this refers to the then recently announced plans of Pinpoint to create the Pinpoint Address Code, progress on which was reported in chapter 4). For unit postcodes, the current point references should be improved to meet users' requirements. To avoid different grid references for the same address or postcode, Government, probably the OS and/or the census Offices, in conjunction with the Post Office, should be responsible for ensuring consistency in grid referencing of addresses and unit postcodes;

41   The Office of Population Censuses and Surveys, in addition to the General Register Office (Scotland), should ensure that the results of the 1991 Census of Population and any future censuses are available, subject to confidentiality, on a unit postcode basis.

Government accepted the thrust of all of these recommendations though it made careful caveats in a few cases. How far have we achieved all these aims five years after the publication of that Report?

The clear import of recommendation 25 is that additional data, known to exist inside government, should be made available. The catalogue of spatial data sets recently compiled by the Association for Geographic Information (AGI), parts of which (those data sets referenced by Postcode or address) are included in appendix 3, suggests that real progress has been made towards this goal. It is, however, somewhat disquieting to note the gaps in the range of data made available and to appreciate that some countries within the UK hold more highly disaggregated data than others, as table 10.1 emphasises. This shows that Northern Ireland holds more data sets than does England in these forms, particularly in address-based form. In reality, the differences are more extreme than the table illustrates since many of the records kept by central government (for example those of the Department of Employment) and categorised below as 'England and Wales' also include the equivalent data for Scotland and (less frequently) for Northern Ireland.

Table 10.1 Postcode and address-based referencing of official data according to the survey carried out by UK government departments under the Tradeable Information Initiative (see appendix 3). *(Source: DoE).*

	England and Wales (some also cover Scotland and Northern Ireland)	Scotland	Northern Ireland
Postcoded data	21	21	9
Address-referenced data	19	16	42
Totals	40	37	51

So far as recommendation 37 is concerned, the answer is that there has been some progress e.g. remote sensing data is now available in a format matching the areas covered by OS maps and on the same map projection. There is, however, still some way to go in so far as many data sets seem not to be geographically referenced or even released: as indicated by the survey, the vast majority of Postcoded data held by government is not available to the public in its most disaggregated form. Recommendation 39 is of course one with which we as authors have much sympathy and our belief is that use of machine-readable versions of both addresses and Postcodes is increasing. So far as having a single, standard set of grid references for Unit Postcodes and of higher quality than that in the PAF on CD and the Central Postcode Directory (Recommendation 40), our findings suggest that this improvement is needed as much now as it was in 1987. Finally, the story of what happened in the 1991 Censuses has already been told (see chapter 6); the statistical unsuitability of the Unit Postcode as the basis for publishing census data – because of its small size, the very basis of its success in other applications – does not obscure the fact that publishing census data for small areas which are amalgamations of these same basic building blocks has considerable value. OPCS have gone part of the way towards this by creating an Enumeration District to Postcode Directory index but GRO(S) built the whole of their census geography on use of the Postcode.

Trends in Postcode usage

Since Postcodes were initiated as a means to facilitate the delivery of mail, much of the early growth in their use has been in activities directly connected to the mailing process, rather than in use by private individuals. A significant part of this is direct marketing controlled by geodemographic profiling. By targeting large mail users through discount schemes such as Mailsort and individual users by Postcode awareness schemes, the correct use of the Postcode had climbed to 71% of all mail posted in 1990/91. These business activities can be characterised as 'hard' uses of the Postcode, since the use is directly related to the end-user's survival. Research carried out on behalf of Royal Mail has indicated that most of the users who do not yet use PAF to validate addresses, but continue to work with the paper Postcode directories, do so only because it is not commercially necessary for them to Postcode mail more efficiently. This may indicate that the 'market' for the efficient postcoding of the mail is reaching saturation and that there is a limit to 'supply-side' incentives from Royal Mail.

By contrast, the 'soft' uses of the Postcode which focus on its application in spatial referencing have clearly not yet reached their potential. These developments may not affect Royal Mail so directly or immediately but can be considered as valuable for raising awareness of the Postcode. For example, Royal Mail business customers in the high volume non pre-sorted business mail category (see chapter 3) may see a number of advantages in developing correctly Postcoded mailing lists in order to pursue the benefits of non-mailing uses of the Postcode. In this case, specific mailing incentives may not be as effective. Royal Mail will then see serendipitous benefits on both sides – higher percentages of Postcoded mail <u>and</u> better sales of the PAF.

The widespread use of the Postcode in this way will encourage businesses, government and individuals to consider the code important, and hence to expand the 'market' of users. This set of 'demand-side' operations will help to build a consensus for the common use of the Postcode by all spatial data users. This in turn helps towards the implementation of the Chorley Report recommendations for the use of the Postcode as the universal spatial unit for socio-economic and related data.

There are likely to be three major developments in the early 1990s which may require postcoding in order to be a success. The first is the development of the Computerised Street Works Register (CSWR), which is required by the 1991 Roads and Street Works Act. The objective of the CSWR is to achieve more efficient scheduling of street works by the utilities and local authorities i.e. to reduce the number of times that the same roads are dug up, especially within short periods of each other, and to reduce the costs incurred to the utilities and the public at large. An interim system must be operational by July 1992 and, on plans at the time of writing, the full system must be ready in 1993. The principal requirement of the CSWR is that it facilitate the exchange of information about the location of street works; hence extensive discussion and consultation has taken place on the issue of spatial referencing. A two level solution to this problem is envisaged *viz.* a 'detailed' level where the works are referenced with a 12 figure (1m) National Grid reference and a 'general' level where a more approximate reference is appropriate. The practical solutions to this latter problem are the creation of a street gazetteer and/or use of the address and Unit Postcode. The National Streetworks Gazetteer produced by the Local Authorities' Geographical Information Advisory Group has been selected as the street referencing standard which means that many new opportunities will open up for the linkage of utility and local authority data and the Postcode.

The second major development is the new National Health Service (NHS) 'internal market' where funds are tied more directly to patients. Since April 1991, the right to free healthcare of an individual in the NHS has been linked to the District Health Authority in which they are resident. Thus there has been a sudden new need to be able to determine a patient's Health Authority of residence. This can be achieved by a linkage between Postcodes and the health code held in PAF. Many Family Practitioner Committees (FPC) have also Postcoded their registers of patients which are linked to patients' NHS numbers.

A further administrative change in the basis of funding local government in 1993 seems likely to provide opportunities for Postcode linkage. It is proposed that every residential property in Britain is to be assigned to one of eight new value 'bands', and that residents would be charged a new 'Council Tax' on the basis of the banding. A natural development of geodemographic profiling will be to link the bands to Unit Postcodes and the PAF, producing a new index of 'wealth' based on the capital value of property. The general availability of this data in disaggregated form should make it popular in this respect.

Technological changes in Royal Mail

Another view of the future concerns the role of technological change inside Royal Mail. A number of developments currently envisaged should lead to further extensions to the Postcode. The first of these developments is the testing of an extension to the Postcode to identify individual premises (the delivery point suffix), and is being tested in the

Bath BA1 Postcode District. The delivery point suffix is composed of two further alphanumeric characters added to the end of the existing Postcode as a suffix. The first character is a number (excluding 0), while the second is an alphabetic character (excluding C, I, K, M, O, V), giving nine and 20 alternatives respectively or a total of 180 possible combinations. Implicitly (as indicated in chapter 2) this should guarantee that there are no more than 180 delivery points per Unit Postcode when and if the delivery point suffix is incorporated.

A second development related to the first is the testing of a Royal Mail bar code to be added to letters. This would store the Postcode and the delivery point suffix in a barcode specially developed for Royal Mail by Postal Technology (the normal retail code does not give a fast enough 'read-rate' and is therefore not suited for Postcodes). The barcode would be placed on the top of the address block (surrounded by a 2mm 'quiet zone') and consist of four types of bar defining four different states. These bars consist of ascenders, descenders, whole bars or track only at a spacing of 20–24 bars per 25mm (figure 10.1). The new barcode will be terminated by a check sum character which validates the form of the Postcode by a

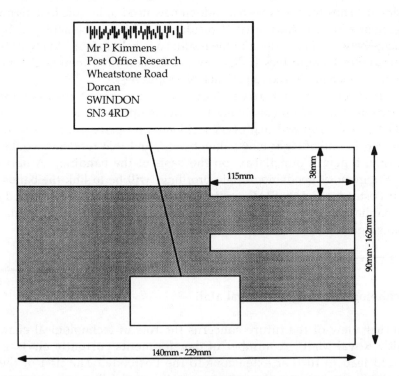

Mr P Kimmens
Post Office Research
Wheatstone Road
Dorcan
SWINDON
SN3 4RD

115mm

38mm

90mm - 162mm

140mm - 229mm

Figure 10.1   The design of the new Royal Mail barcode, showing its position on a standard envelope *(Source: Royal Mail)*

final encoding check. The bars can be considered as alphanumeric characters presented in a more machine-readable format, so that the mail can be automatically sorted to a much finer level. Given the specification of the barcode, it is anticipated that large users of the mail will code their own address labels with it by laser printing.

Since the new barcode is intended to incorporate all prospective forms of the Postcode, table 2.1, (which showed the existing alternative foms of the Postcode), will need to be extended from its current six main alternatives to 24; these are given below in table 10.2. This is to permit the addition of an international prefix and a delivery point suffix.

Table 10.2 Possible future form of the Postcode. N represents a numeric character, A an alphabetic character, C is a checksum digit and S is a start/stop character *(Source: Royal Mail)*

S	NNN	ANA	NAA	NA	C	S
S	NNN	AAN	NAA	NA	C	S
S	NNN	AANN	NAA	NA	C	S
S	NNN	AANA	NAA	NA	C	S
S	NNN	AN	NAA	NA	C	S
S	NNN	ANN	NAA	NA	C	S
S	NNN	ANA	NAA		C	S
S	NNN	AAN	NAA		C	S
S	NNN	AANN	NAA		C	S
S	NNN	AANA	NAA		C	S
S	NNN	AN	NAA		C	S
S	NNN	ANN	NAA		C	S
S		ANA	NAA	NA	C	S
S		AAN	NAA	NA	C	S
S		AANN	NAA	NA	C	S
S		AANA	NAA	NA	C	S
S		AN	NAA	NA	C	S
S		ANN	NAA	NA	C	S
S		ANA	NAA		C	S
S		AAN	NAA		C	S
S		AANN	NAA		C	S
S		AANA	NAA		C	S
S		AN	NAA		C	S
S		ANN	NAA		C	S

These developments to the Postcode itself are to be supported by organisational change in Royal Mail. These changes include the completion of on-line connections from the Postcode duty officer in each of Royal Mail's nine operating divisions to the mainframe computer in Chesterfield where the PAF is located and maintained. In addition, a change in the way the mail is sorted is proposed for 1992, with all manual mail sorting being changed from post town basis to Postcode basis. These changes will extend the sense in which Royal Mail is internally organised by and committed to the Postcode.

Data issues

The other key area of development for postcoding is as part of the rapidly growing market for geographically referenced data. While there are a multiplicity of types of spatial referencing, as this book has exhaustively (!) shown, only the Postcode comprehensively links addresses to 'geography'. We now consider several issues which may control the development of this field.

The first of these issues concerns data protection and the ever-present public concern over confidentiality of information about their private life. During the debating in Parliament of the 1991 Census Enabling Act, several MPs spoke against some of the provisions in the census and absolute guarantees of security of information about the individual were sought. Partly as a consequence, the output criteria for the Census were changed to be even more certain that no small areas with only a few individuals could be targeted and the individuals characterised directly. Looking abroad, in the US the publication of a CD product called MarketPlace by Lotus and Equifax containing lifestyle data about 120 million US households had to be withdrawn when 30,000 households demanded that their details were removed from the disc, in spite of the fact that all the data was already available elsewhere.

This may seem somewhat removed from Postcodes. In reality, however, Postcodes are a finer resolution unit of subdivision than the census ED or any other Basic Spatial Unit used throughout most of government. Although little data is distributed directly for individual Postcodes, much information can be imputed for them using the PAF. This is especially true when Postcodes are linked with databases like ICD's National Consumer database with 43 million consumer names and extended with the delivery point suffix, at which time the Postcode will become unique for each address. Some of the data in such databases will be imputed from census and other statistics for the people as a whole in the small surrounding area and this makes matters even worse since the imputations will occasionally be wrong. The danger is that the Postcode system is seen as part of a process which falls into disrepute and hence itself becomes tarnished. It is possible that such uses of Postcodes might sensibly be considered to come within the remit of the Data Protection Registrar. System operators would therefore be well-advised to ensure all possible care is taken in building, checking, maintaining and using their database, to keep audit trails of all operations and periodically to consider registration under the 1984 Data Protection Act or its successors.

GIS software developments

It is also worthwhile at this stage to consider the role of GIS in the development of Postcoding. Here there are perhaps two groups of issues, the first concerned with the extension of the analytical use of GIS and the second concerned with the maintenance of Postcode information systems under rapid boundary change conditions. GIS use has been growing rapidly in recent years, with take-up being particularly rapid in the utilities and somewhat more slowly in Local Authorities. Inevitably, the start-up phase has concentrated on the implementation issues and GIS functionality has tended to concentrate on data capture and structuring. There are some clear signs, however, that the established users will turn to spatial analysis as a way of adding to the benefits earned from their GIS installation. GIS software vendors are beginning to respond to this development and some recent software releases (e.g. System 9's Analytical Tool Box) have seemed to be aimed at this new market.

The second issue likely to attract greater concern in the years ahead concerns the maintenance of the Postcode data sets in the computer. Many users are at the stage of structuring large area-based boundary data sets or exploring the use of PAF, and relatively few as yet have experience in managing changes and updates to a spatial database. The key decisions will concern the update triggers and what to do with old boundary data sets. In the first case, the choice must be made by the user, perhaps at the rate that PAF is updated and distributed (currently far more rapidly than most other geographical databases); in the second case, it is probably advisable to create a policy of retaining old boundary data sets lest historical analysis of data become impossible as digital representations are simply thrown away with the press of a button, a situation already encountered and regretted in some organisations.

The key issues

In addition to all of the above, a few key issues loom large for the future of Postcoding. No simple solutions to these are available at present but posing them at least advances the chance of solutions being found. They are:

- if the Postcode system is to become truly universal and most other organisations adopt it as the basis on which to spatially reference all their data holdings, can the control of its operations remain solely with Royal Mail? The government Committee of Enquiry referred to above received submissions to the effect that changes made by Royal Mail to facilitate their own internal operations sometimes complicated greatly the operations of Postcode users in other organisations. The very success of the Postcode and its potential for non-mail applications is therefore engendering a problem for Royal Mail. Perhaps the most immediate solution is to create a Postcode Board to discuss policy issues which would contain representatives of the main users, as well as Royal Mail itself;

- the quality of the National Grid references attached to the CPD and to PAF on CD are dangerously poor for England and Wales on the evidence available to us – and notwithstanding the efforts in OPCS to improve them. This may not seem to be directly relevant to Royal Mail – they make little use of the grid references – but they are widely used for non-postal applications and any errors in them reflect badly on their products as a whole. It would seem sensible therefore if they, OS and OPCS considered how best to solve this problem;

- in the course of researching material for this book, we have become acutely aware of the need for a high quality and up-to-date file of addresses for the whole country. We have shown earlier that a version of this is easy to produce from PAF on CD, and Royal Mail already 'spin off' a file of addresses of delivery points from the Main File of PAF (see chapter 4). Nevertheless, we are sure that there is much scope to enhance this by working collaboratively with other organisations to build a file which is not simply related to mail delivery points but attempts to cover all property across the country as a whole. Recent proposals for a land and property database emanating from the Local Authority sector and the proposals for the Domesday 2000 scheme suggest we are not alone in this view. Developments such as the creation of a Council Tax register and the easing of access to some records of HM Land Registry may facilitate such collaboration. As we go to press, discussions initiated by Ordnance Survey on just such a data base are beginning.

- the reaction of government has suggested that relatively few data sets may be released to the general public at Unit Postcode level because of confidentiality constraints. No-one doubts, however, that use of the Postcode facilitates data linkage between data sets which is based on the Postcode 'name' (i.e. 'exact' or 'hierarchical' matching as described in chapter 1) and that minimal aggregations of Postcode Units is the best way to support the needs of data users whilst preserving confidentiality. ˙The ramifications of this are that the data suppliers must have the technical capabilities to produce such 'minimal aggregations' speedily and cheaply from their databases and to document which Postcodes comprise the new 'mega Postcode zones' for which the data are made available. Such new areas should, if at all possible, be consistent between data suppliers. This suggests that the creation and widespread use of a new tier of Postcode tracts, intermediate in size between the Unit Postcode (1.7 million in total) and the Postcode Sector (some 9,000 in total), is appropriate. Ideally, these should be equivalent to the census Output Areas in Scotland and approximately the same size as Enumeration Districts in England and Wales. If possible they should also be a good match to the boundaries of the widely-based Wards.

We would not like the reader to conclude from all this that the Postcode system is beset with problems. Running an organisation the size of Royal Mail is non-trivial and the Postcode system is a central part of their past and future. Considerable efforts and finances are being devoted to minimising the problems with PAF identified earlier, both so far as they affect Royal Mail's own operations and those of non-mail users of the Postcodes. We repeat our earlier conjecture: no other system of identifying position in space has the advantages possessed by the Postcode in being easily related to the physical world through postal addresses; when combined with use of the National Grid, they are a uniquely powerful mechanism for applications limited only by the imagination. Truly, Postcodes *are* the New Geography.

References

Adler M and Raab G M (1988) Exit choice and loyalty: the impact of parental choice on admissions to secondary schools in Edinburgh and Dundee *Journal of Education Policy* **3**, 2, 155–79.

Anthony R N (1965) *Planning and control: a framework for analysis.* Harvard University Press, Boston.

Baker K (1989) Using geodemographics in market research surveys. *Journal of the Market Research Society* **31**, 1, 7–37–44.

Baker M J (1990) One more time – what is marketing? In M J Baker (ed) *The Marketing Book*, 3–9, Heinemann Butterworth, London.

Barnsley M J, Barr S L and Sadler G J (1991) Spatial re-classification of remotely-sensed images for urban land use monitoring. *Proceedings, Spatial Data 2000* , University of Oxford.

Beaumont J R (1991) *An Introduction to Market Analysis.* CATMOG 53, Geo Books, Norwich.

Beaumont C D, Geary K, Halliburton C, Clifford D and Rivers R (1989) Advertising assessment - myth or reality? *Environment and Planning A* **21**, 5, 629–42.

Beaumont J R and Inglis K (1989) Geodemographics in practice: developments in Britain and Europe. *Environment and Planning A* **21**, 5, 587–604.

Beaumont, J R and Clarke M (1992) Strategic information management in practice for marketing. In M J Baker (ed) *Perspectives on Marketing Management,* Vol **2**, John Wiley, London.

Berry J and Maclean F (1989) Managing the development of a customer marketing database. *Environment and Planning A* **21**, 5, 617–24.

Best R H (1981) *Land Use and Living Space.* Methuen, London.

Bibby P R and Shepherd J (1991) *Rates of Urbanization in England.* HMSO, London.

Blakemore M (1991) Managing an operation GIS; the National On-line Manpower Information System (NOMIS). In D J Maguire, M F Goodchild and D W Rhind (eds) *Geographical Information Systems: Principles and Applications,* **I** 503–13, Longman, Harlow.

Boyd P (1991) The Data Protection Implications of the targeting of Direct Mail. *Draft Report by the Office of the Data Protection Registrar,* Manchester.

Boyle P and Dunn, C E (1990) Redefining Enumeration District centroids and boundaries. *North West Regional Research Laboratory, Research Report No. 7.* Lancaster University, Lancaster.

Brown P J B (1991) Exploring geodemographics: a review of recent developments. In I Masser and M Blakemore (eds) *Handling Geographical Information: Methodology and Potential Applications*, 221–58, Longman, London.

Brown P J B and Batey P W J (1990) Geodemographics and the construction of individual-level market classifications: the case of the home-shopping industry. *Working Paper 16*, The Urban Research and Policy Evaluation Regional Research Laboratory, University of Liverpool.

Brownlie D T (1991) Putting the management in marketing management. In M J Baker (ed) *Perspectives on Marketing Management*, Vol 1, John Wiley, London.

Burnhill P M, Dowie P J and Healey R G (1991) Common Service Boundaries: from conflicting to conterminous boundaries. *ESRC Regional Research Laboratory for Scotland Working Paper No. 24*, Edinburgh.

Butcher R (1988) The use of the Postcode Address File as a Sampling Frame. *The Statistician*, 37, 1988, pp 15–24.

Cannon T (1989) International marketing. *Environment and Planning A* **21**, 5, 643–54.

Christopher M, McDonald M and Wills G (1980) *Introducing Marketing.* Pan, London.

Collins A (1989) Store location planning: its role in marketing strategy. *Environment and Planning A* **21**, 5, 625–9.

Coopers and Lybrand (1988) *Local Management of Schools: a report to the DES.* HMSO, London.

Cornish P (1989) Geodemographic sampling in readership surveys. *Journal of the Market Research Society* **31**, 1, 45–52.

Davies H (1991) 1991 Census – Enumeration District/Postcode Directory: its use with SASPAC91. *British Urban and Regional Information Systems Association Newsletter (BURISA)* 101, December 1991, 10–2.

Densham P J (1991) Spatial Decision Support Systems. In D J Maguire, M F Goodchild and D W Rhind (eds) *Geographical Information Systems: Principles and Applications*, **I**, 403–12, Longman, Harlow.

Department of Health (1989) *Caring for People: community care in the next decade and beyond – caring for the 1990s.* Cm 849 London HMSO, London.

Department of the Environment (1987) *Handling geographic information: the report of the government's Committee of Enquiry.* Department of the Environment, London.

Department of Trade and Industry (1990) *Government-held Tradeable Information: guide-lines for government departments in dealing with the private sector.* Department of Trade and Industry, London.

Dibb S, Simkin L, Pride W M and Ferrell O C (1991) *Marketing: Concepts and Strategies.* (European Edition). Houghton-Mifflin Company, London.

Dowie P, Koval S, Burnhill P and Healey R (1991) GIS and community health care: a case study of geriatric service provision. *Proceedings, European Geographical Information Systems Conference, EGIS 91,* Vol **1**, 267–77, Utrecht.

Dunlea M (1991) The use of GIS in mobilising Irish Emergency Services: the CAMP experience. *Paper 2.10, Proceedings, Association for Geographic Information Conference.*

England J R (1985) The Census of Employment. In England J R *et al Information Systems for Policy Planning in Local Government,* (Ch 3.2) Longman, Harlow.

Flowerdew R and Goldstein W (1989) Geodemographics in practice: developments in North America. *Environment and Planning A* **21**, 5, 605–16.

Flowerdew R and Green M (1991) Developments in areal interopolation methods using GIS. *European Regional Science Association Congress,* Lisbon.

Flowerdew R, Green M and Lucas S (1991) Analysing local house price variations with GIS. *Proceedings, Association for Geographic Information Conference 1991, 3.25.1–8.*

Fothergill S and Gudgin G (1982) *Unequal Growth.* Heinemann, London.

Garner C L, Gittings B M and Tolgu K E A (1990) Monitoring the social and spatial impact of educational reform: a geographical information system approach. *Regional Research Laboratory for Scotland, Working Paper No. 9,* February 1990.

Gatrell A C (1989) On the spatial representation and accuracy of address-based data in the United Kingdom. *International Journal of GIS* **3**, 4, 335–48.

Goldstein H and Cuttance P (1988) A note on national assessment and school comparisons. *Journal of Education Policy* **3,** 2, 197–202.

Goodchild M F and Lam N N-S (1980) Areal interpolation: a variant of the traditional spatial problem, *Geo-processing* **1,** 297–312.

Gorry G A and Scott Morton M (1989) A framework for management information systems. *Sloan Management Review* **30,** 3, 49–61.

Green N P A and Shepherd J W (1988) The design and construction of the DoE demonstrators, objectives, execution and software listings. *South East Regional Research Laboratory (SERRL) Working Report No.7,* SERRL, Birkbeck College, London.

Griffiths R (1988) *Community Care: Agenda For Action. A report to the Secretary of State for Social Services.* HMSO, London.

Haines-Young R (1991) The Tradeable Information Initiative: a review. *Paper 1.26, Proceedings, Association for Geographic Information Conference.*

Harley J B (1975) *Ordnance Survey maps - a descriptive manual.* Ordnance Survey, Southampton.

Harrison I D (1986) A basic bibliography on Postcodes and Postcode applications. *City of London Polytechnic Faculty of Computing, Mathematics and Allied Studies, Working Paper 86/07.*

Hawker L and Goodwin R (1991) The computerised Street Works Register – streets ahead? *Paper 1.253 Proceedings Association for Geographic Information Conference.*

Healey M J (ed) (1991) *Economic activity and land use: the changing information base for local and regional studies.* Longman, Harlow.

Higby M A and Farah B N (1991) The status of marketing information systems, decision support systems and expert systems in the marketing function of US firms. *Information and Management* **20** 1, 29–35.

Humby C R (1989) New developments in demographic targeting – the implications of 1991. *Journal of the Market Research Society* **31**, 1, 53-73.

Johnson M (1989) The application of geodemographics to retailing – meeting the needs of the catchment. *Journal of the Market Research Society* **31**, 1, 7–36.

Kendall D G (1971) Construction of maps from 'odd bits of information'. *Nature,* **231**, 158–9.

Knox P (1978) Territorial social indicators and areal profiles, some cautionary observations. *Town Planning Review* **49**, 75–83.

LGMB (1991) *GIS News No. 2.* Local Government Management Board, Luton.

Lievesley D, Breeze E and Owen D (1978) *Postcode Sampling.* OPCS, London.

Longley P, Batty M and Shepherd J (1991) The size, shape and dimension of urban settlements, *Transactions, Institute of British Geographers* **16**, 1, 75–94.

Maguire D J and Raper J F (1991) GIS Design Models, *Computers and Geosciences,* Special Issue **17**, 8.

Maling D H (1973) *Co-ordinate systems and map projections.* Geo. Philips, London.

Martin D (1989) Mapping population data from zone centroid locations. *Transactions, Institute of British Geographers* NS, 14, 2, 90–7.

Martin D (1991) *Using Postcoded information with the 1991 Census.* Geodata Institute, University of Southampton.

Mintzberg H (1989) *Mintzberg on Management.* Free Press, New York.

Norris P and Mounsey H M (1983) Analysing change through time. In D W Rhind (ed) *A Census User's Handbook,* Methuen, London.

Oasis (1989) *Report on the Management of Marketing Information.* Institute of Marketing, London.

OPCS (1984) *Key Statistics for Urban Areas: Great Britain.* HMSO, London.

OPCS (1987) *Central Postcode Directory: Information Guide.* Office of Population Censuses and Surveys, Titchfield.

OPCS (1990) *Central Postcode Directory: Information Guide Version 2.* Office of Population Censuses and Surveys, Titchfield.

OPCS (1991) *Central Postcode Directory: Version Notes on Version I 1991 Base 1981/2 and I/1991/2.* Office of Population Censuses and Surveys, Titchfield.

Openshaw S (1984) Ecological fallacies and the analysis of areal census data. *Environment and Planning A* **16,** 17–31.

Openshaw S (1987) A mark 1 Geographical Analysis Machine for the automated analysis of point data sets. *International Journal of Geographical Information Systems* 1, 335–58.

Openshaw S (1989) Making geodemographics more sophisticated. *Journal of the Market Research Society* **31,** 1, 111–32.

Openshaw S and Goddard J (1987) Some implications of the commodification of information and the emerging information economy for applied information analysis inthe UK. *Environment and Planning A* 19, 1423–39.

Openshaw S, Wymer C and Charlton M (1986) A geographical information and mapping system for the BBC Domesday optical disks. *Transactions, Institute of British Geographers* NS, **11,** 3, 296–304.

OSRC (1979) *Report of the Ordnance Survey Review Committee.* Her Majesty's Stationery Office, London.

Owen D W, Green A E and Coombes M G (1986) Using the social and economic data on the BBC Domesday disk. *Transactions, Institute of British Geographers* NS, **11,** 3, 305–14.

Park R E, Burgess E W and Mackenzie R D (eds) (1925), *The City* University of Chicago Press, Chicago.

Parkinson L K and Parkinson S T (1987) *Using the Micro-computer in Marketing.* McGraw-Hill, New York.

Petch A (1988) Rezoning, an exercise in compromise. In L Bondi and M H Matthew (eds) *Education and Society,* Routledge, London.

Piercy N (1990) Developing marketing information systems. In M J Baker (ed) *The Marketing Book,* 250–269, Heinemann Butterworth, London.

Pugh D, Black T and Mounsey H (1991) A national land and property gazetteer? Opportunities for development. *Paper 1.25, Proceedings Association for Geographic Information Conference.*

Raper J F (1991) User interfaces for GIS. In I Masser and M Blakemore (eds) *Geographical Information Management: Methodology and Potential Applications*, Longman, Harlow: 102–114.

Raper J F and Green N P A (1989) The development of a hypertext based tutor for geographical information systems. *British Journal of Educational Technology* 20, 164–72.

Rapp T and Collins S (1987) *MaxiMarketing*. McGraw Hill, New York.

Rhind D W (ed) (1983) *A Census User's Handbook*. Methuen, London.

Rhind D W, Armstrong P and Openshaw S (1988) The Domesday machine: a nationwide geographic information system, *Geographical Journal* **154**, 56–68.

Scottish Education Department (1989) Placing requests in education authority schools *Statistical Bulletin*, No. 1/B6, Edinburgh.

Sellwood R (1987) Statistics of Changes in Land Use: A New Series. *Statistical News*, November.

Seymour W (1980) *A history of the Ordnance Survey*. Wm Dawson and Sons Ltd, Folkestone.

Shepherd J (1991) Planning settlements and infrastructure. In I Masser and M Blakemore (eds) *Handling Geographical Information: Methodology and Potential Applications*, 181–220, Longman, Harlow.

Singh G (1991) Targeting technology. *What's new in marketing*, March 1991, 13–14.

Sleight P and Leventhal B (1989) Applications of geodemographics to research and marketing. *Journal of the Market Research Society* **31**, 1, 75–102.

Squires S (1988) DEFINE *User Manual*. INFOLINK Limited, Croydon.

Tobler W R (1979) Smooth pycnophylatic interpolation of geographic regions. *Journal of the American Statistical Association* **74**, 519–30.

Thomas F (1991) Digital boundaries for the 1991 Census of Population in Scotland . *Mapping Awareness* **5**, 1, 13–5.

Webber R (1989) Using multiple data sources to build an area classification system: operational problems encountered by MOSAIC. *Journal of the Market Research Society* **B**, 1, 103–10.

Wilson P R and Elliott D J (1987) An evaluation of the Postcode Address File as a Sampling Frame and its use within OPCS. *Journal of Royal Statistical Society A* **150**, 3, 230–40.

APPENDIX 1 Glossary of abbreviations and terms

AA	Automobile Association
ACORN	A Classification Of Residential Neighbourhoods (see Webber 1989)
AGI	Association for Geographic Information
Barcode	Machine readable code made up of vertical bars
BT	British Telecom
CAD	Computer Aided Design
CD	Compact Disc
CISC	Complex Instruction Set Chip
CPD	Central Postcode Directory
CSWR	Computerised StreetWorks Register
DBMS	DataBase Management System
DoE	Department of the Environment
DPP	Direct Product Profitability
DSS	Decision Support System
DTI	Department of Trade and Industry
DTp	Department of Transport
DTp's RHTM	Department of Transport's Regional Highway Traffic Model
ED	Enumeration District
EHCS	English House Condition Survey
EPOS	Electronic Point Of Sale
FES	Family Expenditure Survey
FPC	Family Practitioner Committee
GAM	Geographical Analysis Machine
Geodemographics	Analysis of the spatial aspects of the socio-economic structure of urban areas
GHS	General Household Survey
GIS	Geographical Information System
GRO(S)	General Register Office (Scotland)
IEEE	Institute of Electronics and Electrical Engineers

ISO	International Standards Organisation
LEA	Local Education Authority
LFS	Labour Force Survey
LGMB	Local Government Management Board
LSM	Letter Sorting Machine
MAUP	Modifiable Areal Unit Problem
Mb	Megabytes
MBI	Mapinfo Boundary Interchange
MPS	Mailing Preference Service
NRS	National Readership Survey
MS-DOS	Computer operating system for IBM-compatible personal computers
NFS	National Food Survey
NHS	National Health Service
OA	Output areas used by GRO(S)
OCR	Optical Character Reader
OPCS	Office of Population, Censuses and Surveys
OS	Ordnance Survey of Great Britain
OSNI	Ordnance Survey of Northern Ireland
PAC	Pinpoint Address Code
PAF	Postcode Address File
PAF on CD	Postcode Address File on Compact Disc
PIP	Point-in-Polygon
POAs	Provisional Output Areas
PPI	Postage Paid Impression
PPU	Part Postcode Unit
PRN	Pinpoint Road Network
PSU	Primary Sampling Unit
PTT	Post, Telegraph and Telephone
RAM	Random Access Memory
RDBMS	Relational DataBase Management System
RHTM	Regional Highway Traffic Model
RISC	Reduced Instruction Set Chip
RGS	Royal Geographical Society
SAS	Small Area Statistics
SDDS	Spatial Decision Support System
SIC	Standard Industrial Classification
SQL	Structured Query Language
TCP – IP	Transmission Control Protocol/Internet Protocol
TGI	Target Group Index
UPC	Unit Postcode Centroid
UNIX	Computer operating system for workstations
USPS	US Postal Service
Ward	Basic administrative unit used for local government and elections
Zip code	Postal code in use in the USA

Contact names and
addresses

All UK telephone numbers listed below commence with a zero (0). For use from other countries, the zero should be replaced with 44. Whilst the contact point for Royal Mail is shown in the general list, all of the distributors of official Postcode products are given in a separate section at the end of this appendix.

Abbreviation	Full title and address	Contact 'phone/fax
AA	The Automobile Association, Fanum House, Basing View, Basingstoke RG21 2EA	0256 492111/494651
AGI	Association for Geographic Information, RICS, 12 Great George Street, London SW1P 3AD	071 222 7000/9430
A-Z Maps	Geographers' A-Z Map Company Ltd, Fairfield Road, Borough Green, Sevenoaks, Kent TN15 8PP	0732 781000/780677
Barts	Bartholomew, 12 Duncan Street Edinburgh EH9 1TA	031 667 9341/662 4282

Abbreviation	Full title and address	Contact 'phone/fax
BT	British Telecom CS Directory Products Unit, Columbia Centre Market Street, Bracknell, Berkshire RG12 1JG	0344 861961/860872
CACI	CACI Ltd (Market Analysis), CACI House, Kensington Village, Avonmore Road, London W14 8TS	071 602 6000/603 5682
CAM	Centre for Analysis and Modelling, 126 Cornwall Road, London SE1 8TQ	071 928 2433/2366
CCN	CCN Systems, 39 Houndsditch, London EC3A 7DB	071 623 5551/621 9596
CDMS	Credit and Data Marketing Services Ltd, JM Centre, Old Hall Street, Liverpool L70 1AB	051 235 3092/255 1604
CSO	Central Statistical Office, PO Box 1333, Millbank Tower, Millbank, London SW1H 9NA	071 217 4209
CMT	Computer Marketing Technology Ltd, Teddington House, Broad Street, Teddington TW11 8QZ	081 943 5511/1686
DANI	Northern Ireland Department of Agriculture, Dundonald House, Upper Newtonards Road, Belfast BT4 3SF	0232 650 111
Data Protection Registrar	Office of the Data Protection Registrar, Springfield House, Water Lane, Wilmslow, Cheshire SK9 5AX	0625 535777/524510

Abbreviation	Full title and address	Contact 'phone/fax
DEDNI	Northern Ireland Department of Economic Development, Statistics Research Branch, Netherleigh, Massey Avenue, Belfast BT4 2JP	0232 63244
DEm	Department of Employment, Caxton House, Tothill Street, London SW1H 9NA	071 273 5519
DoE	Department of the Environment 2 Marsham Street, London SW1P 3EB	071 276 3000
DoENI	Northern Ireland Department of the Environment, Parliament Building Belfast, BT4 355	0232 763210
DES	Department of Education and Science, Elizabeth House, York Road, London SE1 7PH	071 934 9046
DFPNI	Northern Ireland Department of Finance and Personnel, Valuation and Land Office, Queen's Court, 56-66 Upper Queen Street, Belfast BT1 6FD	0232 439 303
DHSSNI	Northern Ireland Department of Health and Social Security, Dundonald House, Upper Newtonards Road, Belfast BT4 3SF	0232 650 111
DSS	Department of Social Security, Richmond Ho., 79 Whitehall Lane, London SW1A 2NS	071 210 3000
DTI	Department of Trade and Industry 151 Buckingham Palace Road, London SW1 9WS	071 215 1295
DTp	Department of Transport, Romney House, 43 Marsham Street, London SW1P 3PY	071 276 8776

Abbreviation	Full title and address	Contact 'phone/fax
ESRC	Economic and Social Research Council, Sir David Philips Building, North Star Avenue, Swindon SN2 1UJ	0793 413000/413001
GDC	Graphical Data Capture, 262 Regents Park Road, London N3 3HN	081 346 4959/349 4095
Geodan	Geodan, Overtoom 60, 1054 HK Amsterdam, Netherlands	+31 20 612 5073/9854
GeoMatrix	GeoMatrix Ltd., Sheffield Science Park, Arundel St., Sheffield S1 2NS	0742 724272
Geoplan	Geoplan UK Ltd, 14-15 Regents Parade, Harrogate HG1 5AW	0423 566755/525545
Goad	Chas E Goad, Salisbury Square, Old Hatfield, Herts AL9 5BJ	0707 271171/274641
GRO(S)	General Register Office for Scotland, Ladywell House, Ladywell Road, Edinburgh EH12 7TF	031 314 4254/314 4344
HMLR	Her Majesty's Land Registry, 32 Lincoln's Inn Fields, London WC2A 3PH	071 405 3488
ICD	ICD Marketing Services Ltd, 29 Corsham Street, London N1 6DR	071 251 2883/250 0298
Infolink	Infolink Ltd, Coombe Cross, 2-4 South End, Croydon CR0 1DL	081 686 7777
IR	Inland Revenue, Somerset House, The Strand, London WC2R 1LB	071 438 6622

Abbreviation	Full title and address	Contact 'phone/fax
Kingswood	Kingswood Ltd, 19 Kingswood Road, London W4 5EU	081 994 5404/747 8047
LGMB	Local Government Management Board Arndale House, The Arndale Centre Luton LU1 2TS	0582 451166/412525
Mediapost	Le Miroir, 15-17 Boulevard Charles De Gaulle, 92126 Montrouge CEDEX, France	
MPS	Mailing Preference Service Freepost 22, London W1E 7EZ	071 738 1625
MVA	MVA Systematica, MVA House, Victoria Way, Woking, Surrey GU21 1DD	0483 728051/755207
OPCS	Office of Population Censuses and Surveys, St Catherine's House, 10 Kingsway, London WC2B 6JP	071 242 0262/405 3049
OS	Ordnance Survey, Romsey Road, Maybush, Southampton SO4 9DH	0703 792000 (general) 792912 (marketing) 0703 792888 (fax)
OSNI	Ordnance Survey Northern Ireland, Colby House, Stranmillis Court, Belfast BT9 5BJ	0232 661 244
Pinpoint	Pinpoint Analysis Ltd, Tower House, Southampton Street, London WC2E 7HN	071 836 1511/497 8610
RDC	Rural Development Commission, 11 Cowley Street, London SW1P 3NA	071 276 6969/6940

Abbreviation	Full title and address	Contact 'phone/fax
RGS	Royal Geographical Society, I Kensington Gore, London N1P 1PA	071 589 5466
Royal Mail	Royal Mail National Postcode Centre 3 & 4 St George's Business Centre, St George's Square, Portsmouth, PO1 3AX	0705 838515 (general) 0705 870307 (customer services) 0705 838518 (fax)
RS	Registers of Scotland, Meadowbank House, 153 London Road, Edinburgh EH8 7AU	031 659 6111
SERRL	South East Regional Research Laboratory, Birkbeck College, 7 - 15 Gresse St., London W1P 1PA	071 631 6483/ 6498 (fax)
SO	Scottish Office St. James' Centre, Edinburgh EH1 3SX	031 244 4990
Thomson Directories	Thomson Directories 296 Farnborough Rd., Farnborough Hants. GU14 7NU	0252 516111

Suppliers of postcode-related products and services

Acxiom UK Ltd
Becket House
60-80 St Thomas Street
LONDON
SE1 3QU
Tel: 071 378 7244

Allies Computing
12 Alexandra Avenue
GREAT YARMOUTH
Norfolk
NR30 4ED
Tel: 0493 855338

Anadata Ltd
Kings Chambers
Queens Road
COVENTRY
Warwickshire
CV1 3EH
Tel: 0203 553911

Archetype Systems Ltd
7 The Courtyards
The Croxley Centre
Hatters Lane
WATFORD
WD1 8YH
Tel: 0923 210280

AT & T Istel Ltd
Isys House
PO Box 36
County Trading Estate
Watlington Road
OXFORD
OX4 5LR
Tel: 0865 716179

CACI Ltd
CACI House
Avonmore Road
Kensington Village
LONDON
W14 8TS
Tel: 071 602 6000

Capscan Ltd
Tranley House
Tranley Mews
144 Fleet Road
LONDON
NW3 2QW
Tel: 071 267 7055

CCN Systems Ltd
Abbey House
Abbeyfield Road
NOTTINGHAM
NG7 2SW
Tel: 0602 863864

CDMS (Credit and Data Marketing Services)
JM Centre
Old Hall Street
LIVERPOOL
L70 1AB
Tel: 051 235 3293

Centre-File Ltd
75 Leman Street
LONDON
E1 8EX
Tel: 071 410 3000

Suppliers of postcode-related products and services (*continued*)

Claymore Services Ltd
Station House
Whimple
EXETER
EX5 2QJ
Tel: 0404 823097

Corporate Publishing Software Ltd
Terminal House
Station Approach
SHEPPERTON
Middlesex
TW17 8AS
Tel: 0932 221212

Equifax Europe Ltd
Anchor House
Ingleby Road
BRADFORD
West Yorkshire
BD99 2XG
Tel: 0274 579544

Hopewiser Ltd
Tatton House
20-22 Tipping Street
ALTRINCHAM
Cheshire
WA14 2EZ
Tel: 061 941 6001

Lindor Ltd
The Colston Centre
Colston Avenue
BRISTOL
BS1 4UH
Tel: 0272 291571

Codedit Services Ltd
14A New Street
STOURPORT-ON-SEVERN
Worcestershire
DY13 8UW
Tel: 02993 77087

Eltec Ltd
2 Campus Road
Listerhills Science Park
BRADFORD
BD7 1HR
Tel: 0274 309999

GB Mailing Systems Ltd
Border House
High Street
Farndon
CHESTER
CH3 6PT
Tel: 0829 270714

Information for Marketing
Ltd
31 Bell Lane
LONDON
E1 7LN
Tel: 071 247 9486

Mail Marketing (Bristol) Ltd
Springfield House
West Street
Bedminster
BRISTOL
BS3 3NX
Tel: 0272 666900

Suppliers of postcode-related products and services *(continued)*

Optech Ltd
East Street
FARNHAM
Surrey
GU9 7XX
Tel: 0252 714340

Pinpoint Analysis
Tower House
Southampton Street
LONDON
WC2E 7HN
TEL: 071 836 1511

Printronic International
6 Alexandra Road
CROYDON
CR0 6EU
Tel: 081 654 0692

Quick Address Systems
1 Taylors Yard
67 Alderbrook Road
LONDON
SW12 8AD
Tel: 081 675 6690

ROCC Computers Ltd
Kelvin Way
CRAWLEY
West Sussex
RH10 2LY
Tel: 0293 531211

Root 3 Systems Ltd
Hawks View
Guildford Road
LEATHERHEAD
Surrey
KT22 9DS
Tel: 0372 370051,
0272 314424 or
0222 566310

Sintrom Electronics
Arkwright Road
READING
RG7 0LS
Tel: 0734 311088

Technical Information Ltd
15 Belsize Park
LONDON
NW3 4ES
Tel: 071 794 5040

The Computing Group
Beech House
Betts Way
CRAWLEY
West Sussex
RH10 1GB
Tel: 0293 561666

The WSA Consultancy Ltd
Mill Studio Business Centre
Crane Mead
WARE
Herts
SG12 9PY
Tel: 0920 444217/218

Suppliers of postcode-related products and services *(continued)*

Words and Numbers
Tudor House
Hackney Terrace
WOODBRIDGE
Suffolk
IP12 1NS
Tel: 0394 386315

Suppliers of GIS and related software for handling Postcode and similar data which were mentioned in the text

ARC/INFO	ESRI (UK), Doric House, 23 Woodford Road, Watford, Herts WD1 1PB	(0923) 210450
ERDAS	Remote Sensing Services., Lychgate House, 24 High Street, Ramsbury, Wiltshire SN8 2PH	(0672) 20226
GenaMap	Genasys UK Ltd, Manchester Science Park, Lloyd Street North, Manchester M15 4EN	(061) 232 9444
GIMMS	Gimms Ltd, 30 Keir Street, Edinburgh EH3 9EU	(031) 668 3046
GISTutor	Department of Geography, Birkbeck College, 7-15 Gresse Street, London W1P 1PA	(071) 631 6577
INFO-MAP	Claymore Services Ltd, Station House, Whimple, Exeter EX5 2QJ	(0392) 210600
MapGrafix	Admiral Computing, 193-199 London Road, Camberley, Surrey, GU15 3JT	(0276) 692269
MapInfo	MapInfo Corp., 200 Broadway Troy, NY 12180 USA	+1 (800) 327 8627

Metropolis	Laser-Scan, Cambridge Science Park Milton Road, Cambridge CB4 4FY	(0223) 420414
MGE	Intergraph (UK) Ltd, Delta Business Park, Great Western Way, Swindon, Wilts SN5 7XP	(0793) 619999
ProSpex	GeoMatrix Ltd, Sheffield Science Park, Arundel St., Sheffield S1 2NS	(0742) 724272
SmallWorld	SmallWorld Systems Ltd, Burleigh House, 13-15 Newmarket Road, Cambridge CB5 8EG	(0223) 460199
SPANS	Tydac Technologies Ltd, Chiltern House, 45 Station Rd., Henley-upon-Thames, Oxon. RG9 1AT.	(0491) 411100
System 9	Prime Computer (UK) Ltd, Beech House, 373-399 London Road, Camberley, Surrey GU15 3HR	(0276) 682821

Postcoded data sets held by
British government
departments and agencies

Under a Prime Ministerial directive to set up the Tradeable Information
Initiative, British government departments were asked in 1989/90 to
consider which of their data holdings might be made available for wider
use. The objective was to generate revenue and (wherever possible)
involve the private sector (DTI 1990). Geographical data was seen as just
one part of the whole. It has long been recognised that a knowledge of
what is available is essential so the Association for Geographic
Information (AGI) pressed government to set up a catalogue of spatial (or
geographically referenced) data. In the event, this was finally assembled
by AGI under contract to the Department of the Environment (DoE) and
taking advantage of the preceding work of an inter-departmental working
group on the topic.

This appendix is in three sections. The first, reproduced below, is the
AGI description of the catalogue as a whole and its sources: updates for it
may be obtained from the AGI. The second section is a listing of specific
data sets. Thanks are due to the DoE for permission to publish it though
the material remains Crown Copyright. The first part of this second
section is of those data sets known to contain a Postcode locational
reference while the second is of those data sets whose records contain at
least a postal address; in the latter case, even if Postcodes are not included
they can be introduced by various address matching organisations and,
under certain circumstances, by Royal Mail for customers.

The data sets are classified on whether they are available in machine-
readable (computer) form, as indicated in the last column. Some of them
are not available to the public in their detailed geographical form (if
shown as true under the Category D heading); this results from their
collection under legislation such as the Statistics of Trade Act which
precludes release of the data except to duly authorised bodies, almost

invariably for government administration purposes. Even in these cases, however, it may well be possible to obtain less geographically specific versions of the files. It is easy to aggregate the data to larger areas using the Postcode and hence provide confidentiality yet make available useful information. Geography thus becomes a screening device - generalised data are often adequate for certain purposes. Finally, the third section describes the products available from perhaps the most sophisticated single Postcoded data source currently available: the data from the 1991 Population Census carried out for Scotland by the General Register Office for Scotland. We include this because we expect it to act as a model for other products in the future.

The AGI catalogue of government spatial data

The Government's Tradeable Information Initiative Working Group (TIIWG) issued a questionnaire to government departments in order to bring together information about datasets held by central government. After considering how best to disseminate this information, the TIIWG decided that an information service should be provided and a database of information set up.

The database of spatial information held by central government is held at the AGI Secretariat and holds information on 454 data sets, 301 of which are accessible. Twenty seven government departments were involved in the initiative as listed overleaf.

The information held for each data set is:

Department where data set is held
    Dataset Title
    Data Category - is it available to the public
    Associated products
    Time Span
    Series
    Update frequency
    Purpose
    Collection method - whether by census, interview, postal survey,
       request, statistical return, field survey or derived data
    Sampling detail
    Sources
    Limitations

Raw/Processed Data Locational Reference - coastal division, Enumeration District, grid reference (OSGB/OSNI), health district, health region, location authority code, local authority name, lake name, point, Postcode Sector, postal address, region name, Scottish region, tax district, user area code, ward code, water supply zone

Grid reference detail

Accuracy

Smallest area collected/smallest area released - coastal zone, county council, district council, education authority, enterprise zone, Enumeration District, health district, lake, local authority area metropolitan borough, NRA region, parish point, property/parcel region, schools, Scottish region, tax district, tile, town, ward, water supply zone

Area covered

Computer - mainframe/micro/magnetic tape/hard disk

Manual records held

Store software/Extract software

Whether personal data held/registered under Data Protection Act

Who uses data outside government and how frequently

When data will be available - if not already available

Conditions of use

Where to get further information

Contact department details

The database can be queried using any of the 22 types of information above or any combination of these. The information describes a very wide variety of datasets - from pig species to large scale construction plans. It contains details of how the data were collected, by whom and how they are spatially referenced. The next phase in the development of the database will be to categorise the datasets. The AGI is currently investigating the different ways in which the information may be disseminated.

Government Departments involved in the Tradeable Information Initiative:

Central Statistical Office

Department of the Environment – Nature Conservancy Council/Countryside Commission/Rural Development Commission/Natural Environment Research Council

Department of Education and Science
Department of Social Security
Department of Transport
Department of Energy
Department of Employment
Department of Trade and Industry
General Records Office (Scotland)
Home Office
HM Land Registry
Inland Revenue
Ministry of Defence/Meteorological Office
Ministry of Agriculture, Fisheries and Food
Northern Ireland – Department of Finance and Personnel
Northern Ireland – Department of Education
Northern Ireland – Department of Economic Development
Northern Ireland – Geological Survey
Northern Ireland – Housing Executive
Northern Ireland – Department of Health and Social Services
Northern Ireland – Department of the Environment - Roads Service/Ordnance Survey/Work Service/Housing Division/Land Registry/Conservation Service/Water Service/Planning Service
Northern Ireland - Department of Agriculture
Ordnance Survey
Office of Population Censuses and Surveys
Registers of Scotland
Scottish Office
Welsh Office

Data known to be Postcoded

Government source	Dataset title	Category D	Machine form
Department of the Environment	Civil Estate Record Information System (CERIS)	True	True
Department of the Environment	Open University Survey of Background Noise 1985 Onward	False	True
Department of the Environment	Public attitudes to the Environment 1986 & 1989	False	True

Government source	Dataset title	Category D	Machine form
Department of the Environment	Domestic addresses in London Docklands area, as held in Valuation Office records, April 1990	True	False
Department of Education and Science	Schools Census	False	True
Central Statistical Office	Annual Census of Production	True	True
Central Statistical Office	Business Register	True	True
Northern Ireland – Department of Economic Development	Computerised Unemployment Statistics (COMPUS)	False	True
Northern Ireland – Department of Economic Development	Census of Employment (NI)	False	True
Northern Ireland – Department of Health & Social Services	Mental Health Record Scheme	True	True
Northern Ireland – Department of the Environment – Planning Service	Register of Planning Applications	False	True
Northern Ireland – Department of Agriculture	Northern Ireland Farm Census: Names File	True	True
Northern Ireland – Department of Agriculture	Farm Business Survey (NI)	True	True
Northern Ireland – Department of Agriculture	Food Industry Database	True	False
Northern Ireland – Department of Agriculture	Mailing List for "Agriculture in Northern Ireland"	False	True
Northern Ireland - Department of Agriculture	Herd Owner File	False	True

Government source	Dataset title	Category D	Machine form
Department of Social Security	Income Support Quarterly Statistical Enquiry	True	True
Department of Social Security	Income Support Annual Statistical Enquiry	True	True
Department of Social Security	Family Credit Statistical Sample	False	True
Department of Transport	GB Vehicle Keeper Register	True	True
Inland Revenue	Domestic Rating Records Database	False	False
Inland Revenue	Non-Domestic Rating Records Database	False	True
Inland Revenue	Revenue and Compensation Database (including property transactions in England and Wales)	False	True
General Records Office (Scotland)	Statutory Registers of Births	False	True
General Records Office (Scotland)	Statutory Register of Marriages	False	True
General Records Office (Scotland)	Statutory Register of Deaths	False	True
Office of Population Censuses & Surveys	Infant Mortality Linked Data Files	False	True
Office of Population Censuses & Surveys	Cancer Annual Primary Files 1971 onwards	True	True
Department of Employment	Juvos Database	False	True
Department of Employment	Juvos Cohort File	False	True

Government source	Dataset title	Category D	Machine form
Department of Employment	Census of employment. A survey to businesses on the number of employees in employment.	False	True
Department of Employment	VAT Small Firms File	False	True
Scottish Office	General Medical Practitioner Practice Information	False	True
Scottish Office	Registered private nursing homes and hospitals ISD(S)34	True	True
Scottish Office	Scottish Morbidity Records: 1st entry. Inpatient & Day Case Record – Summary Sheet (form SMR1)	True	True
Scottish Office	Scottish Morbidity Records: 2nd entry – Maternity discharge record.	False	True
Scottish Office	Scottish Morbidity Records: 3rd Entry – Mental Health – Inpatient Admission/ Discharge (SMR4)	False	True
Scottish Office	Scottish Morbidity Records: 4th entry - Scottish Cancer Registration Case Abstract Card (SMR6)	False	True
Scottish Office	Scottish Morbidity Records: 5th entry – Handicapped Children's Register (SMR7)	False	True
Scottish Office	Scottish Morbidity Records: 6th entry - Scottish Neonatal Discharge record (SMR11)	False	True

Government source	Dataset title	Category D	Machine form
Scottish Office	Scottish Morbidity Records: 7th entry - Community Dental Treatment Record (SMR13)	False	True
Scottish Office	Scottish Morbidity Records: 8th entry – Scottish Cardiac Surgery Register (SMR20)	True	True
Scottish Office	Monitoring of Scottish Wider Access Programme, SWAP	True	True
Scottish Office	Beef Special Premium Scheme – BSPS	True	True
Scottish Office	Cereal Certification	True	True
Scottish Office	Farmers' Name, Address and Holding Description – Parish List	True	True
Scottish Office	Potato Cyst Nematodes – pre crop soil tests additional info (all current soil test results taken as requirement)	True	True
Scottish Office	Census of Employment Local Units in Scotland. Subsets available for 1981, 1984 and now for 1987	True	True
Scottish Office	Publicly Owned Factories Record	True	True
Scottish Office	Regional Data System	False	True
Scottish Office	Public Sector Dwelling Sales	True	True

Government source	Dataset title	Category D	Machine form
Department of Trade and Industry	Basic Information about all Limited Companies	False	True
Department of Trade and Industry	Systematic Index (of need for employment opportunities) Database	True	True

Data known at least to include postal addresses on records

Government source	Dataset title	Category D	Machine form
Department of the Environment	Derelict Land Grant Applications	True	False
Department of the Environment	Builders Address File – Register of Construction Firms	True	True
Department of the Environment	Enterprise Zone (EZ) Employment Survey	False	True
Department of the Environment	Sitefile	True	True
Department of the Environment	European Regional Development Grants for English Infrastructure projects for Local and Public bodies (including bodies acting in the public interest) managed by DoE	False	True
Department of the Environment	Monitored Domestic Energy use Archive	False	True
Department of the Environment	1986 English House Condition Survey	False	True
Departement of the Environment	Statutory Lists of Buildings of special Architectural or Historic Interest	False	False

Government source	Dataset title	Category D	Machine form
Department of the Environment	Domestic addresses in London Docklands area as held in Valuation Office records, April 1990.	True	False
Department of Education and Science	Exam Results & First Destination Survey	False	True
Department of Education and Science	Further Education Statistical Record (FESR)	False	True
Northern Ireland – Department of Finance & Personnel	VALCOM	True	True
Northern Ireland – Department of Economic Development	Sponsors of the Northern Ireland Training & Employment Agency's Action for Community Employment (ACE) Scheme	False	True
Northern Ireland – Department of Economic Development	Trading Standards Traders Records	True	True
Northern Ireland – Department of Health & Social Services	Property Estates Records	True	True
Northern Ireland - Department of Health & Social Services	Registered Adoption Societies in Northern Ireland	False	False
Northern Ireland - Department of Health & Social Services	Registered Voluntary Children's Homes in Northern Ireland	False	False
Northern Ireland - Department of Health & Social Services	Regional Voluntary Child Care organisations Grant-aided by the Department	False	False

Government source	Dataset title	Category D	Machine form
Northern Ireland – Department of Health & Social Services	Other Regional Voluntary Organisations Grant aided by the Department	False	True
Northern Ireland – Department of Health & Social Services	Cancer Registration Scheme (Northern Ireland)	True	True
Northern Ireland – Department of the Environment - Roads Service	Northern Ireland Bitmac Specification Compliance procedure	True	True
Northern Ireland – Department of the Environment – Conservation Service	List of Buildings of Special Architectural or Historic Interest	False	False
Northern Ireland – Department of the Environment – Water Service	DoE(NI) Water Service – Records of Work Done	False	True
Northern Ireland – Department of the Environment - Water Service	DoE(NI) Water Service – Statistical Information on Volumes and Qualities of Supply and Treatment	False	True
Northern Ireland – Department of the Environment - Water Service	DoE(NI) Water Service – Assets Records for Water mains, Sewerage, Structures, Land and Plant	False	True
Northern Ireland - Department of Agriculture	Herd/Animals File	True	True
Northern Ireland - Department of Agriculture	Northern Ireland Farm Census: Names File	True	True
Northern Ireland - Department of Agriculture	Register of Milk Quota Holders	False	True
Northern Ireland - Department of Agriculture	Potato Land Test History	True	True

Government source	Dataset title	Category D	Machine form
Northern Ireland – Department of Agriculture	Seed Potato Grower Cards	True	False
Northern Ireland – Department of Agriculture	Ware Potatoes: Area Registration Scheme – Growers Cards	True	False
Northern Ireland – Department of Agriculture	Registered Grower - Salesmen	True	False
Northern Ireland – Department of Agriculture	Registered Merchants	True	False
Northern Ireland - Department of Agriculture	Mailing list for 'Agriculture in Northern Ireland	False	True
Northern Ireland – Department of Agriculture	Statistical Data on N.I. Meat Exports, Slaughterings and Condemnations	True	True
Northern Ireland – Department of Agriculture	Names & Addresses of People Applying for Planting Grants & Areas Planted (hectares or acres)	True	False
Northern Ireland – Department of Agriculture	Producers in the less favoured areas of N.I. who are claiming payment of Hill Livestock Compensatory Allowance	False	True
Northern Ireland – Department of Agriculture	N.I. Sheepmeat producers claiming payment of EC Premium on Ewes	False	True
Northern Ireland – Department of Agriculture	(a) Suckle Cow Premium Scheme; (b) Beef Special Premium Scheme	False	False

Government source	Dataset title	Category D	Machine form
Northern Ireland – Department of Agriculture	Merchants Licensed to send Potatoes to non-EC Countries during a Crop Year	True	False
Northern Ireland – Department of Agriculture	Milk Licence Holders	True	False
Northern Ireland – Department of Agriculture	County office Records: Holdings	True	False
Northern Ireland – Department of Agriculture	Capital Grant Expenditure Cards (one set for each scheme)	True	False
Northern Ireland – Department of Agriculture	Farm Safety Files	True	False
Northern Ireland - Department of Agriculture	Agriculture and Seeds Act Files	False	True
Northern Ireland - Department of Agriculture	Medicated Feed Register	False	True
Northern Ireland - Department of Agriculture	Register of Egg Packers	True	False
Northern Ireland – Department of Agriculture	Registered Poultry Premises	True	False
Northern Ireland – Department of Agriculture	Agricultural and Horticultural Advisory Cases	False	True
Northern Ireland – Department of Agriculture	Register of Fish Farms based in Northern Ireland	True	False

Government source	Dataset title	Category D	Machine form
Northern Ireland – Department of Agriculture	Register of Commercial Dealers in Salmon and Trout	True	False
Northern Ireland - Department of Agriculture	Register of Commercial Permit Holders in Lough Erne	True	False
Northern Ireland - Department of Agriculture	Fishing Vessel Register of Northern Ireland	True	False
Northern Ireland - Department of Agriculture	Register of Angling Clubs in Northern Ireland	False	False
Rural Development Commission	Loans, Redundant Building Grants, Client Records	False	True
Registers of Scotland	Land Register for Scotland (Replacement for Register of Sasine (Scotland) – partial cover at present – see also Register of Sasine (Scotland)	False	True
Registers of Scotland	Register of Sasine (Scotland) Register of Deeds affecting heritable property in Scotland excluding those on the Land Register (See also Land Register for Scotland)	False	False
HM Land Registry	The Register of Title to Land	False	True
General Records Office (Scotl.)	Census Enumeration Transcript Books	False	False

Government source	Dataset title	Category D	Machine form
Department of Employment	ES554 - Quarterly Occupational Classification Analysis of Job Centre Vacancies and Placings by Jobseeker Type	False	False
Department of Employment	ES 555 - Quarterly Industrial Classification Analysis of Job Centre Vacancies and Placings	False	False
Department of Employment	ES 5600 - Monthly Analysis of Job Centre Performance – Jobstart and YTS Orders	True	False
Department of Employment	ES 561 - Job Centre Placings by Registrant Characteristics – Long Term Unemployed	True	False
Department of Employment	Restart Interview Form Survey	False	True
Department of Employment	Determinants of Jobclub Performance	False	False
Department of Employment	Postal Survey of individuals who joined Jobclubs in Autumn 1987	False	True
Scottish Office	General Medical Practitioner Practice Information	False	True
Scottish Office	Laboratory Statistics ISD(S) 14 – 18 Statistics	False	True
Scottish Office	Crofter's Building Grant and Loan Scheme – Index of Applications for assistance under CBGLS	True	False

Government source	Dataset title	Category D	Machine form
Scottish Office	Farm Capital Grants – covers FHGS/AHGS,GHDS/ AHDS,AID(EC)&(N), FCGS(EC)&(N)	True	True
Scottish Office	Farm Structure (payment to outgoers) Scheme	True	True
Scottish Office	Index of Agricultural Holdings for Wages Enforcement	True	False
Scottish Office	Waste Disposal Survey – 1988	False	True
Scottish Office	Housing Land Annual Return - HLAR	True	True
Scottish Office	Industrial Sites Register – ISR	True	True
Scottish Office	Planning Appeals	False	True
Scottish Office	Scottish Vacant Land Survey - SVLS, vacant and derelict land included	True	True
Scottish Office	Threatened Buildings (including industrial) Survey reference and monitoring indexes and files	False	False
Scottish Office	Scottish Industrial Archaeology Survey Catalogue 1977-85 - SIAS	False	True

Postal areas and their codes

The table below shows the 120 Postal Areas and the towns with which they are primarily associated. Note that, for reasons of space, the town names are given in lower case letters but for mail purposes they should always be in upper case ones i.e. capital letters. Royal Mail also publishes a more detailed file of Post Towns, the 'Post Town Gazetteer' containing about 3,000 records. This contains details of the range of Postcode sectors associated with each post town.

AB	Aberdeen	DY	Dudley	LN	Lincoln	SL	Slough
AL	St Albans	E	London E	LS	Leeds	SM	Sutton
B	Birmingham	EC	London EC	LU	Luton	SN	Swindon
BA	Bath	EH	Edinburgh	M	Manchester	SO	Southampton
BB	Blackburn	EN	Enfield	ME	Medway	SP	Salisbury
BD	Bradford	EX	Exeter	MK	Milton Keynes	SR	Sunderland
BH	Bournemouth	FK	Falkirk	ML	Motherwell	SS	Southend on Sea
BL	Bolton	FY	Blackpool (Fylde Coast)	N	London N	ST	Stoke on Trent
BN	Brighton	G	Glasgow	NE	Newcastle upon Tyne	SW	London SW
BR	Bromley	GL	Gloucester	NG	Nottingham	SY	Shrewsbury
BS	Bristol	GU	Guildford	NN	Northampton	TA	Taunton
BT	Belfast	HA	Harrow	NP	Newport	TD	Galashiels
CA	Carlisle	HD	Huddersfield	NR	Norwich	TF	Telford
CB	Cambridge	HG	Harrogate	NW	London NW	TN	Tonbridge
CF	Cardiff	HP	Hemel Hempstead	OL	Oldham	TQ	Torquay
CH	Chester	HR	Hereford	OX	Oxford	TR	Truro

CM	Chelmsford	HU	Hull	PA	Paisley	TS	Cleveland
CO	Colchester	HX	Halifax	PE	Peterborough	TW	Twickenham
CR	Croydon	IG	Ilford	PH	Perth	UB	Southall
CT	Canterbury	IP	Ipswich	PL	Plymouth	W	London W
CV	Coventry	IV	Inverness	PO	Portsmouth	WA	Warrington
CW	Crewe	KA	Kilmarnock	PR	Preston	WC	London WC
DA	Dartford	KT	Kingston on Thames	RG	Reading	WD	Watford
DD	Dundee	KW	Kirkwall	RH	Redhill	WF	Wakefield
DE	Derby	KY	Kirkcaldy	RM	Romford	WN	Wigan
DG	Dumfries	L	Liverpool	S	Sheffield	WR	Worcester
DH	Durham	LA	Lancaster	SA	Swansea	WS	Walsall
DL	Darlington	LD	Llandrindod Wells	SE	London SE	WV	Wolverhampton
DN	Doncaster	LE	Leicester	SG	Stevenage	YO	York
DT	Dorchester	LL	Llandudno	SK	Stockport	ZE	Lerwick

The British National Grid system

The National Grid was devised by Ordnance Survey (OS), the British national mapping organisation. It provides a consistent way of specifying the position of any point in Britain. By increasing the number of digits used, the position may be specified with greater and greater precision. Though devised before the computer age, the National Grid is well-suited to use in making maps by computer and carrying out certain types of analysis. Indeed, it is highly complementary to the Postcode as a way of describing position in space. For that reason, Royal Mail includes grid references of Postcodes in its PAF and many other organisations use numerous grid coordinates as the basis for defining the boundaries of Postcode Sector and other areas (see chapter 5). The following description is based upon that given in Harley (1975); it is more technical than that given in the penultimate section of chapter 2.

Though grids had been printed on earlier OS maps, the vital decision to produce one which would be common to all scales of map came from a recommendation in the Report of the Davidson Committee. This Committee examined the future role of OS and reported in 1938 (Seymour 1980). The international metre was proposed as the unit on which the grid should be based.

The relationship over Great Britain of the lines of the National Grid to the Transverse Mercator projection graticule (representing lines of latitude and longitude) is indicated in figure A5.1. Although the small longitudinal extent of the British Isles prevents any serious divergence of the two systems, an exact fit and graticule cannot of course be achieved. The difference in direction between the grid and graticule lines is known as *convergence*; the value of the convergence is zero along the meridian 2° W but varies over the rest of the projection (figure A5.2).

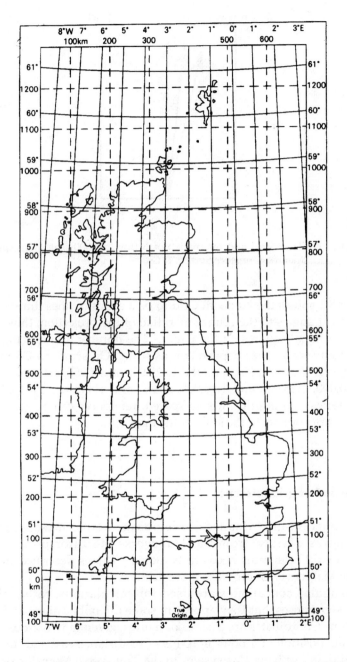

Figure A5.1   Relationship of the Transverse Mercator graticule to the National
Grid system on Ordnance Survey maps. The continuous lines
represent the projection, the broken lines the National Grid.
(Source: Ordnance Survey. © Crown Copyright)

297

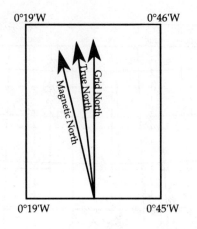

0°19'W   0°46'W

0°19'W   0°45'W

Figure A5.2   True, grid and magnetic north (for 1:50,000 scale map sheet 196). *(Source: Ordnance Survey. © Crown Copyright)*

Figure A5.1 shows the National Grid to be a series of lines drawn parallel and at right angles to the central meridian of the projection, thus forming a series of equal squares on the paper. The number and spacing of grid lines for any map series depends on its scale. On standard OS maps the grid interval shown is 10km on the 1:625,000 and 1:250,000 series; 1km on the 1:50,000, 1:25,000 and 1:10,000 series; and 100m on the 1:2,500 and 1:1,250 series. From grid lines so spaced, references can be given with a precision appropriate to the scale of the map.

The method of grid reference

The distinction in Ordnance Survey usage between rectangular co-ordinates as derived from the Transverse Mercator projection and National Grid references needs to be noted. This is described in outline here but Maling (1973) provides more detail.

Rectangular coordinates are used for calculations, rather than for reference purposes, but they appear in some OS publications and require definition. Coordinates are a series of figures, given in two groups, which define the position of a point in terms of its distance east and north from an origin. In applying this system to the Transverse Mercator projection covering Great Britain, the true origin of which is 2°West 49° North, a false origin is employed. Were rectangular coordinates to be calculated from the true origin, the positions lying west of the central meridian would be

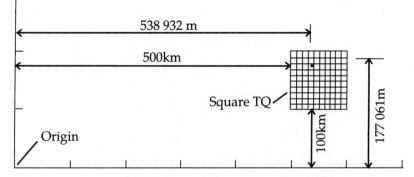

Figure A5.3 The position of a point P (whose National Grid reference is TQ 38932 77061) in relation to the origin of the Grid. *(Source: Ordnance Survey. © Crown Copyright)*

negative and the northings, although all positive, would exceed 1000 km for some points in north Scotland. To avoid inconvenience, 400km are added to all easting coordinates and 100km subtracted from all northing co-ordinates. Rectangular coordinates quoted by OS are thus related to a false or working origin, approximately Latitude 49°46′N; Longitude 7°33′W of Greenwich, slightly south west of the Isles of Scilly. This ensures that coordinates of all points on the mainland of Great Britain are positive and less than 1000km from that false origin. Since the linear unit adopted by the OS is the metre, coordinates are expressed in metres and decimals of a metre according to the standard of precision required. Figure A5.3 illustrates a simple example in which the National Grid rectangular coordinates of a point P in London are 538932 East and 177061 North.

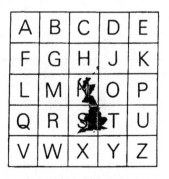

Figure A5.4(a) The National Grid reference system of Great Britain. 500 kilometre squares of the National Grid. *(Source: Ordnance Survey. © Crown Copyright)*

(b)

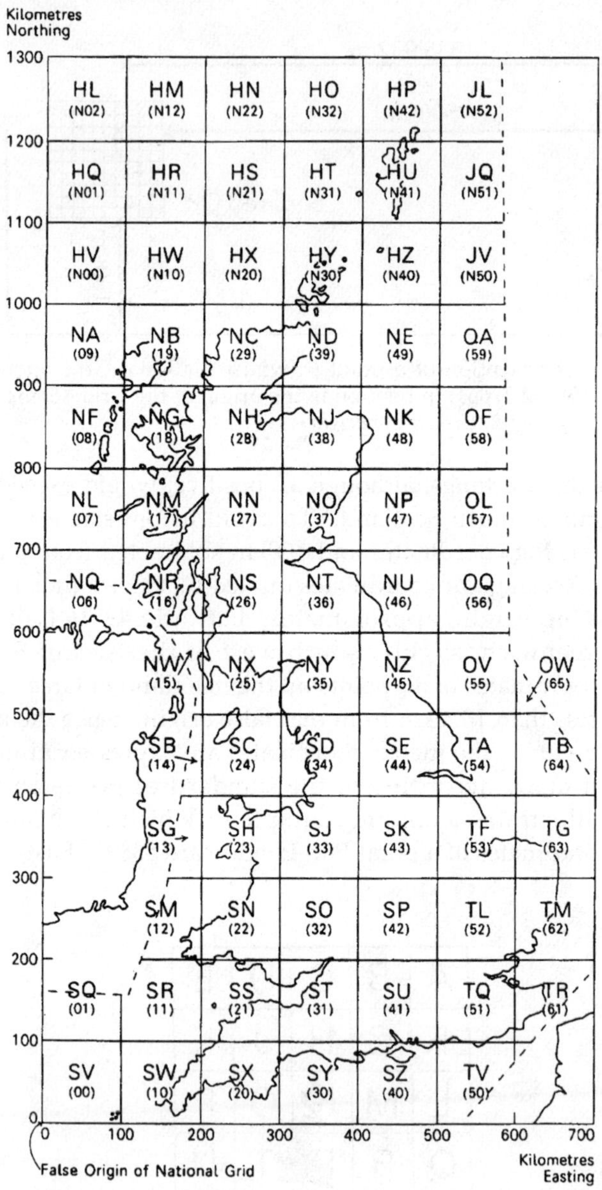

Figure A5.4(b) The National Grid reference system of Great Britain. 100 kilometre squares of the National Grid covering Great Britain with their reference letters and (in brackets) the numbers formerly used. *(Source: Ordnance Survey. © Crown Copyright)*

Grid references, however, although they are also related to the same false origin off the Isles of Scilly, do not give the actual distances from this point but employ combinations of letters and numbers in the National Grid system to denote location. This convention was introduced to help the user who might well have problems dealing with, say, 12 digit (one metre) grid references. As a result, the National Grid consists of a systematic breakdown of the grid areas into progressively smaller squares identified by letters and then by numbers. The largest units are 500 km squares, each designated by a prefix letter – the first letter to be quoted in the National Grid reference (figure A5.4 (a)). The 500km squares are then broken down into twenty-five 100km squares: normally these are also designated by a prefix letter - the second letter of the grid reference - although originally they were referenced by figures. Figure A5.4 (b), representing the grid of 100km squares covering Great Britain, identifies these letters and beneath these (in brackets) are the numbers they replaced; the latter are shown because there are still a few OS maps held by users which are referenced in this way. No two 100km squares can now have the same combination of prefix letters.

Within the 100km squares, each smaller grid square (of 10km, 1km or 100m side length) is designated by the distance of its *south-west* corner from the west (eastings) and south (northings) margins, respectively, of the 100 km square in which it lies. To enable these distances, or coordinates, to be found easily, their values are printed in the map margins against the grid lines concerned. These provide the numbers – two, four or six digits – which identify each particular grid square. A point or feature within one of the smallest grid squares can be indicated still more closely by estimating the tenths of the appropriate grid square either by eye or by means of a romer (a simple measuring device). Whilst this sounds complex, use of the National Grid is very easy in practice.

Examples of grid references

In the National Grid reference system the initial two prefix letters immediately locate the 100 km square in which the point falls. The remaining figures, the number of which depends on the scale of the map and the level of detail chosen by the user, enable the point to be located with reference to the west and south sides of the 100 km square concerned. The point can normally be located to one-tenth of the grid interval as shown in the map margin.

When giving a National Grid reference for any point, the distance eastward (eastings) is always given before the distance northwards (northings). Eastings and northings must always be recorded in the same number of figures, even though some of these may be zero.

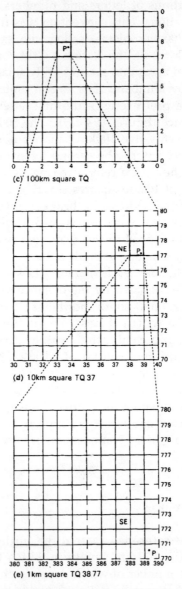

(c) 100km square TQ

(d) 10km square TQ 37

(e) 1km square TQ 38 77

Figure A5.5   Examples of the Grid reference of Point P at different levels of resolution; the area in which the point lies is expanded down the page so that more detail may be given for the location. Thus the first (top) diagram shows only a Grid reference to the nearest 100km, the next is shown to the nearest 10km and the third (bottom) is shown correct to 1km. *(Source: Ordnance Survey. © Crown Copyright)*

Examples of full grid references at various scales, illustrated in figure A5.5, are given in table A5.1. In these examples, a full grid reference is given in all cases. This is unique within Great Britain and there is no other grid reference exactly the same. If, however, the first letter (T) is omitted, all references will be repeated in the adjoining 500km squares; if the second letter (Q) is omitted as well, the same reference will be repeated in the adjacent 100km square. Prefix letters can only be omitted therefore when there is no likelihood of ambiguity arising from a reference being repeated elsewhere at 500km or 100km distance.

Table A5.1   Grid references for a point, P* which has National Grid rectangular co-ordinates (to the nearest metre) of 538932 East and 177061 North (see figure A5.3), at various scales

Map scale	Grid interval of	Grid reference	Precision
1:625,000	10,000 metres	TQ 38 77	1000 metres
1:250,000	10,000 metres	TQ 38 77	1000 metres
1:50,000	1,000 metres	TQ 389 770	100 metres
1:25,000	1,000 metres	TQ 389 770	100 metres
1:10,000	1,000 metres	TQ 389 770	100 metres
1:2500	100 metres	TQ 3893 7706	10 metres
1:1250	100 metres	TQ 3893 7706	10 metres

Note that TQ replaces the 5 prefix to the easting rectangular cordinate and the 1 prefix to the northing (see figure A5.5). Note also that the precisions shown may be improved by a factor of 10 by estimation between the units marked on the map margins i.e. grid references can be estimated to the nearest metre on 1:1,250 and 1:2,500 scale maps.

Sheet numbering of National Grid maps

A further application of the National Grid is that it enables the 1:25,000 and all map series at larger scales published by the OS to be numbered in accordance with the grid reference of their south west corner. Although maps at scales smaller than 1:25,000 all carry the National Grid, sheet numbering is based on different principles and does not conform to the system outlined below. The 204 map sheets covering Britain at 1:50,000 scale for instance overlap in many places to ensure towns, etc are shown on both map sheets and to avoid large 'blank' areas of sea.

The way in which OS large scale maps are numbered (or identified) is shown below:

1:25,000 maps A 1:25,000 sheet is denoted by the grid reference of its south west corner to the nearest ten km, e.g. TQ37. In the Second Series, where each sheet covers two adjacent 10 km squares, each unit was originally numbered separately by its south west corner e.g. TQ27 and TQ37, but they are now designated in the form TQ27/37.

1:10,000 maps Each sheet covers a five km by five km area. The sheets in these series are denoted by the addition of quadrant letters to the 1:25,000 sheet reference e.g. TQ37NE.

1:2,500 maps Since each standard sheet covers an area one km by one km, a 1:2,500 sheet is denoted by the grid reference of its south-west corner to the nearest km, e.g. TQ3877. For convenience of users, however, 1:2500 plans are normally paired into a sheet representing an area of two square km and these are referenced by the south west corner of each component km square e.g. TQ3877 and TQ3977.

1:1250 maps A 1:1250 sheet covers an area of 500m by 500m and is denoted by the addition of quadrant letters to the 1:2,500 map reference e.g. TQ3877SE.

From 1991 onwards, OS is progressively withdrawing such standard map sheets and replacing them with maps printed (by computer) to meet the needs of individual users. This facility is termed the Superplan service and permits users to specify exactly where the map is to be centred, at what scale the plot is to be made and what infromation is to be shown. The map database is held in OS major agents and is updated each night.

Boundary Products from the Scottish Census

The following is a slightly amended version of General Register Office for Scotland, *Boundary Products Prospectus*, August, 1991. It retains the same format of the original. A contact address for obtaining further information or any of the products is given in appendix 2.

1. Introduction

1.1 The Registrar General for Scotland offers for sale information defining the boundaries of Scottish Postcodes and areas for the Small Area Statistics (SAS) from the 1991 Census of Population. GRO(S) also make available a number of indexes which will enhance the use of this boundary information.

1.2 These products are available in a number of data formats thus making them accessible to a wide range of users from those with little or no access to computers to those with sophisticated Geographic Information Systems (GIS).

1.3 Users of Small Area Statistics (SAS) will find it easier to use the census data if they also have the area boundaries to which the SAS relate.

1.4 Customers may also find the products in this prospectus of assistance when analysing any Postcoded data sets or in producing new information by bringing together different data sets on a common geographic basis in the manner envisaged by the Chorley Report on handling of Geographic Information.

1.5 Postcode boundaries can be used for many purposes. For example, with census or other data for assessing traffic planning applications; for positioning emergency services; for identifying areas for special marketing initiatives or promotions.

1.6 The General Register Office for Scotland (GRO(S)) has, since 1973, maintained a unique set of maps on which the Office has drawn the boundaries of Postcodes to cover the whole land area of Scotland. GRO(S) is currently digitizing the boundaries of all these mapped Postcodes in order to divide the smallest areas to be used for producing SAS from the 1991 Census. These areas will be created in two stages, first as Provisional Output Areas (POAs) and later as Final Output Areas (OAs). Since these areas will be aggregates of Postcodes, digital boundaries will be produced for Output Areas as well as Postcodes.

1.7 In summary, the various boundary products are:

  (i) Postcode boundaries available in digital format on disk or tape or as clear film map overlays. These boundaries will also be shown on the maps returned to GRO(S) by census enumerators. These maps may be made available on permanent loan to local authorities.

  (ii) Census Area Output boundaries available in digital format on disk or tape or as clear film map overlays.

  (iii) Index Files (linking Postcodes or Census Output Areas to each other or to higher areas). These files are available on disk or tape or on paper. With the index file linking Postcodes to OAs, local authorities may draw OA boundaries on the enumerator maps referred to at (i) above.

1.8 This prospectus describes the products available, the media on which they are available and states price and conditions of supply. An additional related product is the Scottish Postcode Directory which consists of a series of locational codes for each Postcode in Scotland. Further information about the Directory is available on request.

1.9 The Registrar General is *not* offering for sale any software to manipulate computer-readable products.

2. The Products

2.1 The products offered for sale have been grouped below into 3 categories: Postcode boundaries; 1991 Census Boundaries (Provisional) and 1991 Census Boundaries (Final). The first group should be of interest to all customers who are looking beyond the immediate requirements of the 1991 Census. Some Census customers may prefer to wait for the availability of the final products described in the third group rather than use the provisional boundaries.

2.2 *Postcode boundaries*

This group comprises the 2 versions (machine-readable and hard-copy) of Postcode boundaries. The products are:

Product 1: Postcode boundary file: a file containing the digitized boundary of each Postcode. The data are divided into sets, one for each local government district.

Product 2: Postcode overlay: digitized boundaries plotted out on clear film overlay.

These products will be revised constantly before Postcodes are 'frozen' to ensure a static set is available for processing the 1991 Census. The frequency of updating thereafter has still to be determined.

With the Scottish Postcode Directory, users can either automatically or manually create the boundaries of each of the area types coded on the Directory. Alternatively, GRO(S) will supply boundaries of 'higher areas' (see below).

2.3 *1991 Census Area Boundaries (Provisional)*

This group of products will be available before the Census is processed. These products describe the Provisional Output Areas (POAs). Users with products from this group will be able to:

• comment on the POAs and their suitability as potential OAs, and

• make preparations for the receipt of Census data for OAs e.g. by planning the collection or allocation of non-Census data to POA boundaries.

The products are:

Product 3: Postcode - POA index file: a file containing for each Postcode (a) the Provisional Output Area (POA) to which it has been assigned and (b) a size measure, the estimated household value.

This file, plus Product 1 (Postcode boundary file) or Product 2 (Postcode overlay) will give the user the opportunity to comment on the creation of POAs and to plan the collection of non-Census data to the same boundaries.

Product 4: POA - Postcode index file: this file lists POAs and shows the Postcode content of each and the estimated household value for each Postcode. This file is a sorted version of Product 3.

Product 5: POA - Best Neighbour index file: a file containing for each POA the neighbouring POA considered to be the best neighbour for merger if the actual 1991 Census household and resident counts warrant a merger on the grounds of confidentiality. The file will also contain the estimated value of the POA to help the user comment on the allocation of best neighbours.

Product 6: POA boundary file: a file containing the digitized boundaries of POAs to enable users to comment on how well the provisional areas meet users' needs.

Product 7: POA overlay: this is the hard copy (clear film) version of Product 6 for use with other maps and overlays.

These products will be revised constantly before Postcodes are 'frozen' to ensure a static set is available for processing the 1991 Census.

2.4 *1991 Census Boundaries (Final)*

The third group of products will become available after the Census has been processed and OAs created. These are:

Product 8: Postcode OA index file: a file containing for each Postcode the Output Area to which it has been assigned. This file is similar to Product 3 but created after POAs have been changed as necessary to produce OAs. With Product 1 and this file, users will be able to create for themselves the boundaries of OAs (Product 10) for use with 1991 Census Small Area Statistics (SAS).

Product 9: OA - Postcode index file: this file lists Output Areas and shows the Postcode content of each. This is a sorted version of Product 8.

Product 10: OA boundary file: this file is similar to Product 6 but created after POAs have been changed as necessary to produce OAs. The file can be used with 1991 Census SAS for OAs to create maps displaying SAS data.

Product 11: <u>OA overlay</u>: this is the hard copy (clear film) version of Product 10.

Product 12: <u>OA - Higher Area index file</u>: this file contains for each OA the codes for various types of 'higher area' to which the OA belongs or has been assigned. The higher areas included are listed in Table A.

For any local authority region, these products will become available at about the same time as the main Small Area Statistics tables from the 1991 Census became available for that region (i.e in the period October 1991 to August 1992). The products will not be updated. The Postcodes on Products 8 and 9 will be those 'frozen' for processing the 1991 Census. However the 1991 OA code will be added to the area types contained on the Scottish Postcode Directory and all new Postcodes added to the Directory will be assigned to a 1991 OA.

2.5   GRO(S) will also be able to produce the boundaries of aggregations of Postcodes or OAs to higher areas coded, respectively, on the Scottish Postcode Directory or Product 12. These boundaries would be available as boundary files or overlays. Users may wish to produce these boundaries themselves.

Table A3.1 sets out whether Postcodes and OAs fit exactly into the higher areas to which they have been assigned.

Table A3.1   The fit of Postcodes and Census Output Areas to standard geographical units

	Exact fit from	
Area type	Postcodes	OAs
Local government Region or Islands Area	Yes	Yes
Local government district	Yes	Yes
Postcode sector	Yes	No
Health Board area	Yes	Yes
District ward	No	No
New town	No	No
Civil parish	No	No
Inhabited island	No	No
Urban-rural type	Yes	Yes (1)
Locality	Yes	Yes (1)
1981 Enumeration District (frozen at 1981)	No	No
1981 Enumeration District	Yes (2)	Yes (3)
1991 output area	Yes	

Note 1: Localities and urban-rural type will initially be defined in terms of Postcodes. Once OAs have been created the boundary of the locality and urban-rural type will be adjusted to fit OA boundaries.

Note 2: All Postcodes are allocated to a 1981 ED including those created since the 1981 Census.

Note 3: Except where confidentiality thresholds are not attained.

The fit of OAs to higher areas is necessarily coarser than that provided by Postcodes, but the areas in this file will match exactly those for which 1991 SAS will be produced. This is because 1991 Census results will be produced only for OAs or aggregations of OAs.

Uses of the Central Postcode
Directory surveyed for
Royal Mail and OPCS

The following table sets out the use made of the Central Postcode
Directory by the following types of organisations sampled in a survey
carried out for Royal Mail and OPCS in 1987.

Key: AI= Academic Institute; ARM= Armed Services; LG= Local
Government; NGD= National government department; RHA= Regional
Health Authority; UTL= Utility organisation; SER= Consultancy/Service
Bureau; MR= Market Research firm (Source: MVA Final Report
'Improvements to the Central Postcode Directory' to Royal Mail/OPCS)

Organisation Type Code
Summary of Current Uses – Question 2.6

AI   Matching EDs to Postcodes for subsequent mapping or analysis

ARM   Postcodes/OSGR used as the basic validation check for creation
        of a property-based street index giving geographic location.
        Resolution to 10m OSGRs undertaken manually as required

LG   1. Postcode-based referencing of information for local directories:

                e.g.   – Census of Employment data
                        – Shopping interview analyses
                        – Mortality data
                        – Housing management areas
                        – Residential locations of school children

2. Traffic analysis

3. Mapping and/or location of addresses from questionnaires, surveys and records, including allocation of Postcode-based zones

4. Checking of accuracy of local data

NGD　1. Production of small area statistics

　　　　e.g. – by enterprise zone
　　　　　　 – by travel-to-work area

2. Geocoding of statistics; e.g. allocation of unemployment benefit claimants to wards

3. Selection of samples by area

4. Eligibility checks – e.g. eligibility for DTI assistance can be checked by entry of Postcode to on-line database

5. Identification of OSGR from Postcode used in Land Registry

RHA　1. Provision of geographically-based statistics to NHS, OPCS and for research purposes

　　　　　　　　e.g.　　　– births
　　　　　　　　　　　　　 – deaths
　　　　　　　　　　　　　 – maternity admissions
　　　　　　　　　　　　　 – child health
　　　　　　　　　　　　　 – cancer cases

2. Planning of services provided to doctors on a demographic basis according to patient characteristics in the area

3. Validation of Postcodes

e.g.　 – on hospital maternity admission forms
　　　　 – on patient information systems

4. To assign NHS Area codes, County District and Electoral Ward Codes to Postcoded patient records

UTL   1. Mail targeting
2. Market/sales analysis
3. Delivery programming schedules
4. Identification of consumers on any given transformer
5. Identification of station, sub-station and transformers in conjunction with OS maps
6. Calculation of the number of consumers allocated to a particular transformer
7. Computerised system to determine water supply usage on geographical basis

SER   1. Analysis of demographic characteristics of client files
2. Proximity analysis of customers to branches
3. Mapping of customer addresses
4. Segmentation of direct mail
5. To match census information to Postcode geography to assist client targeting
6. Traffic analysis and transport planning
7. Route guidance programs - definition of origin and destination of journeys

MR   Selection of samples by area

Index